D0990111

THE ANHARMONIC CRYSTAL

Philippe Choquard
Battelle Memorial Institute
Geneva, Switzerland

W. A. BENJAMIN, INC., New York · Amsterdam 1967

Frontiers in Physics

DAVID PINES, Editor

S. L. Adler and R. F. Dashen
CURRENT ALGEBRAS AND APPLICATIONS TO PARTICLE PHYSICS

P. W. Anderson **CONCEPTS IN SOLIDS:** *Lectures on the Theory of Solids*

N. Bloembergen **NONLINEAR OPTICS:** *A Lecture Note and Reprint Volume*

N. Bloembergen **NUCLEAR MAGNETIC RELAXATION:** *A Reprint Volume*

R. Brout **PHASE TRANSITIONS**

G. F. Chew **S-MATRIX THEORY OF STRONG INTERACTIONS:** *A Lecture Note and Reprint Volume*

P. Choquard **THE ANHARMONIC CRYSTAL**

P. G. de Gennes and Philip A. Pincus (Trans.)
SUPERCONDUCTIVITY OF METALS AND ALLOYS

R. P. Feynman **QUANTUM ELECTRODYNAMICS:** *A Lecture Note and Reprint Volume*

R. P. Feynman **THE THEORY OF FUNDAMENTAL PROCESSES:** *A Lecture Note Volume*

H. L. Frisch and J. L. Lebowitz
THE EQUILIBRIUM THEORY OF CLASSICAL FLUIDS: *A Lecture Note and Reprint Volume*

H. Frauenfelder **THE MÖSSBAUER EFFECT:** *A Review—With a Collection of Reprints*

S. C. Frautschi **REGGE POLES AND S-MATRIX THEORY**

M. Gell-Mann and Y. Ne'eman
THE EIGHTFOLD WAY: *A Review—With a Collection of Reprints*

W. A. Harrison **PSEUDOPOTENTIALS IN THE THEORY OF METALS**

R. Hofstadter **ELECTRON SCATTERING AND NUCLEAR AND NUCLEON STRUCTURE:** *A Collection of Reprints with an Introduction*

M. Jacob and G. F. Chew
STRONG-INTERACTION PHYSICS: *A Lecture Note Volume*

L. P. Kadanoff and G. Baym
QUANTUM STATISTICAL MECHANICS: *Green's Function Methods in Equilibrium and Nonequilibrium Problems*

I. M. Khalatnikov and Pierre C. Hohenberg (Trans.)
AN INTRODUCTION TO THE THEORY OF SUPERFLUIDITY

A. M. Lane — **NUCLEAR THEORY:** *Pairing Force Correlations to Collective Motion*

T. Loucks — **AUGMENTED PLANE WAVE METHOD:** *A Lecture Note and Reprint Volume*

A. B. Migdal — **THE QUASIPARTICLE METHOD IN NUCLEAR THEORY**

P. Nozières — **THEORY OF INTERACTING FERMI SYSTEMS**

R. Omnès and M. Froissart
MANDELSTAM THEORY AND REGGE POLES: *An Introduction for Experimentalists*

G. E. Pake — **PARAMAGNETIC RESONANCE:** *An Introductory Monograph*

D. Pines — **THE MANY-BODY PROBLEM:** *A Lecture Note and Reprint Volume*

J. R. Schrieffer — **THEORY OF SUPERCONDUCTIVITY**

E. J. Squires — **COMPLEX ANGULAR MOMENTA AND PARTICLE PHYSICS:** *A Lecture Note and Reprint Volume*

L. Van Hove, N. M. Hugenholtz, and L. P. Howland
PROBLEMS IN QUANTUM THEORY OF MANY-PARTICLE SYSTEMS: *A Lecture Note and Reprint Volume*

The Anharmonic Crystal

Library of Congress Catalog Card Number 67-31222
Manufactured in the United States of America

This book was published December 30, 1967

to Noëlle

W. A. Benjamin, Inc.

New York, New York 10016 123456M216987

EDITOR'S FOREWORD

The problem of communicating in a coherent fashion the recent developments in the most exciting and active fields of physics seems particularly pressing today. The enormous growth in the number of physicists has tended to make the familiar channels of communication considerably less effective. It has become increasingly difficult for experts in a given field to keep up with the current literature; the novice can only be confused. What is needed is both a consistent account of a field and the presentation of a definite "point of view" concerning it. Formal monographs cannot meet such a need in a rapidly developing field, and, perhaps more important, the review article seems to have fallen into disfavor. Indeed, it would seem that the people most actively engaged in developing a given field are the people least likely to write at length about it.

"Frontiers in Physics" has been conceived in an effort to improve the situation in several ways. First, to take advantage of the fact that the leading physicists today frequently give a series of lectures, a graduate seminar, or a graduate course in their special fields of interest. Such lectures serve to summarize the present status of a rapidly developing field and may well constitute the only coherent account available at the time. Often, notes on lectures exist (prepared by the lecturer himself, by graduate students, or by postdoctoral fellows) and have been distributed in mimeographed form on a limited basis. One of the principal purposes of the "Frontiers in Physics" series is to make such notes available to a wider audience of physicists.

It should be emphasized that lecture notes are necessarily rough and informal, both in style and content, and those in the series will prove no exception. This is as it should be. The point of the series is to offer new, rapid, more informal, and, it is hoped, more effective ways for physicists to teach one another. The point is lost if only elegant notes qualify.

A second way to improve communication in very active fields of physics is by the publication of collections of reprints of recent articles. Such collections are themselves useful to people working in the field. The value of the reprints would; however, seem much enhanced if the collection would be accompanied by an introduction of moderate length, which would serve to tie the collection together and, necessarily, constitute a brief survey of the present status of the field. Again, it is appropriate that such an introduction be informal, in keeping with the active character of the field.

A third possibility for the series might be called an informal monograph, to connote the fact that it represents an intermediate step between lecture notes and formal monographs. It would offer the author an opportunity to present his views of a field that has developed to the point at which a summation might prove extraordinarily fruitful, but for which a formal monograph might not be feasible or desirable.

Fourth, there are the contemporary classics - papers or lectures which constitute a particularly valuable approach to the teaching and learning of physics today. Here one thinks of fields that lie at the heart of much of present-day research, but whose essentials are by now well understood, such as quantum electrodynamics or magnetic resonance. In such fields some of the best pedagogical material is not readily available, either because it consists of papers long out of print or lectures that have never been published.

"Frontiers in Physics" is designed to be flexible in editorial format. Authors are encouraged to use as many of the foregoing approaches as seem desirable for the project at hand. The publishing format for the series is in keeping with its intentions. In most cases both paperbound and clothbound editions of each book are available.

Finally, suggestions from interested readers as to format, contributors, and contributions will be most welcome.

David Pines

Urbana, Illinois
August 1964

PREFACE

In February 1964, at the invitation of Professor J. Bardeen, I gave a series of seminar lectures entitled "Selected Topics in Lattice Dynamics" at the University of Illinois. This research monograph, which grew out of these lectures, covers a molecular field theory of the equilibrium properties of anharmonic crystals. Chapters 1 to 4 and a part of Chapter 6 deal with the classical aspect of the theory; the remainder treats most of its quantum theoretical counterpart.

Various aspects of the theory of anharmonicity had captured my attention since my days as a student under the late Professor W. Pauli at the E. T. H. in Zürich. Some ten years ago I developed a renewed interest in the subject during some investigations on the high temperature limit of the thermal conductivity of insulators. It became apparent that the newly-established theories of irreversible processes could not directly be applied to this problem owing to the presence, in an infinite series, of non-dissipative first-order phonon-phonon interactions. Together with some older preoccupations of mine this prompted me to reconsider the whole equilibrium theory of anharmonic crystals. The approach, first outlined in Ref. 13, was subsequently developed at Illinois. The idea of writing this monograph was born there.

The material of Chapters 1 to 3 and, in part, of Chapter 6, is the content of my 1964 Illinois lecture notes. Some of the research needed to prepare Chapter 4 also was conducted at Illinois in the spring of 1965. Chapters 5 and 6 are, respectively, part of the material of a graduate course on solid-state theory held at the University of Lausanne in 1965-66 and of seminar lectures delivered at the University of Geneva in 1966-67.

The presentation of the monograph is primarily inductive, parallelling the original development of the research. The text is almost entirely self-contained; a few calculations have occasionally been left as exercises. Most of the numerical examples are given in the last chapter, together with a discussion of further applications and possible developments of the theory.

This monograph is intended primarily for theoreticians. However, I have tried to make the sections dealing with the thermal properties useful to experimentalists. The reader having a basic training in quantum mechanics, statistical mechanics, and solid-state physics should be able to follow the text.

It is a pleasure to acknowledge the inspiration, the support, and the assistance received from the following sources.

Through a couple of decisive questions, Professors L. V. Hove and W. Kohn contributed to the orientation of my research work. The development of my investigations was stimulated by enriching comments and suggestions from Professors G. Baym, L. P. Kadanoff, D. Pines, and J. Bardeen. Confrontation of ideas and results with Professors R. H. Brout and, lately, L. H. Nosanow was most helpful. Numerous discussions with Dr. E. Ascher deeply influenced the last stage of this work. The great help and encouragements of these authors are most gratefully acknowledged.

I should like to express my gratitude to Professor D. Pines for suggesting this monograph and my indebtedness to the governing bodies and the directors of the Battelle Memorial Institute, the University of Illinois, the Universities of Lausanne, Neuchâtel, and Geneva, through the Intercantonal convention for graduate teaching in physics, for making this project possible and for the generous support granted to me during the preparation of the text.

I wish to thank Dr. S. Zimering and M. R. Ritter for their alert and helpful assistance in mathematical and numerical analysis. The manuscript has been reviewed by Mr. A. F. Kugler, Miss M. Beer and Mr. P. Fabesch, to whom I should like to express my deep-felt appreciation. The latter also goes to Mme L. Amiguet and Mlle E. Zioerjen for their patient and skillful cooperation in the preparation of the typescript, and to M. R. Bosson for his expert execution of the drawings.

Ph. Choquard

Geneva

September, 1967

CONTENTS

Chapter 1

INTRODUCTION

In this chapter we wish to formulate the problem of the vibrating crystal lattice, thereby introducing some of the concepts important for the subsequent development of the theory. In the first section we lay down the assumptions on which the former will be built. Next, suitable expressions for the crystal potential are established and compared with standard ones. Finally, in the third section the classical problem of the specific heat at constant volume is discussed in the traditional manner, and used to indicate one of the reasons motivating the development of an improved theory of anharmonicity.

1-1 ASSUMPTIONS

Let us consider a non-conducting ideal crystal lattice. Let $\underset{\sim}{a}_1$, $\underset{\sim}{a}_2$ and $\underset{\sim}{a}_3$ be the primitive translation vectors of the elementary cell of the lattice, assumed to contain N such cells. Let $\underset{\sim}{R}_s$ be a crystal translation vector, given by an integral linear combination of the primitive translation vectors, that is

$$\underset{\sim}{R}_s = s_1 \underset{\sim}{a}_1 + s_2 \underset{\sim}{a}_2 + s_3 \underset{\sim}{a}_3 \; ^{\dagger} \tag{1-1}$$

Let each cell contain n_o atoms. The static equilibrium position of a nucleus n in a cell s will be designated by $\underset{\sim}{R}_{sn}$ and the actual position by

$$\underset{\sim}{r}_{sn} = \underset{\sim}{R}_{sn} + \underset{\sim}{u}_{sn} \tag{1-2}$$

$\underset{\sim}{u}_{sn}$ being the nuclear displacement vector from its static equilibrium position $\underset{\sim}{R}_{sn}$.

The crystal lattice energy is written as

$$E = T + V \tag{1-3}$$

The kinetic energy reads

$$T = 1/2 \sum_{sn} M_n \dot{\underset{\sim}{u}}_{sn}^2 \tag{1-4}$$

where M_n stands for the mass of an atom of type n . The potential energy will be assumed to consist of a sum of two, three, and more body interaction energies, that is

$$V = V(\text{2-body}) + V(\text{3-body}) + \ldots\ldots \tag{A-1}$$

where

---

† Note that here s is an index which labels a given cell and represents a set of three integers.

$$V(\text{2-body}) = 1/2 \sum_{(sn) \neq (s'n')} \varphi_{(2)} (\underset{\sim}{r}_{s'n'} - \underset{\sim}{r}_{sn}) \tag{1-5}$$

$$V(\text{3-body}) = 1/3! \sum_{\substack{(sn) \neq (s'n') \\ (s'n') \neq (s''n'') \\ (s''n'') \neq (sn)}} \varphi_{(3)} (\underset{\sim}{r}_{s'n'} - \underset{\sim}{r}_{sn}; \underset{\sim}{r}_{s''n''} - \underset{\sim}{r}_{sn}) \tag{1-6}$$

each $\varphi_{(m)}$ being derived from molecular physics calculations which consist of the elimination of the electronic coordinates from the total system nuclei and electrons under application of the adiabatic hypothesis ([1] Ch. IV § 14). Despite the relative importance of three and more body interaction energies, the present analysis will be limited to taking into account V(2-body) with central forces only while keeping in mind that the methods developed here will have to be applicable to the other contributions as well †. The crystal potential considered here will therefore read

$$V = 1/2 \sum_{(sn) \neq (s'n')} \varphi(|\underset{\sim}{r}_{s'n'} - \underset{\sim}{r}_{sn}|) \ ‡ \tag{1-7}$$

The next assumption, commonly made in lattice dynamics, is that $\varphi(r)$ belongs to the class of functions infinitely differentiable, except at $r = 0$, that is

$$\varphi(r) \in C_\infty, \quad r \neq 0 \tag{A-2}$$

---

† A systematic study of the effects of three-body forces on the absolute stability of rare gas crystals, alkali-halides, II-VI and III-V compounds, conducted in our Institute by L. Jansen and collaborators, has indeed proved to solve many puzzling questions of crystal physics. (See f.i. L. Jansen, Phys. Rev. A 135, 1292-1306, 1964; E. Lombardi & L. Jansen, Phys. Rev. A 136, 1011-1023, 1964.)

‡ $\varphi_{(2)}$ is written without index for simplicity of notation. Further, $|\underset{\sim}{X}| = X$ means absolute value of the vector $\underset{\sim}{X}$.

Third, the periodic boundary conditions of Born and von Kàrmàn will be assumed in the description of the ideal crystal lattice considered. This permits the introduction of lattice wave coordinates by means of the unitary transformation

$$\underset{\sim}{u}_{sn} = \frac{1}{\sqrt{N}} \sum_{\underset{\sim}{q}} e^{i\underset{\sim}{q}\underset{\sim}{R}_s} \underset{\sim}{u}_{\underset{\sim}{q}n} \tag{A-3}$$

where $\underset{\sim}{q}$ is a wave vector belonging to the first Brillouin zone of the reciprocal lattice. If this lattice has primitive translation vectors designated by $\underset{\sim}{b}_1$, $\underset{\sim}{b}_2$, $\underset{\sim}{b}_3$ and if one sets $N = L^3$, one has

$$\underset{\sim}{q} = \frac{2\pi}{L} (n_1\underset{\sim}{b}_1 + n_2\underset{\sim}{b}_2 + n_3\underset{\sim}{b}_3) \tag{1-8}$$

where n_1, n_2 and n_3 are integers running from 1 to L or from $-\frac{L}{2} + 1$ to $+\frac{L}{2}$. The complex amplitude $\underset{\sim}{u}_{\underset{\sim}{q}n}$ satisfies the reality condition

$$\underset{\sim}{u}_{-\underset{\sim}{q}n}^{*} = \underset{\sim}{u}_{\underset{\sim}{q}n} \tag{1-9}$$

where * means complex conjugate. Owing to the orthogonality relations

$$\underset{\sim}{b}_i \cdot \underset{\sim}{a}_k = \delta_{ik} \tag{1-10}$$

where δ_{ik} is the Kronecker symbol, a matrix element of the transformation reads

$$\frac{1}{\sqrt{L^3}} \exp (i\underset{\sim}{q}.\underset{\sim}{R}_s) \equiv \frac{1}{\sqrt{L^3}} \exp \left[\frac{2i\pi}{L} (n_1s_1 + n_2s_2 + n_3s_3) \right] \tag{1-11}$$

and in fact it is in this form that the introduction of lattice wave coordinates has to be understood for any crystal lattice.

From the coordinates $\underset{\sim}{u}_{\underset{\sim}{q}n}$ one usually goes over to normal mode coordinates by means of an additional transformation, namely

$$\underset{\sim}{u}_{\underset{\sim}{q}n} = \frac{1}{\sqrt{M_n}} \sum_j \underset{\sim}{e}_n^{\,j}(\underset{\sim}{q})\, Q_{\underset{\sim}{q}j} \tag{1-12}$$

where j is a branch index running from 1 to 3 n_o and $\underset{\sim}{e}_n^{\,j}(\underset{\sim}{q})$ are polarization vectors, the latter being the eigenvectors of a certain eigenvalue problem. Whereas this problem has to be formulated in some scheme of approximations, the unitary transformation (A-3) is, on the contrary, model independent. The lattice wave coordinates $\underset{\sim}{u}_{\underset{\sim}{q}n}$ so introduced represent an excellent choice of collective coordinates well suited to convey interparticle motional correlation in ordered systems. In such systems the particle indices can be identified with lattice site indices, no permutation of site assignement having to be considered. The absolute amplitudes of motion of the particles, however, are not limited to the cells within which their mean positions are located.

Lastly, and for illustrative purposes, it will often be instrumental to supplement assumption (A-2) by a stronger one, namely that $\varphi(r)$ be Fourier analyzable. In these cases we shall set

$$\begin{aligned} \varphi(\underset{\sim}{r}) &= \sum_{\underset{\sim}{k}} e^{i\,\underset{\sim}{k}\cdot\underset{\sim}{r}}\, \overline{\varphi}(\underset{\sim}{k}) \\ \overline{\varphi}(\underset{\sim}{k}) &= \frac{1}{\upsilon} \int_{\upsilon} d^3r\, e^{-i\,\underset{\sim}{k}\cdot\underset{\sim}{r}}\, \varphi(r) \end{aligned} \tag{A-2a}$$

where υ is the volume of the crystal. That this assumption is stronger than (A-2) can readily be seen in noticing that for $\overline{\varphi}(o)$ to exist, $\varphi(r)$ has not to be more singular than $r^{-2}.\ \ell n\ r$.

1-2 EXPRESSIONS FOR THE CRYSTAL POTENTIAL

One problem in lattice dynamics is to write down convenient expressions for the crystal potential. For the case of a Bravais lattice ($n_o = 1$), to begin with, the potential energy

$$V = 1/2 \sum_{s \neq s'} \varphi(|\underset{\sim}{R}_{s'} - \underset{\sim}{R}_s + \underset{\sim}{u}_{s'} - \underset{\sim}{u}_s|) \tag{1-7}$$

will be expressed as follows : First, we introduce relative indices and translation vectors by setting

$$s' - s = \rho \qquad \rho = 1, \ldots. N-1 \tag{1-13}$$

$$\underset{\sim}{R}_{s'} - \underset{\sim}{R}_s = \underset{\sim}{R}_\rho{}^{\dagger} \tag{1-14}$$

Second, and with the help of the unitary transformation (A-3), we have

$$\underset{\sim}{u}_{s'} - \underset{\sim}{u}_s = \underset{\sim}{u}_{(s+\rho)} - \underset{\sim}{u}_s = \frac{1}{\sqrt{N}} \sum_{\underset{\sim}{q}} (e^{i\underset{\sim}{q}\underset{\sim}{R}_\rho} - 1)\, e^{i\underset{\sim}{q}\underset{\sim}{R}_s}\, \underset{\sim}{u}_{\underset{\sim}{q}} \tag{1-15}$$

The quantity in parenthesis

$$\exp(i\underset{\sim}{q}\underset{\sim}{R}_\rho) - 1 \equiv \eta_\rho(\underset{\sim}{q}) \tag{1-16}$$

---

† Again ρ is an index which labels neighboring cells and represents a set of three integers.

can conveniently be defined as eigenvalue of the difference and displacement operator

$$\eta_\rho \cdot \equiv \left\{ \exp(\underset{\sim}{R}_\rho \, \partial / \partial \underset{\sim}{R}_s) - 1 \right\}^{\dagger} . \tag{1-17}$$

applying to the partial wave $e^{i\underset{\sim}{q}\underset{\sim}{R}_s}$. The relative nuclear displacement vectors can then be written as

$$\underset{\sim}{u}_{s'} - \underset{\sim}{u}_s = \eta_\rho \underset{\sim}{u}_s \tag{1-18}$$

in such a way that

$$\varphi(|\underset{\sim}{R}_{s'} - \underset{\sim}{R}_s + \underset{\sim}{u}_{s'} - \underset{\sim}{u}_s|) \rightarrow \varphi(|\underset{\sim}{R}_\rho + \eta_\rho \underset{\sim}{u}_s|) \tag{1-19}$$

Assuming for the moment Eq. (A-2a) and substituting $\underset{\sim}{R}_\rho + \eta_\rho \underset{\sim}{u}_s$ for $\underset{\sim}{r}$, the potential energy takes the illustrative form

$$V = 1/2 \sum_{s\rho\underset{\sim}{k}} \exp(i\eta_\rho \underset{\sim}{u}_s \cdot \underset{\sim}{k}) \quad \exp(i\underset{\sim}{k}\underset{\sim}{R}_\rho) \, \overline{\varphi}(\underset{\sim}{k}) \tag{1-20}$$

More generally, however, making use only of the differentiability assumption (A-2) and defining

$$\partial / \partial \underset{\sim}{r} \, \varphi(r) \equiv \underset{\sim}{p} \, \varphi(r) \tag{1-21}$$

for all $r \neq 0$, the r.h.s. of (1-19) can be expanded in a Taylor series of the relative nuclear displacement vectors $\eta_\rho \underset{\sim}{u}_s$, so that Eq. (1-7) can formally be written as

---

† Note that by definition $R_\rho \neq \underset{\sim}{R}_s$ so that $\underset{\sim}{R}_\rho$ commutes with $\partial / \partial \underset{\sim}{R}_s$. Furthermore, $\eta_\rho(\underset{\sim}{q})$ is independent of the lattice constant by virtue of Eq. (1-11).

$$V = 1/2 \sum_{s\rho} \exp(\eta_\rho \underset{\sim}{u}_s \cdot \underset{\sim}{p})\, \varphi(R_\rho) \tag{1-22}$$

$$\equiv 1/2 \sum_{s\rho} \Big(1 + \eta_\rho \underset{\sim}{u}_s \cdot \underset{\sim}{p} + 1/2\,(\eta_\rho \underset{\sim}{u}_s \cdot \underset{\sim}{p})^2$$

$$+ \frac{1}{3!}(\eta_\rho \underset{\sim}{u}_s \cdot \underset{\sim}{p})^3 + \frac{1}{4!}(\eta_\rho \underset{\sim}{u}_s \cdot \underset{\sim}{p})^4 + \ldots\Big)\, \varphi(R_\rho) \tag{1-22a}$$

It is the compact operator form (1-22) of the crystal potential which will mostly be used throughout this monograph.

If three-body interactions have to be considered, a second set of relative indices, translation vectors and operators are introduced, namely

$$s'' - s = \rho' \qquad \rho' = 1, \ldots\ldots N-2$$

$$\underset{\sim}{R}_{s''} - \underset{\sim}{R}_s = \underset{\sim}{R}_{\rho'}$$

$$\underset{\sim}{u}_{s''} - \underset{\sim}{u}_s = \eta_{\rho'} \underset{\sim}{u}_s$$

$$\underset{\sim}{p}' \cdot \varphi(\underset{\sim}{r}, \underset{\sim}{r}') = \partial/\partial \underset{\sim}{r}'\, \varphi(\underset{\sim}{r}, \underset{\sim}{r}')$$

Assuming $\varphi_{(3)}(\underset{\sim}{r}, \underset{\sim}{r}')$ twice Fourier analyzable, that is

$$\varphi_{(3)}(\underset{\sim}{r}, \underset{\sim}{r}') = \sum_{\underset{\sim}{k}\underset{\sim}{k}'} \exp(i\underset{\sim}{k} \cdot \underset{\sim}{r} + i\underset{\sim}{k}' \cdot \underset{\sim}{r}')\, \overline{\varphi}_{(3)}(\underset{\sim}{k}, \underset{\sim}{k}')$$

$$\overline{\varphi}_{(3)}(\underset{\sim}{k}, \underset{\sim}{k}') = \frac{1}{\upsilon^2} \int d^3r \int d^3r' \exp(-i\underset{\sim}{k} \cdot \underset{\sim}{r} - i\underset{\sim}{k}' \cdot \underset{\sim}{r}')\, \varphi_{(3)}(\underset{\sim}{r}, \underset{\sim}{r}')$$

the three-body contribution reads

$$V(\text{3-body}) = \frac{1}{3!} \sum_{s\rho\rho'\underset{\sim}{k}\underset{\sim}{k}'} \exp(i\eta_\rho \underset{\sim}{u}_s \cdot \underset{\sim}{k} + i\eta_{\rho'} \underset{\sim}{u}_s \cdot \underset{\sim}{k}')$$

$$\times \quad \exp(i\underset{\sim}{k} \cdot \underset{\sim}{R}_\rho + i\underset{\sim}{k}' \cdot \underset{\sim}{R}_{\rho'})\, \overline{\varphi}_{(3)}(\underset{\sim}{k}, \underset{\sim}{k}') \qquad (1\text{-}23)$$

More generally this contribution assumes the operator form

$$V(\text{3-body}) = \frac{1}{3!} \sum_{s\rho\rho'} \exp(\eta_\rho \underset{\sim}{u}_s \cdot \underset{\sim}{p} + \eta_{\rho'} \underset{\sim}{u}_s \cdot \underset{\sim}{p}')\, \varphi_{(3)}(\underset{\sim}{R}_\rho, \underset{\sim}{R}_{\rho'}) \qquad (1\text{-}24)$$

Finally, for polyatomic lattices, we further define

$$n' - n = \nu$$

$$\underset{\sim}{R}_{s'n'} - \underset{\sim}{R}_{sn} = \underset{\sim}{R}_{\rho\nu}$$

$$\underset{\sim}{u}_{s'n'} - \underset{\sim}{u}_{sn} = \eta_{\rho\nu} \underset{\sim}{u}_{sn}$$

$$= \frac{1}{\sqrt{N}} \sum_{\underset{\sim}{q}} \left[\exp(i\underset{\sim}{q} \cdot \underset{\sim}{R}_\rho)\, \underset{\sim}{u}_{q(n+\nu)} - \underset{\sim}{u}_{qn}\right] \exp(i\underset{\sim}{q}\underset{\sim}{R}_s) \qquad (1\text{-}25)$$

and, in the case of two-body forces, the summations over sns'n' become $\sum_{sn\rho\nu}$ whereby $\sum_{sn}$ amounts to Nn_o whereas

$$\sum_{\rho\nu} = \sum_{(\rho=0),\,\nu} + \sum_{(\rho\neq 0),\,\nu} = (n_o - 1) + n_o(N - 1) = n_oN - 1 \,,$$

the total being $Nn_o(Nn_o - 1)$ as it should be.

It is worth discussing now the traditional expression for the crystal potential. For a Bravais lattice, this is obtained by breaking the series expansion (1-22a) after the quartic term, that is

$$V_t = 1/2 \sum_{s\rho} \Big(1 + \eta_\rho \underset{\sim}{u}_s \cdot \underset{\sim}{p} + 1/2\, (\eta_\rho \underset{\sim}{u}_s \cdot \underset{\sim}{p})^2$$

$$+ 1/3!\, (\eta_\rho \underset{\sim}{u}_s \cdot \underset{\sim}{p})^3 + 1/4!\, (\eta_\rho \underset{\sim}{u}_s \cdot \underset{\sim}{p})^4 \Big)\, \varphi(R_\rho) \qquad (1\text{-}26)$$

where the subscript t stands for "truncated". The first term represents the static crystal potential energy

$$V_{st} = 1/2\, N \sum_\rho \varphi(R_\rho) \qquad (1\text{-}27)$$

The second term vanishes for the usual reason that the lattice sites are points of static equilibrium. Alternatively, this also follows from an important property of the factor $\sum_s \exp(i\underset{\sim}{q}\underset{\sim}{R}_s)$, namely

$$\sum_s \exp(i\underset{\sim}{q}\underset{\sim}{R}_s) = \Delta(\underset{\sim}{q}) = \begin{cases} N & \text{for } \underset{\sim}{q} = 0 \text{ or } 2\pi\underset{\sim}{\tau} \\ 0 & \text{otherwise} \end{cases} \qquad (1\text{-}28)$$

where $\underset{\sim}{\tau}$ is a translation vector of the reciprocal lattice given by $\tau_1 \underset{\sim}{b}_1 + \tau_2 \underset{\sim}{b}_2 + \tau_3 \underset{\sim}{b}_3$, τ_1, τ_2 and τ_3 being any positive or negative integers. For, applying the relation (1-28) to the second term of V_t yields contributions proportional to $\eta_\rho(2\pi\underset{\sim}{\tau})\, u_{2\pi\underset{\sim}{\tau}}$ which vanish identically by virtue of Eqs (1-16) and (1-10).

The third term is the harmonic part of the crystal potential which usually serves to define an unperturbed Hamiltonian, a set of polarization vectors $\underset{\sim}{e}^j(\underset{\sim}{q})$ and frequencies $\omega_{\underset{\sim}{q}j}$ of harmonic oscillators. In writing indices α or β, for the x, y, z components of a vector, this part reads, with the subscript h standing for harmonic

$$V_h = 1/4 \sum_{s\rho\alpha\beta} (\eta_\rho u_{s\alpha}\, \eta_\rho u_{s\beta} p_\alpha p_\beta)\, \varphi(R_\rho) \qquad (1\text{-}29)$$

With Eqs (A-3), (1-28) and (1-9) it becomes

$$V_h = 1/2\, M \sum_{\underset{\sim}{q}\alpha\beta} D_{\alpha\beta}(\underset{\sim}{q}) u_{\underset{\sim}{q}\alpha} u_{\underset{\sim}{q}\beta}^{*} \qquad (1\text{-}30)$$

where the elements of Born's dynamical matrix $D(\underset{\sim}{q})$ are given by

$$D_{\alpha\beta}(\underset{\sim}{q}) = \frac{1}{M}\frac{1}{2} \sum_{\rho} \eta_\rho(q)\eta_\rho^{*}(\underset{\sim}{q}) p_\alpha p_\beta\, \varphi(R_\rho)$$

$$= \frac{1}{M} \sum_{\rho} (1 - \cos \underset{\sim}{q}\underset{\sim}{R}_\rho)\ \varphi_{\alpha\beta}(R_\rho) \qquad (1\text{-}31)$$

where

$$\varphi_{\alpha\beta}(R_\rho) = p_\alpha p_\beta\, \varphi(R_\rho) \qquad (1\text{-}32)$$

Whenever assumption (A-2a) applies it may be convenient to rewrite the dynamical matrix in terms of the Fourier components of the potential $\varphi(r)$, since this enables us to carry out the summation over the neighboring R_ρ, that is

$$D_{\alpha\beta}(\underset{\sim}{q}) = \frac{1}{M} \sum_{\rho \underset{\sim}{k}} \left[1 - 1/2 \left\{\exp(i\underset{\sim}{q}\underset{\sim}{R}_\rho) + \exp(-i\underset{\sim}{q}\underset{\sim}{R}_\rho)\right\}\right] \times \exp(i\underset{\sim}{k}\underset{\sim}{R}_\rho)\ \bar{\varphi}_{\alpha\beta}(\underset{\sim}{k}) \qquad (1\text{-}33)$$

where

$$\bar{\varphi}_{\alpha\beta}(\underset{\sim}{k}) = -k_\alpha k_\beta\, \bar{\varphi}(\underset{\sim}{k}) \qquad (1\text{-}34)$$

In inverting the ρ and $\underset{\sim}{k}$ summations and noticing that one can add the term with $\rho = 0$ since it yields nothing, one obtains with Eq. (1-28)

$$D_{\alpha\beta}(\underset{\sim}{q}) = \frac{1}{M} \sum_{\underset{\sim}{k}} \left(\Delta(\underset{\sim}{k}) - 1/2 \left(\Delta(\underset{\sim}{k} + \underset{\sim}{q}) + \Delta(\underset{\sim}{k} - \underset{\sim}{q})\right) \right) \bar{\varphi}_{\alpha\beta}(\underset{\sim}{k}) \quad 1\text{-}35)$$

which can be rewritten formally as

$$D_{\alpha\beta}(\underset{\sim}{q}) = \frac{1}{M} \sum_{\underset{\sim}{k}} \left\{ (1 - \operatorname{Cosh} \underset{\sim}{q}.\partial/\partial \underset{\sim}{k}) \, \Delta(\underset{\sim}{k}) \right\} \bar{\varphi}_{\alpha\beta}(\underset{\sim}{k}) \qquad (1\text{-}36)$$

or, more compactly, as

$$D_{\alpha\beta}(\underset{\sim}{q}) = N \frac{1}{M} \sum_{\underset{\sim}{K}} (1 - \operatorname{Cosh} \underset{\sim}{q}.\partial/\partial \underset{\sim}{K}) \; \bar{\varphi}_{\alpha\beta}(\underset{\sim}{K}) \qquad (1\text{-}37)$$

where Cosh means hyperbolic cosine and $\underset{\sim}{K} = 2\pi\underset{\sim}{\tau}$, $\underset{\sim}{\tau}$ being a translation vector of the reciprocal lattice. If the normal coordinates are now introduced by means of the transformation

$$u_{\underset{\sim}{q}\alpha} = \frac{1}{\sqrt{M}} \sum_{j} e_{\alpha}^{j}(\underset{\sim}{q}) \, Q_{\underset{\sim}{q}j} \qquad (1\text{-}12)$$

the eigenvalue problem becomes

$$\sum_{\beta} D_{\alpha\beta}(\underset{\sim}{q}) \, e_{\beta}^{j}(\underset{\sim}{q}) = e_{\alpha}^{j}(\underset{\sim}{q}) \omega_{\underset{\sim}{q}j}^{2} \quad (j = 1, 2, 3) \qquad (1\text{-}38)$$

and V_h reads accordingly

$$V_h = 1/2 \sum_{\underset{\sim}{q}j} \omega_{\underset{\sim}{q}j}^{2} Q_{\underset{\sim}{q}j} . Q_{\underset{\sim}{q}j}^{*} \qquad (1\text{-}39)$$

Together with the kinetic energy written in terms of the momenta

$$P_{\underset{\sim}{q}j} = \dot{Q}_{\underset{\sim}{q}j} \tag{1-40}$$

the crystal Hamiltonian in the harmonic approximation takes the standard form

$$H_h = 1/2 \sum_{\underset{\sim}{q}j} \left\{ P_{\underset{\sim}{q}j} P_{\underset{\sim}{q}j}^* + \omega_{\underset{\sim}{q}j}^2 Q_{\underset{\sim}{q}j} Q_{\underset{\sim}{q}j}^* \right\} \tag{1-41}$$

It is sometimes convenient to go over from the normal coordinates to the set of action-angle variables which define the complex amplitudes of the elastic waves

$$a_{qj} \equiv \sqrt{A_{\underset{\sim}{q}j}} \exp(i\alpha_{\underset{\sim}{q}j}) \tag{1-42}$$

by means of the canonical transformation

$$Q_{\underset{\sim}{q}j} = \sqrt{\frac{1}{2\omega_{\underset{\sim}{q}j}}} \left(a_{\underset{\sim}{q}j} + a_{-\underset{\sim}{q}j}^* \right) \tag{1-43}$$

$$iP_{\underset{\sim}{q}j} = \sqrt{\frac{\omega_{qj}}{2}} \left(a_{\underset{\sim}{q}j} - a_{-\underset{\sim}{q}j}^* \right) \tag{1-44}$$

With these variables H_h becomes

$$H_h = \sum_{\underset{\sim}{q}j} \omega_{\underset{\sim}{q}j} a_{\underset{\sim}{q}j}^* a_{\underset{\sim}{q}j} = \sum_{\underset{\sim}{q}j} \omega_{\underset{\sim}{q}j} A_{\underset{\sim}{q}j} \tag{1-45}$$

Alternatively $Q_{\underset{\sim}{q}j}$ can be resolved into real and imaginary parts

$$Q_{\underset{\sim}{q}j} = c_{\underset{\sim}{q}j} + id_{\underset{\sim}{q}j} \tag{1-46}$$

The reality condition (1-9) then becomes

$$c_{\underset{\sim}{q}j} = c_{-\underset{\sim}{q}j}$$

$$d_{\underset{\sim}{q}j} = -d_{-\underset{\sim}{q}j}$$

and the harmonic Hamiltonian reads

$$H_h = \sum_{\underset{\sim}{q}j}{}' (\dot{c}_{\underset{\sim}{q}j}^2 + \dot{d}_{\underset{\sim}{q}j}^2) + \omega_{\underset{\sim}{q}j}^2 (c_{\underset{\sim}{q}j}^2 + d_{\underset{\sim}{q}j}^2) \tag{1-47}$$

Here the $'$ means that one has to sum over half of the first Brillouin zone since half of the c_{qj} and d_{qj} variables are linearly independent. We shall not deal further with the theory of lattice dynamics in the harmonic approximation but refer the reader to the recent and most comprehensive monograph on this subject by A.A. Maradudin, E.W. Montroll and G.H. Weiss for more information [2].

Before entering the discussion of the anharmonic terms of V_t, a key quantity relevant to the entire analysis will be introduced here : It is the space average product of any two components of the relative nuclear displacement vectors $\eta_\rho \underset{\sim}{u}_s$, or their correlation function at equal times, namely

$$\begin{aligned} \Lambda_\rho^{\alpha\beta} &\equiv \frac{1}{N} \sum_s \eta_\rho u_{s\alpha} \; \eta_\rho u_{s\beta} \\ &= \frac{1}{N} \sum_{\underset{\sim}{q}} \eta_\rho(\underset{\sim}{q}) \; \eta_\rho^*(\underset{\sim}{q}) \; u_\alpha(\underset{\sim}{q}) \, u_\beta^*(\underset{\sim}{q}) \\ &= \frac{2}{NM} \sum_{\underset{\sim}{q}jj'} (1-\cos \underset{\sim}{q}\underset{\sim}{R}_\rho) \; e_\alpha^j(\underset{\sim}{q}) \; e_\beta^{j'}(-\underset{\sim}{q}) \; Q_{\underset{\sim}{q}j} \cdot Q_{\underset{\sim}{q}j'}^* \end{aligned} \tag{1-48}$$

With this definition, the following relation has to be noticed

$$1/4 \sum_{\rho\alpha\beta} \Lambda_{\rho}^{\alpha\beta} \quad \varphi_{\alpha\beta}(R_{\rho})$$

$$= 1/2 \ 1/NM \sum_{\underset{\sim}{q}jj'} \sum_{\rho\alpha\beta} (1-\cos \underset{\sim}{q}\underset{\sim}{R}_{\rho}) \ e_{\alpha}^{j} (\underset{\sim}{q}) \ e_{\beta}^{j'} (-\underset{\sim}{q})$$

$$\times \ \varphi_{\alpha\beta}(R_{\rho})Q_{\underset{\sim}{q}j}Q_{\underset{\sim}{q}j}^{*} = \frac{1}{N} \frac{1}{2} \sum_{\underset{\sim}{q}j} \omega_{\underset{\sim}{q}j}^{2} Q_{\underset{\sim}{q}j} Q_{\underset{\sim}{q}j}^{*}$$

that is

$$1/4 \sum_{\rho\alpha\beta} \Lambda_{\rho}^{\alpha\beta} \ \varphi_{\alpha\beta}(R_{\rho}) = 1/N \ V_{h} \qquad (1\text{-}49)$$

The fourth and fifth terms of Eq. (1-26) represent the cubic and quartic anharmonic interaction energies designated by V_{3-a} and V_{4-a} respectively. The cubic part reads

$$V_{3-a} = 1/2 \sum_{s\rho} 1/3! \ (\eta_{\rho}\underset{\sim}{u}_{s} \cdot \underset{\sim}{p})^{3} \ \varphi(R_{\rho})$$

$$= 1/2 \ . \ 1/3! \sum_{\rho, \underset{\sim}{q}, \underset{\sim}{q}', \underset{\sim}{q}''} \frac{\Delta(q+q'+q'')}{(NM)^{3/2}} \ \eta_{\rho} \ \eta_{\rho}' \ \eta_{\rho}''$$

$$\times \ \varphi_{(III)} \ ee'e''QQ'Q'' \qquad (1\text{-}50)$$

where a self-explanatory shorthand notation has been used. The summation over ρ , however, has intentionally not been absorbed in the coefficients of the normal mode coordinates. Out of the trilinear sum let us consider in particular the contribution arising from any pairing between two wave vectors, for example, $\underset{\sim}{q} = -\underset{\sim}{q}'$. This makes the third vector vanish owing to the Δ function. For a Bravais lattice this particular contribution is therefore 0 since $\eta_{\rho}(0) = 0$. For a polyatomic lattice however, optical modes of 0 wave vector exist. So, if this contribution is written

$$V^{12}_{3-a} = \sum_{\gamma j''} \frac{1}{\sqrt{M}} G_\gamma \cdot e^{j''}_\gamma (0) \, Q_{0j''} \tag{1-51}$$

then, examination of the coefficient G_γ reveals the occurrence of the correlation function defined above, namely

$$G_\gamma = 3.1/3! \;\; 1/2 \; \sqrt{N} \sum_{\rho\alpha\beta} \Lambda^{\alpha\beta}_\rho \; \varphi_{\alpha\beta\gamma}(R_\rho) \tag{1-52}$$

or, in tensor form

$$G_\gamma = \sqrt{N} \;\; 1/2 \sum_\rho (1/2 \;\; \Lambda_\rho : \underset{\sim}{p}\underset{\sim}{p}) \; \varphi_\gamma \, (R_\rho) \tag{1-53}$$

The other contributions to the trilinear form (1-50) will not be further discussed here, but in the next section. As to the quartic term, it reads

$$\begin{aligned} V_{4-a} &= 1/2 \sum_{s\rho} 1/4! \;\; (\eta_\rho \underset{\sim}{u}_s \cdot \underset{\sim}{p})^4 \, \varphi(R_\rho) \\ &= 1/2 \;\; 1/4! \sum_{\rho \underset{\sim}{q}\underset{\sim}{q}'\underset{\sim}{q}''\underset{\sim}{q}'''} \frac{\Delta(q+q'+q''+q''')}{(NM)^2} \\ &\quad \times \;\; \eta_\rho \; \eta_\rho{}' \; \eta_\rho{}'' \; \eta_\rho{}''' \;\; ee'e''e'''QQ'Q''Q''' \varphi_{(IV)} \end{aligned} \tag{1-54}$$

There is again a particular contribution of interest to pick out of this quadrilinear form by pairing two by two the wave vectors, for instance $\underset{\sim}{q} = -\underset{\sim}{q}'$ and $\underset{\sim}{q}'' = -\underset{\sim}{q}'''$. There are three pairing possibilities. If this contribution is called V^{22}_{4-a} the following enlightening expression arises

$$V^{22}_{4-a} = N\ 1/2 \sum_{\rho\alpha\beta\gamma\delta} 3/4!\quad \Lambda^{\alpha\beta}_{\rho}\ \Lambda^{\gamma\delta}_{\rho}\ \varphi_{\alpha\beta\gamma\delta}\ (R_\rho) \tag{1-55}$$

or, in tensor form, and in distributing conveniently the factor $3/4! = (1/2)^3$

$$V^{22}_{4-a} = N\ 1/2 \sum_{\rho} 1/2\ (1/2\ \Lambda_\rho : \underset{\sim}{p}\underset{\sim}{p})^2\ \varphi(R_\rho) \tag{1-56}$$

The manipulations performed above permit us to anticipate the potential interest of the reduction procedure made possible by the introduction of the correlation functions $\Lambda^{\alpha\beta}_{\rho}$. However, before proceeding with the generalization of the method, the real need for an improved theory of anharmonicity has first to be established. This need will be exemplified in the next section with the classical problem of the specific heat C_υ (T) at high temperature.

1-3 CLASSICAL THEORY OF THE SPECIFIC HEAT C_υ (T)

It is generally accepted that at high temperature several effects can contribute to a temperature dependence of the specific heat at constant volume, thus yielding deviations to the classical Dulong-Petit law, which predicts a constant value of 1 K per degree of freedom. Not considering electronic contributions explicitly, there are effects due to lattice defects and to their interaction with the lattice waves, others due to the interaction between optical and acoustical modes or between optical and optical modes in polyatomic lattices, all of them adding to a background of effects due to interactions between the acoustic modes. Since this background is always present, it seems wise trying first to exhaust the possibilities offered by the interactions between acoustic modes only and establish thereby a firm step toward a clear cut interpretation of the set of high temperature specific heat data actually available. This is, among other things, what we intend to achieve in this monograph.

To get acquainted with the problem it is worth beginning with a standard path calculation of $C_\upsilon(T)$ for the supposedly well established, positive or negative, linear deviation to the Dulong - Petit law, a deviation which is assigned to the effects of four mode interactions in first order and three mode interactions in second order of perturbation theory.

The starting quantity is the partition function of the system which for a classical canonical ensemble of $3(N-1)$ degrees of freedom (a Bravais lattice at rest) reads

$$Z = \left(\frac{1}{h^3}\right)^{(N-1)} \int d\Omega \, \exp(-\beta H) \tag{1-57}$$

$$Z = e^{-\beta F} \tag{1-58}$$

where $d\Omega$ is the volume element in phase space, h is Planck's constant and $\beta = 1/KT$. Here, K stands for the Boltzmann constant and F is the free energy. Further, the internal energy U reads

$$U = -\frac{\partial}{\partial \beta} \ln Z$$

$$= kT^2 \frac{\partial}{\partial T} \ln Z \tag{1-59}$$

and the specific heat at constant volume

$$C_\upsilon = \frac{\partial U}{\partial T} = K \frac{\partial}{\partial T} T^2 \frac{\partial}{\partial T} \ln Z$$

$$= K\beta^2 \frac{\partial^2}{\partial \beta^2} \ln Z \tag{1-60}$$

Alternatively if one defines the mean value of a function 0 of the coordinates and momenta of the system by

$$\langle 0\rangle = \frac{\int d\Omega\, 0\, e^{-\beta H}}{\int d\Omega\, e^{-\beta H}} \tag{1-61}$$

then Eqs (1-59) and (1-60) take the often convenient form

$$U = \langle H\rangle \tag{1-62}$$

$$C_\upsilon = K\beta^2 \left(\langle H^2\rangle - \langle H\rangle^2\right) \tag{1-63}$$

As to the volume element $d\Omega$, if action-angle variables are used, it reads

$$d\Omega = \prod_{\underset{\sim}{q}j} dA_{\underset{\sim}{q}j} \cdot d\alpha_{\underset{\sim}{q}j} \tag{1-64}$$

and, for an harmonic crystal, for instance, one has the very familiar formula

$$\begin{aligned} Z_h &= \prod_{\underset{\sim}{q}j} \frac{1}{h} \int_0^\infty dA_{\underset{\sim}{q}j} \int_0^{2\pi} d\alpha_{\underset{\sim}{q}j} \cdot \exp(-\beta\omega_{\underset{\sim}{q}j} A_{\underset{\sim}{q}j}) \\ &= \prod_{\underset{\sim}{q}j} \frac{1}{\beta\hbar\omega_{\underset{\sim}{q}j}} \end{aligned} \tag{1-65}$$

where $\hbar$ has been set for $h/2\pi$. Since, for an ideal crystal lattice, the crystal potential is a function of the normal coordinates only, it will be more convenient to work with the $Q_{\underset{\sim}{q}j}$ and their conjugated momenta $P_{\underset{\sim}{q}j}$. The partition function is thereby written as a product of kinetic and potential contributions, the latter being evaluated in various approximations. With these variables the volume element reads

$$d\Omega = \prod_{\underset{\sim}{q}j}{}' \, dP_{\underset{\sim}{q}j} \cdot dP^*_{\underset{\sim}{q}j} \cdot dQ_{\underset{\sim}{q}j} \cdot dQ^*_{\underset{\sim}{q}j} \tag{1-66}$$

where the ' means that the product has to be taken over half of the set of wave vectors $\underset{\sim}{q}$. More precisely this number will be designated by N' with the relation

$$N = 2N' + 1$$

In introducing polar coordinates

$$P_{\underset{\sim}{q}j} = \sqrt{I_{\underset{\sim}{q}j}} \exp(-i\chi_{\underset{\sim}{q}j}) \tag{1-67}$$

$$Q_{\underset{\sim}{q}j} = \sqrt{J_{\underset{\sim}{q}j}} \exp(i\Psi_{\underset{\sim}{q}j}) \tag{1-68}$$

whereby the reality condition is noticed to imply

$$I_{\underset{\sim}{q}j} = I_{-\underset{\sim}{q}j} \qquad \chi_{\underset{\sim}{q}j} = -\chi_{\underset{\sim}{q}j}$$

$$J_{\underset{\sim}{q}j} = J_{-\underset{\sim}{q}j} \qquad \Psi_{\underset{\sim}{q}j} = -\Psi_{-\underset{\sim}{q}j}$$

the kinetic contribution to the partition function will be set

$$Z_{KE} \equiv \left(\frac{2\pi}{h^2}\right)^{3N'} \prod_{qj}{}' \int_0^\infty dI_{\underset{\sim}{q}j} \int_0^{2\pi} d\chi_{\underset{\sim}{q}j} \exp(-\beta I_{\underset{\sim}{q}j})$$

$$= \left(\frac{1}{\hbar^2 \beta}\right)^{3N'} \tag{1-69}$$

and the potential contribution

$$Z_V = \left(\frac{1}{2\pi}\right)^{3N'} \prod_{\underset{\sim}{q}j}{}' \int_0^\infty dJ_{\underset{\sim}{q}j} \int_0^{2\pi} d\Psi_{\underset{\sim}{q}j} \exp(-\beta V(\{J_{\underset{\sim}{q}j}\}, \{\Psi_{\underset{\sim}{q}j}\}))$$

(1-70)

The relative dimensions of Z_{KE} and Z_V are in principle arbitrary. Writing $[Z_V]$ for the dimension of Z_V, we have actually

$$\left[Z_V\right] = \left[J\right]^{3N'} = \left[M\ell^2\right]^{3N'}$$

Note also that a convenient normalization of Eq. (1-70) has been introduced for easying the calculation of phase averages.

We are now going to perform a calculation of $\ell n\, Z$ to the order which yields the first deviation of $C_\upsilon(T)$ from its constant Dulong-Petit value. This will be shown to arise from the following approximation, established on the basis of an expansion of the Boltzmann factor in a power series of the anharmonic crystal potential

$$\ell n\, Z = -\beta V_{st} + \ell n\, Z_h - \beta \langle V_{4-a} \rangle_h + 1/2\, \beta^2 \langle (V_{3-a})^2 \rangle_h \tag{1-71}$$

where $\langle .. \rangle_h$ means that the mean values are calculated in the harmonic approximation, that is with a weight factor $\exp(-\beta V_h)$. The first term is just the one due to the static potential energy, V_{st}, the second is the usual harmonic term

$$\begin{aligned} \ell n\, Z_h &= \ell n\, Z_{KE} + \ell n\, Z_{V,h} \\ &= 3N' \,\ell n \frac{1}{\hbar^2 \beta} + \sum_{\underset{\sim}{q}j}{}' \ell n \frac{1}{\beta \omega^2_{\underset{\sim}{q}j}} \end{aligned} \tag{1-72}$$

The third is the mean value of the quartic anharmonic part of the crystal potential. Now the mean value implies phase average and amplitude average. The phase average procedure yields the pairing rule between the wave numbers and polarization indices of any two modes occurring in the quantity to be averaged. If one designates by an upper bar the result of this operation, one recognizes that according to Eqs (1-48) and (1-54)

$$\overline{V}_{4-a} = N\, 1/2 \sum_{\substack{\rho \\ \alpha\beta\gamma\delta}} \frac{1}{8}\, \overline{\Lambda}_{\rho}^{\alpha\beta}\, \overline{\Lambda}_{\rho}^{\gamma\delta}\, \varphi_{\alpha\beta\gamma\delta}(R_\rho) \tag{1-73}$$

where

$$\overline{\Lambda}_{\rho}^{\alpha\beta} = \frac{1}{NM} \sum_{\underset{\sim}{q}j} \eta_\rho(\underset{\sim}{q})\, \eta_\rho(-\underset{\sim}{q})\, e_\alpha^j(\underset{\sim}{q})\, e_\beta^j(-\underset{\sim}{q})\, J_{\underset{\sim}{q}j} \tag{1-74}$$

and where $\Delta(0)$ has been set $= N$. In order to save some space let us define the coefficients

$$\frac{1}{M}\, \eta_\rho(\underset{\sim}{q})\, \eta_{\rho'}(-\underset{\sim}{q}')\, e_\alpha^j(\underset{\sim}{q})\, e_{\alpha'}^{j'}(-q') \equiv f_{\rho\rho'\alpha\alpha'}^{qq'jj'} \tag{1-75}$$

and agree that, wherever two indices of f are identical, they will not be repeated ; for instance

$$\overline{\Lambda}_{\rho}^{\alpha\beta} = \frac{1}{N} \sum_{\underset{\sim}{q}j} f_{\rho\alpha\beta}^{qj}\, J_{\underset{\sim}{q}j}$$

In carrying out the phase average of the fourth term in Eq. (1-71) one gets to pair one mode of the first V_{3-a} with any one of the second; there are 3! possibilities of pairing. Thus one obtains a tri-linear combination of amplitudes $J_{\underset{\sim}{q}j}$ of the form

$$\overline{(V_{3-a})^2} = N\, 1/3! \sum_{\substack{\underset{\sim}{q}\underset{\sim}{q}'\underset{\sim}{q}'' \\ jj'j''}} B_{\underset{\sim}{q}j\underset{\sim}{q}'j'\underset{\sim}{q}''j''}\, \frac{\Delta(q+q'+q'')}{N^3}\, J_{\underset{\sim}{q}j}\, J_{\underset{\sim}{q}'j'}\, J_{\underset{\sim}{q}'j'} \tag{1-76}$$

where

$$B_{\underset{\sim}{q}j\underset{\sim}{q}'j'\underset{\sim}{q}''j''} = 1/4 \sum_{\substack{\rho\rho' \\ \alpha\beta\gamma \\ \alpha'\beta'\gamma'}} f_{\rho\rho'\alpha\alpha'}^{qj}\, f_{\rho\rho'\beta\beta'}^{q'j'}\, f_{\rho\rho'\gamma\gamma'}^{q''j''} \times \varphi_{\alpha\beta\gamma}(R_\rho) \cdot \varphi_{\alpha'\beta'\gamma'}(R_{\rho'}) \tag{1-77}$$

and where the factor N comes from the relation

$$\Delta^2(\underset{\sim}{q}) = N\Delta(\underset{\sim}{q})$$

The amplitude average remains to be carried out. With

$$\langle J_{\underset{\sim}{q}j}\rangle_h = \frac{\int_0^\infty dJ_{\underset{\sim}{q}j}\, J_{\underset{\sim}{q}j}\, e^{-\beta J_{\underset{\sim}{q}j}\omega^2_{\underset{\sim}{q}j}}}{\int_0^\infty dJ_{\underset{\sim}{q}j}\, e^{-\beta J_{\underset{\sim}{q}j}\omega^2_{\underset{\sim}{q}j}}} = \frac{1}{\beta\omega^2_{\underset{\sim}{q}j}} \tag{1-78}$$

the third and fourth terms of (1-71) become

$$-\beta\langle V_{4-a}\rangle_h = -NKT\ 1/16 \sum_{\substack{\rho\alpha\beta\gamma\delta\\ \underset{\sim}{q}j\underset{\sim}{q}'j'}} f^{\underset{\sim}{q}j}_{\rho\alpha\beta}\frac{1}{\omega^2_{\underset{\sim}{q}j}} f^{\underset{\sim}{q}'j'}_{\rho\gamma\delta}\frac{1}{\omega^2_{\underset{\sim}{q}'j'}}$$

$$\times\ \varphi_{\alpha\beta\gamma\delta}(R_\rho)^{\dagger} \tag{1-79}$$

$$1/2\ \beta^2\langle (V_{3-a})^2\rangle_h = 1/2\ NKT\ 1/3! \sum_{\substack{\underset{\sim}{q}\underset{\sim}{q}'\underset{\sim}{q}''\\ jj'j''}} \frac{\Delta(q+q'+q'')}{N^3}$$

$$\times\ B_{\underset{\sim}{q}j\underset{\sim}{q}'j'\underset{\sim}{q}''j''}\cdot\frac{1}{\omega^2_{\underset{\sim}{q}j}\,\omega^2_{\underset{\sim}{q}'j'}\,\omega^2_{\underset{\sim}{q}''j''}} \tag{1-80}$$

---

† For the case where $(\underset{\sim}{q},j) = (\underset{\sim}{q}',j')$ the pairing possibilities are reduced by a factor 2 which is cancelled by the 2 arising from $\langle J^2_{\underset{\sim}{q}j}\rangle_h = 2\langle J_{\underset{\sim}{q}j}\rangle^2_h$ (see Eq.(2-26)) so that Eq. (1-79) is correct in all cases. The same consideration applies to Eq. (1-80).

Application of Eqs (1-59) and (1-60) show then that Eqs (1-79) and (1-80) contribute a correction to the internal energy proportional to T^2, and a correction to the specific heat C_υ proportional to T. One further notices that according to whether the r.h.s. of Eq. (1-79) is larger or smaller than the r.h.s. of Eq. (1-80) the slope of the linear deviation is negative or positive. One therefore observes a possibility of competition between four mode interactions in first order and three mode interactions in second order. If higher corrections to the specific heat are calculated along the same lines, more and more contributions of different origin and sign are mixed. For instance, the correction to $C_\upsilon(T)$ which is quadratic in T is the result of contributions which arise from the following interactions, where m stands for mode

6 m	1° order
4 m - 4 m; 3 m - 5 m	2° order
3 m - 4 m - 3 m	3° order
3 m - 3 m - 3 m - 3 m	4° order

The situation soon becomes hopeless, since there is no a priori reason to neglect for instance 6 mode interactions in first order versus 4 mode interactions in second order or 3 mode interactions in fourth order, as would be done with higher order calculations based on a truncated crystal potential like Eq. (1-26). It is not so much the power series expansion method applied to $\varphi(|\underset{\sim}{R}_\rho + \eta_\rho \underset{\sim}{u}_s|)$ which is questionable but its truncation and, more so, the way in which anharmonicity effects are collected so as to yield for $C_\upsilon(T)$ a power series in the temperature. Practically nothing can be said about the convergence of this series, in particular at elevated temperatures. The alternative method, developed below, will be to group together all mode interactions in first order (4, 6, .. 2n, ..), then all mode interactions in second order and so on. In this approach our key quantities will be the equilibrium correlation functions which in the harmonic approximation read

$$\langle \Lambda_\rho^{\alpha\beta} \rangle_h \equiv \lambda_\rho^{\alpha\beta} = \frac{1}{N} \sum_{\underset{\sim}{q}j} f_{\rho\alpha\beta}^{\underset{\sim}{q}j} \frac{KT}{\omega_{\underset{\sim}{q}j}^2} \tag{1-81}$$

or, in matrix form

$$\lambda_\rho = \frac{2KT}{MN} \sum_{\underset{\sim}{q}} (1 - \cos \underset{\sim}{q}\, \underset{\sim}{R}_\rho)\, D_{\underset{\sim}{q}}^{-1} \tag{1-82}$$

Appropriate summations of anharmonicity effects will then enable us to make a satisfactory theory of $C_\upsilon(T)$. Since C_υ data are derived from measurements of C_P and other thermodynamic quantities, a consistent interpretation and conversion of such data, as regards taking anharmonicity into account, is required. This will therefore necessitate a simultaneous treatment of all the relevant thermodynamic quantities within the framework of one theory, an objective toward which this monograph is aimed. Entailed in this program will be a departure from existing theories and interpretations of anharmonic thermal properties ([3], [4], [5]).

Chapter 2

PERTURBATION CALCULUS

The program sketched at the end of Chapter 1 represents a fairly vast enterprise which will be taken up in successive steps of approximations. In this Chapter, the problem of handling first and higher order anharmonic interactions will be treated in the framework of a many particle perturbation theory of classical statistics. In order to get acquainted with the method of dealing with anharmonic effects, as outlined in section (1-3), we shall begin this development with a calculation of the harmonic mean value $\langle V \rangle_h$ of V and discuss several aspects of the expressions obtained. Next, we shall establish a fundamental theorem of harmonic oscillator statistics, known as the pairing theorem. Then, the calculation of the moment and cumulant expansion of the partition function will be taken up. Finally, closed form expressions of the cumulants will be given and their properties discussed in some details.

2-1 HARMONIC MEAN VALUE OF V

Starting from the compact operator form (1-22) for the crystal potential V we wish to carry out the expectation value

$$\langle V \rangle_h = \frac{1}{2} \sum_{s\rho} \langle \exp(\eta_\rho \underset{\sim}{u}_s \cdot \underset{\sim}{p}) \rangle_h \, \varphi(R_\rho) \qquad (2\text{-}1)$$

by introducing the normal mode coordinates of amplitudes $Q_{\underset{\sim}{q}j}$ and harmonic frequency $\omega_{\underset{\sim}{q}j}$. One way of doing this is to consider that Eq. (2-1) can be written as a sum of products of independent mean values since one deals with N' independent complex amplitudes. Thus,

$$\langle V \rangle_h = \frac{1}{2} \sum_{s\rho}{}' \prod_{\underset{\sim}{q}j}{}' \left\langle \exp\left(\frac{1}{\sqrt{NM}} e^{i\underset{\sim}{q}\underset{\sim}{R}_s} \eta_\rho(\underset{\sim}{q}) \, \underset{\sim}{e}^j(\underset{\sim}{q}) \cdot \underset{\sim}{p} Q_{\underset{\sim}{q}j} + \text{c.c.} \right) \right\rangle_h$$

$$\times \; \varphi(R_\rho) \qquad (2\text{-}2)$$

where c.c means complex conjugate. If one writes $z_{s\rho}^{qj}$ for the coefficient of $Q_{\underset{\sim}{q}j}$ and suppresses the indices for evaluating a representative element of the above product, one gets

$$\langle \exp(zQ + z^* Q^*) \rangle_h$$

$$= \beta\omega^2 \frac{1}{2\pi} \int dQ dQ^* \exp(zQ + z^* Q^*) \exp(-\beta\omega^2 Q Q^*) \qquad (2\text{-}3)$$

Introducing the polar coordinates

$$Q = \sqrt{J} \exp(i\,\varphi)$$

$$z = \sqrt{|z|} \exp(i \arg z)$$

and setting for the integration variables

$$x = \beta\omega^2 J$$

$$\theta = \varphi + \arg z$$

(2-3) becomes

$$\frac{1}{2\pi}\int_0^\infty dx \int_0^\pi d\theta \, \exp\left(2\sqrt{\frac{zz^*}{\beta\omega^2}}\, x\cos\theta\right) \exp(-x)$$

$$= \int_0^\infty dx \sum_{n=0}^\infty \frac{1}{n!\,n!}\left(\frac{zz^*}{\beta\omega^2}\, x\right)^n \exp(-x)$$

$$= \sum_{n=0}^\infty \frac{1}{n!}\left(\frac{zz^*}{\beta\omega^2}\right)^n$$

$$= \exp\left(\frac{zz^*}{\beta\omega^2}\right)$$

a result obtained after interchanging summation and integration. Noticing that, according to Eqs (1-81) and (1-82)

$$\sum_{\tilde{q}j}{}' z_{s\rho}^{qj} z_{s\rho}^{qj*} \frac{1}{\beta\omega_{\tilde{q}j}^2}$$

$$= \frac{1}{2}\sum_{\substack{\tilde{q}j\\ \alpha\beta}} \frac{1}{NM}\,(2-2\cos \underset{\sim}{q}\underset{\sim}{R}_\rho)\, e_\alpha^j(\underset{\sim}{q})\, e_\beta^j(-\underset{\sim}{q})\,.$$

$$\times \frac{KT}{\omega_{\tilde{q}j}^2}\, p_\alpha p_\beta = \frac{1}{2}\langle \Lambda_\rho : \underset{\sim}{p}\underset{\sim}{p}\rangle_h \equiv \frac{1}{2}\lambda_\rho : \underset{\sim}{p}\underset{\sim}{p} \qquad (2\text{-}4)$$

Eq. (2-2) reads then

$$\langle V \rangle_h = N \frac{1}{2} \sum_{\rho} \exp(\frac{1}{2} \lambda_\rho : \underset{\sim}{p}\underset{\sim}{p}) \, \varphi(R_\rho) \tag{2-5}$$

the factor N arising from the summation over the lattice sites s .

Eq. (2-5) tells us that the problem of calculating the mean potential energy $\langle V \rangle_h$ amounts to calculating mean interatomic potentials and to summing up their contributions arising from successive shells of neighbors. Designating by $\Phi(\underset{\sim}{R}_\rho, \lambda_\rho)$ these mean potentials, one can write

$$\langle V \rangle_h = N \frac{1}{2} \sum_{\rho} \Phi(\underset{\sim}{R}_\rho, \lambda_\rho) \tag{2-6}$$

with

$$\Phi(\underset{\sim}{R}_\rho, \lambda_\rho) \equiv \exp(\frac{1}{2} \lambda_\rho : \underset{\sim}{p}\underset{\sim}{p}) \, \varphi(R_\rho) \tag{2-7}$$

It is readily observed that the operator on the r.h.s. of Eq. (2-7) represents the formal solution of a diffusion equation, the diffusion "constant" being here replaced by a diffusion "tensor". A partial differential equation for any one of the mean potentials can best be derived by extracting from λ_ρ its temperature factor and thus re-writing Eq. (1-81) as

$$\lambda_\rho \equiv T \, \sigma_\rho \tag{2-8}$$

One then finds from Eq. (2-7) that $\Phi(\underset{\sim}{R}_\rho, T\sigma_\rho)$ satisfies the equation

$$\frac{\partial}{\partial T} \Phi = \frac{1}{2} \sigma_\rho : \underset{\sim}{p}\underset{\sim}{p} \, \Phi \tag{2-9}$$

If the initial and boundary conditions are specified, the solutions of Eq. (2-9) are known to be uniquely determined and most suitably constructed with the help of the Green's function technique. Here, the fundamental kernel of Eq. (2-9) assumes the following form

$$G(\underset{\sim}{R}_\rho - \underset{\sim}{R}, T\sigma_\rho) = \frac{1}{\sqrt{(2\pi T)^3 |\sigma_\rho|}} \times \exp\left(-\frac{1}{2T} \sigma_\rho^{-1} : (\underset{\sim}{R}_\rho - \underset{\sim}{R})(\underset{\sim}{R}_\rho - \underset{\sim}{R})\right) \tag{2-10}$$

where σ_ρ^{-1} is the inverse tensor of σ_ρ and $|\sigma_\rho|$ its determinant. Although no explicit example will be given here, the general knowledge that one has from similar problems in physics permits us to assert that the effect of the thermal fluctuations of the atomic nuclei will be to "smear out" the molecular potential $\varphi(R_\rho)$ thus producing a shift in both its minimum position and value. An instructive visualization of the process of thermal expansion is thereby obtained. Another consequence of the smearing effect is that while $\varphi(R_\rho)$ is of spherical symmetry, $\Phi(\underset{\sim}{R}_\rho, \lambda_\rho)$ will be of lower symmetry, namely that of the crystal, mediated by the correlation functions $\lambda_\rho^{\alpha\beta}$. Though qualitative, the above considerations should suffice to make it clear that with the method so far employed one fully exploits the basic parameter of the anharmonic crystal problem which is represented by the ratio of the r.m.s. of the nuclear motional fluctuations to the lattice spacing. While this ratio does not exceed 12 % for most solids up to their triple point, and only amounts to a few per cent or less at moderate and low temperatures, it can be as large as 30 % in the solid heliums. A comprehensive theory of anharmonicity should also encompass the latter situation.

It may be useful to discuss another aspect of the above method in terms of its connection with the scattering theory of X-rays, neutrons and electrons by crystals. For, we rewrite Eq. (2-5) in assuming that $\varphi(r)$ is Fourier analyzable. In this case we readily find

$$\langle V \rangle_h = N \frac{1}{2} \sum_{\rho k} \exp(-\frac{1}{2} \lambda_\rho : \underset{\sim}{k}\underset{\sim}{k} + i\, \underset{\sim}{k} . \underset{\sim}{R}_\rho)\, \overline{\varphi}(\underset{\sim}{k}) \tag{2-11}$$

and wish to compare the coefficient of $\frac{1}{2}\, \overline{\varphi}(\underset{\sim}{k})$ in the above equation with the intensity factor occurring in X-ray scattering theory. In the first Born approximation and for a harmonic lattice (see f. ex. [2], p. 246) the intensity of the scattered X-ray beam is seen to be

$$I(\underset{\sim}{k}) \sim N\left(1 + \sum_{\rho=1}^{N-1} \exp(-1/2\ \lambda_\rho : \underset{\sim}{k}\underset{\sim}{k} + i \underset{\sim}{k}\underset{\sim}{R}_\rho)\right) \tag{2-12}$$

the factor 1 coming from an additional term corresponding to $\rho = 0$ which is by definition excluded in our problem since ρ labels neighboring atoms. For closer comparison with the customary intensity expression, let us write

$$\lambda_\rho : \underset{\sim}{k}\underset{\sim}{k} \equiv 4w - 4w'_\rho$$

with

$$w'_\rho = \frac{1}{2} \sum_{\substack{\underset{\sim}{q}j \\ \alpha\beta}} \cos(\underset{\sim}{q}\underset{\sim}{R}_\rho)\, e^j_\alpha(\underset{\sim}{q})\, e^j_\beta(-\underset{\sim}{q})\, \frac{KT}{\omega^2_{\underset{\sim}{q}j}}\, k_\alpha k_\beta$$

and

$$w'_o \equiv w = \frac{1}{2} \langle (\underset{\sim}{k}\underset{\sim}{u}_s)^2 \rangle_h$$

then (2-12) becomes

$$I(\underset{\sim}{k}) \sim N\Big(1 + \sum_{\rho=1}^{N-1} \exp(-2w + 2w'_\rho + i\underset{\sim}{k}\underset{\sim}{R}_\rho)$$

$$= N \exp(-2w) \cdot \sum_{\rho=0}^{N-1} \exp(2w'_\rho + i\underset{\sim}{k}\underset{\sim}{R}_\rho) \qquad 2\text{-}13)$$

The quantity in front of the sum is noticed to be the famous Debye-Waller factor. The above comparison clearly shows how anharmonicity theory can be viewed as a theory of interatomic scattering in solids, and conversely that one can pictorially speak of a Debye-Waller approach to the anharmonic crystal problem.

Let us now feed the evaluation of $\langle V\rangle_h$ into the calculation of the free energy of the anharmonic crystal in first order of perturbation theory. With the subscript a standing for anharmonic, we write the crystal potential as

$$V = V_{st} + V_h + V_a \qquad (2\text{-}14)$$

where V_a is the untruncated anharmonic part of V, namely

$$V_a = \frac{1}{2} \sum_{s,\rho} \sum_{m=3}^{\infty} \frac{1}{m!} (\eta_\rho \underset{\sim}{u}_s \cdot \underset{\sim}{p})^m \varphi(R_\rho) \qquad (2\text{-}15)$$

From a straightforward power series expansion of the Boltzmann factor $\exp[-\beta(V_{st} + V_h + V_a)]$ in V_a, one has in first order

$$-\beta F_1 = \ell n\, Z_1$$

with

$$\ell n\, Z_1 = -\beta V_{st} + \ell n\, Z_h - \beta \langle V_a \rangle_h \qquad (2\text{-}16)$$

In adding and subtracting

$$\beta \langle V_h \rangle_h = 3N' \tag{2-17}$$

on the right hand side of Eq. (2-16), the mean value of the total crystal potential can be reconstructed and Eq. (2-16) becomes

$$\ell n\, Z_1 = \ell n\, Z_h + 3N' - \beta \langle V \rangle_h = -\beta F_1 \tag{2-18}$$

Then, according to Eqs (1-59) and (1-61) the internal energy in this approximation reads

$$U_1 = - \frac{\partial}{\partial \beta} \ell n\, Z_1$$

$$= 3(N-1)KT + (1 - T \frac{\partial}{\partial T}) \langle V \rangle_h \tag{2-18a}$$

and the specific heat $C_\upsilon(T)$ becomes correspondingly

$$C_{\upsilon_1} = 3(N-1)K - T \frac{\partial^2}{\partial T^2} \langle V \rangle_h \tag{2-18b}$$

One thus notices that, in this approximation, the mean harmonic potential energy directly enters into the calculation of the thermodynamic quantities of interest. To say something about the temperature dependence of $\langle V \rangle_h$, it is clear that the expansion of the exponential operator in Eq. (2-6) generates the series

$$\langle V \rangle_h = V_{st} + \langle V_h \rangle_h + \langle V_{4-a} \rangle_h + \ldots + \langle V_{2n-a} \rangle_h + \ldots \tag{2-19}$$

the term $\langle V_{2n-a} \rangle_h$ being proportional to T^n. A power series expansion of Φ in T, introduced in Eq. (2-9), makes this property immediately apparent. What about the hypothetical limit $T \to \infty$? There is a case where this question can easily be answered and also be given a straightforward theoretical meaning. It is when $\varphi(r)$ is Fourier analyzable. Inspection of Eq. (2-11) shows indeed that in this limit the only non-vanishing contribution to $\langle V \rangle_h$ comes from the term with $k = 0$, in which case we find

$$\lim_{T \to \infty} \langle V \rangle_h = N \frac{1}{2} \sum_{\rho} \bar{\varphi}(0)$$

$$= \frac{1}{2} N(N-1) \frac{1}{\upsilon} \int_{\upsilon} d^3R \; \varphi(R) \tag{2-20}$$

This is a rather interesting result which tells us that we have just found the value of the mean potential energy of an imperfect gas in first order of perturbation theory. Eq. (2-20) thus provides an upper bound to the variation of $\langle V \rangle_h$ as a function of T , the lower bound being V_{st} at $T = 0$. If $\varphi(r)$ is subject only to the weaker differentiability assumption (A.2), and accordingly can exhibit a singularity at the origin stronger than $r^{-2} \ell n \, r$, we face what one usually calls the hard core problem. It is, however, well known that this problem cannot be dealt with in the framework of a first order perturbation theory of imperfect gases. On the other hand, this problem is completely absent in the traditional theory of anharmonicity, based on a truncated V_t of V . Yet the latter approach yields an unbounded polynomial expansion in T for $\langle V_t \rangle_h$, also an unsatisfactory situation. In the present scheme, characterized by the diffusion equation (2-9), the hard core problem assumes a new and different aspect which will capture our attention at a later stage of the developments. It is anyhow not important in most manifestations of the thermal properties of the solid state, but matters in questions related to the dynamical stability of this phase of matter. At this stage we have a more urgent program to cope with. To mention only one point, we have thus far, and purposely, bypassed the many-particle character of the theory. This aspect comes up as soon as second and higher order perturbation calculations are carried out, which, however, necessitate introducing first some vital apparatus.

2-2 THE PAIRING THEOREM

In this section we shall establish what is called the pairing theorem which plays a central role in any harmonic mean value problem, and thus provides a key ingredient for the perturbation theory to be developed afterwards.

Let Y_m be a symmetric multilinear form in the normal modes amplitudes $Q_{\underset{\sim}{q}j}$ with coefficients $C_{\underset{\sim}{q}_1 j_1 \cdots \underset{\sim}{q}_m j_m}$. The question is to calculate

$$\langle Y_m \rangle_h = \sum_{\underset{\sim}{q}_1 j_1 \cdots \underset{\sim}{q}_m j_m} C_{\underset{\sim}{q}_1 j_1 \cdots \underset{\sim}{q}_m j_m} \times \langle Q_{\underset{\sim}{q}_1 j_1} \cdots Q_{\underset{\sim}{q}_m j_m} \rangle_h \tag{2-21}$$

i. e. to deal with the combinatorial and algebraic problems of mode pairing and amplitude averages over a canonical ensemble of harmonic oscillators. We first set $m = 2\nu$ to express the fact that by virtue of phase averages only even combinations of modes yield non-vanishing mean values, and define the above quantity by

$$y_\nu = \langle Y_{2\nu} \rangle_h$$

Next, we introduce restricted summations over the wave vectors in order to facilitate the counting of identities among the indices of originally different pairs such as $Q_{qj}\, Q^*_{qj}$, $Q_{q'j}\, Q^*_{q'j}$, since they can occur in setting $\underset{\sim}{q}' = \underset{\sim}{q}$ and $\underset{\sim}{q}' = -\underset{\sim}{q}$. That means we substitute $\varepsilon\, \underset{\sim}{q}$

for $\underset{\sim}{q}$ with $\varepsilon = \pm 1$ and accordingly split

$$\sum_{\underset{\sim}{q}j} = \sum_{\varepsilon=\pm 1} \sum_{\underset{\sim}{q},j}{}^{'}$$

Finally, and for simplicity of notation, the convention will be made from now on unless otherwise specified that

$$\underset{\sim}{q}j \equiv q$$

and

$$-\underset{\sim}{q}j \equiv -q$$

in such a way that the set $(\underset{\sim}{q}_1 j_1 \ldots \underset{\sim}{q}_{2\nu} j_{2\nu})$ simply reads $(q_1 \ldots q_{2\nu})$. In this way the problem becomes formulated as follows

$$y_\nu = \sum_{\varepsilon_1 \ldots \varepsilon_{2\nu}} \sum_{q_1 \ldots q_{2\nu}}{}^{'} C_{\varepsilon_1 q_1 \ldots \varepsilon_{2\nu} q_{2\nu}} \times \langle Q_{\varepsilon_1 q_1} \ldots Q_{\varepsilon_{2\nu} q_{2\nu}} \rangle_h \tag{2-22}$$

The result, which turns out to be remarkably simple, will first be conjectured out of two examples and then proved in general. The first example consists in calculating the contribution to Eq. (2-22) arising from pairing the 2ν modes into ν independent pairs. This is of course possible provided $\nu < N'$ which will be assumed for the purpose of the exercise. To begin with the restricted q' s the number of ways in which they can be made two by two equal is : $(2\nu-1)$ for the first product times $(2\nu-3)$ for the second one times... etc. $= (2\nu-1)(2\nu-3) \ldots 5.3.1$ and this number is designated by

$$(2\nu-1)!! \equiv (2\nu-1)(2\nu-3)\dots 5.3.1 = \frac{2\nu!}{2^{\nu}\nu!} \tag{2-23}$$

As regards the ε's, the phase average requires that within each product $Q_{\varepsilon q} Q_{\varepsilon' q}$ $\varepsilon = \pm 1 = -\varepsilon' = \mp 1$, that means two possibilities for each pair, 2^{ν} total. The contribution of this particular configuration to (2-22) thus amounts to

$$(2\nu-1)!!\ 2^{\nu} \sum_{q_1 \neq q_2 \neq \dots q_\nu \neq q_1}{}' \times C_{q_1 - q_1 \dots q_\nu - q_\nu} \langle J_{q_1} \dots J_{q_\nu} \rangle$$

and since all q's are different by assumption, in this example, the average of the product of J_q equals the product of averages. In defining

$$\langle J_q \rangle_h = \frac{1}{\beta \omega_q^2} \equiv L_q \tag{2-24}$$

the above sum becomes

$$(2\nu-1)!!\ 2^{\nu} \sum_{q_1 \neq q_2 \neq \dots \neq q_\nu \neq q_1}{}' C_{q_1 - q_1 \dots q_\nu - q_\nu} L_{q_1} L_{q_2} \dots L_{q_\nu} \tag{2-25}$$

The second example consists in calculating the contribution to (2-22) due to the configurations where all restricted q's are identical. One is thus left with the ε's partitioning within the product $Q_{\varepsilon_1 q} \dots Q_{\varepsilon_{2\nu} q}$. Again the phase average requires the same number of positive as negative signs and the number of ways in which this can be done is just

$$\binom{2\nu}{\nu} = \frac{2\nu!}{\nu!\ \nu!}$$

In this case, therefore, the contribution amounts to

$$\frac{2\nu!}{\nu!\ \nu!} \sum_{q}{}' C_{q-q\ q-q \ldots q-q} \langle J_q^{\ \nu} \rangle_h$$

and since

$$\langle J_q^{\ \nu} \rangle_h = \nu! \left(\frac{1}{\beta \omega_q^2} \right)^{\nu} = \nu!\ L_q^{\ \nu} \qquad (2\text{-}26)$$

one of the $\nu!$ of the combinatorial factor is cancelled by the $\nu!$ of the statistical weight. Together with the relation (2-23) the above contribution yields

$$(2\nu-1)!!\ 2^{\nu} \sum_{q}{}' C^{(n)}_{q-q\ q-q \ldots q-q} \cdot L_q^{\ \nu} \qquad (2\text{-}27)$$

It is immediately noticed that the numerical factors in front of (2-25) and (2-27) are the same. It thus looks as if, in forcing all q's in (2-25) to become identical, which contradicts the assumptions made in calculating that example, the correct expression for the second example is obtained. The reason why it works like that is the cancellation observed in the second example, of combinatorial factors which divide the maximum number of configurations in the case of identical modes by the enhanced mean value of the amplitudes of these modes when raised to the power of 1/2 the number of identical indices. This is a capital and distinct property of harmonic oscillator statistics and represents the classical parallel of a well known theorem in Quantum Mechanics due originally to Wick. It is therefore conjectured that the limitations $q_1 \neq q_2 \neq \ldots \neq q_\nu \neq q_1$ in (2-25) can be lifted and that this equation describes the general result. If so, the restricted summations over the q's can be deleted, which amounts to absorbing the factor 2^ν, and the result conjectured reads

$$\langle Y_{2\nu} \rangle_h \overset{?}{=} (2\nu-1)!! \sum_{q_1 \ldots q_\nu} \times C_{-q_1 q_1 \ldots -q_\nu q_\nu} L_{q_1} \ldots L_{q_\nu} \tag{2-28}$$

If correct, this formula means that $\langle Y_{2\nu} \rangle_h$ is simply obtained by pairing $(\underset{\sim}{q}'j' = -\underset{\sim}{q}\, j)$ two by two the 2ν modes in $(2\nu-1)!!$ ways and averaging the amplitudes $J_{\underset{\sim}{q}j} = Q_{\underset{\sim}{q}j}\, Q_{-\underset{\sim}{q}j} \equiv Q_{\underset{\sim}{q}j} \cdot Q^*_{\underset{\sim}{q}j}$ as if they were all independent from one another, i.e. irrespective of the possible identities among their indices.

The conjecture (2-28) will now be proved. In order to take care of all possible configurations, y_ν as defined by (2-22) is resolved into sums of products of amplitudes with 2, 4, ... 2k, ... 2ν identical restricted q indices, the associated ε's being so far arbitrary. Several products may have the same number of identical restricted q's but the latter will be different for each of them since if two q's were equal, the corresponding product would merge and enter the class of products having twice as many identical q's. If n_{2k} designates the number of products having 2k identical restricted q's, this resolution is accomplished in decomposing the number 2ν as follows

$$2\nu = 2n_2 + 4n_4 + \ldots + 2kn_{2k} + 2\nu n_{2\nu} \tag{2-29}$$

and in summing over all possible n_{2k} compatible with (2-29) as well as over all combinations of modes which realize each configuration characterized by a set of n_{2k}. The sum over the q's is finally supposed to be carried out. The number of ways in which each configuration can be made with the 2ν modes available is given by what is called the polynomial coefficient of degree 2ν, whereby however all odd powers of the variables (Q_q here) are missing. This coefficient is

$$2\nu! \prod_{k=1}^{\nu} \frac{1}{n_{2k}!\,(2k!)^{n_{2k}}} \qquad (2\text{-}30)$$

with the restriction (2-29)

$$2\nu = \sum_{k=1}^{\nu} 2kn_{2k}$$

So much concerning the partition of the restricted q's. As regards the ε's which have to be equally shared in positive and negative signs within each product, one gets simply a product of binomial coefficients raised to the appropriate power n_{2k}, namely

$$\prod_{k=1}^{\nu} \binom{2k}{k}^{n_{2k}} = \prod_{k=1}^{\nu} \frac{(2k!)^{n_{2k}}}{(k!)^{2n_{2k}}} \qquad (2\text{-}31)$$

Multiplying (2-30) by (2-31) one obtains the total number of phase averaged combinations of modes which realize the configuration $\{n_{2k}\}$. Noticing the cancellation of the factors $(2k!)^{n_{2k}}$ one gets

$$2\nu! \prod_{k=1}^{\nu} \frac{1}{n_{2k}\,(k!)^{2n_{2k}}} \qquad (2\text{-}32)$$

Next comes the evaluation of the amplitude averages of the product of J_q's associated with each configuration. This product can be written for a particular set of q's

$$\prod_{k=1}^{\nu} \prod_{\varkappa=1}^{n_{2k}} J^k_{q_{n_{2k},\varkappa}}$$

and since all $q_{n_{2k},\varkappa}$ are different from one another by assumption, the mean value of the above product is the product of the mean values, that is

$$\prod_{k=1}^{\nu} \prod_{\varkappa=1}^{n_{2k}} \langle J^k_{q_{n_{2k},\varkappa}} \rangle_h = \prod_{k=1}^{\nu} \prod_{\varkappa=1}^{n_{2k}} k!\ L^k_{q_{n_{2k},\varkappa}}$$

$$= \prod_{k=1}^{\nu} (k!)^{n_{2k}} \prod_{\varkappa=1}^{n_{2k}} L^k_{q_{n_{2k},\varkappa}} \tag{2-33}$$

In multiplying (2-33) by (2-32) one notices the cancellation of a factor $(k!)^{n_{2k}}$; this represents the generalisation of what had been observed in calculating the second example for which $n_{2k} = 0$ except $k = \nu$ with $n_{2\nu} = 1$. The factor multiplying the product of L_q's is therefore

$$2\nu! \prod_{k=1}^{\nu} \frac{1}{n_{2k}!\,(k!)^{n_{2k}}} \tag{2-34}$$

At this point it is revealing to redefine the set of numbers $\{n_{2k}\}$ to be a set $\{\ell_k\}$ with

$$\ell_k = n_{2k}$$

and convert the restriction (2-29) into

$$\sum_{k=1}^{\nu} k\ell_k = \nu \tag{2-35}$$

where a trivial division by 2 has been performed. The factor (2-34) redefined reads

$$2\nu! \prod_{k=1}^{\nu} \frac{1}{\ell_k!\,(k!)^{\ell_k}}$$

and, in eliminating $2\nu!$ by means of Eq. (2-23), becomes

$$(2\nu-1)!!\; 2^{\nu}\; \nu! \prod_{k=1}^{\nu} \frac{1}{\ell_k!\,(k!)^{\ell_k}} \tag{2-36}$$

Then, together with the restriction (2-35), the factor

$$\nu! \prod_{k=1}^{\nu} \frac{1}{\ell_k!\,(k!)^{\ell_k}} \tag{2-37}$$

contained in (2-36) is noticed to be anew a polynomial coefficient of degree ν which now includes both odd and even powers of the variables L_q as contrasted with the polynomial coefficient (2-30) of degree 2ν which included the even powers of the variables Q_q only. The nature of (2-37) being recognized, the contributions to the mean value (2-22) of all configurations can be rewritten in unresolved multilinear forms. Absorbing again the factor 2^{ν} by unrestricted summations over the q's , the fundamental pairing theorem conjectured above is proved, namely

$$y_\nu = \sum_{q_1 \dots q_{2\nu}} C_{q_1 \dots q_{2\nu}} \langle Q_{q_1} \dots Q_{q_{2\nu}} \rangle_h$$

$$= (2\nu - 1)!! \sum_{q_1 \dots q_\nu} C_{-q_1\, q_1 \dots q_\nu\, q_\nu} L_{q_1} \dots L_{q_\nu} \qquad (2\text{-}38)$$

This equation will now be given an alternative, projection operator formulation, best suited to the forthcoming developments. In taking advantage of the property that

$$L_q = L_{-q}$$

which is due to the parity of ω_q^2, this formulation amounts to double again the number of summations in Eq. (2-38) and write

$$y_\nu = P \sum_{q_1 q_2 \dots q_{2\nu}} C_{q_1\, q_2 \dots q_{2\nu}} \sqrt{L_{q_1} L_{q_2} \dots L_{q_{2\nu}}} \qquad (2\text{-}38a)$$

where, symbolically, P means the summation over all possibilities (here $(2\nu - 1)!!$) of pairing two by two the indices of the set $(q_1 \dots q_{2\nu})$. P will be named pairing operator. Its introduction enables us to lift the symmetry hypothesis of the form (2-21) owing to the symmetry character of the product of L_q's. Its usefulness lies furthermore in the fact that we have reproduced on the right hand side of (2-38a) the original form $Y_{2\nu}$ with the significant difference however that the variables Q_q are replaced by the square root of the mean values L_q. This function will be designated by $\overline{Y}_{2\nu}$, that is

$$\overline{Y}_{2\nu} = Y_{2\nu}(\dots \sqrt{L_q} \dots)$$

and thus

$$y_\nu = P\,\overline{Y}_{2\nu} \tag{2-38b}$$

A straightforward generalisation of Eq. (2-38b) can be made whenever the problem is to calculate the mean value of a product of two forms $Y_m \cdot Y_{m'}$. Then we have

$$\langle Y_m \cdot Y_{m'} \rangle_h = P\,\overline{Y}_m \cdot \overline{Y}_{m'}$$

where now the summation has to be carried out over all possibilities of pairing within and between the two functions. At this point it will be useful to split them by introducing the following resolution of the identity, namely

$$P\,\overline{Y}_m \cdot \overline{Y}_{m'} \equiv P\,\overline{Y}_m \cdot P\,\overline{Y}_{m'} + \left\{ P\,\overline{Y}_m \cdot \overline{Y}_{m'} - P\,\overline{Y}_m \cdot P\,\overline{Y}_{m'} \right\}$$

The first term is, by virtue of (2-38b) the product of the mean values $\langle Y_m \rangle_h \cdot \langle Y_{m'} \rangle_h$ and the remainder will be designated by

$$P_L\,\overline{Y}_m \cdot \overline{Y}_{m'} \equiv \langle Y_m\, Y_{m'} \rangle_h - \langle Y_m \rangle_h \langle Y_{m'} \rangle_h \tag{2-39}$$

the subscript L , for link, meaning that at least one of the indices belonging to $\overline{Y}_m$ has to be paired with one belonging to $\overline{Y}_{m'}$ and P_L signifies the summation over all pairing possibilities subject to this condition. It is customary to write for (2-39) the alternative definition

$$\langle Y_m\, Y_{m'} \rangle_{h,L} \equiv P_L\,\overline{Y}_m\,\overline{Y}_{m'} \tag{2-39a}$$

2-3 MOMENT AND CUMULANT EXPANSION OF Z_V

With this apparatus we take up the next step of the developments which is to calculate the partition function of our anharmonic crystal by means of perturbation theory. The starting point is the expansion of the Boltzmann factor in a power series of the anharmonic part of the crystal potential

$$V = V_{st} + V_h + V_a$$

$$\exp - \beta V = \exp - \beta(V_{st} + V_h) \cdot \left\{ \sum_{n=o}^{\infty} \frac{(-\beta)^n}{n!} V_a{}^n \right\} \tag{2-40}$$

With this expansion the potential part of the Partition Function Z_V becomes

$$Z_V = \exp(-\beta V_{st}) \cdot Z_{V,h} \cdot \left\{ \sum_{n=o}^{\infty} \frac{(-\beta)^n}{n!} \langle V_a{}^n \rangle_h \right\} \tag{2-41}$$

a series designated as the moment expansion of Z_V, whereby the moments μ_n are defined by

$$\mu_n = \langle V_a{}^n \rangle_h \tag{2-42}$$

In order to calculate (2-41), the suitable expression (2-15) for V_a has to be introduced. We shall set

$$V_a = \frac{1}{2} \sum_{s\rho} \sum_{m=3}^{\infty} \frac{1}{m!} (\eta_\rho \underset{\sim}{u}_s \cdot \underset{\sim}{p})^m \varphi_\rho \tag{2-15a}$$

where φ_ρ stands as an abbreviation for $\varphi(R_\rho)$. If the transformation to normal modes is carried out, V_a^n, written explicitly, becomes a sum of multilinear forms in the amplitudes $Q_{\underset{\sim}{q}j}$ with complicated coefficients, each interaction contributing to these forms by as many modes as wanted. Yet, for the immediate purpose of calculating globally μ_n only the total number of modes occurring in each form matters and not their origin which can be permuted at will. Thus, (2-41a) can be converted into a sum of symmetric forms of the type (2-21), namely

$$\mu_n = \sum_{\nu=2}^{\infty} \sum_{q_1 \ldots q_{2\nu}} C^{(n)}_{q_1 \ldots q_{2\nu}} \langle Q_{q_1} \ldots Q_{q_{2\nu}} \rangle_h \tag{2-43}$$

in which, fortunately the coefficients will not have to be written explicitly. With (2-38a) the above expansion becomes

$$\mu_n = \sum_{\nu=2}^{\infty} P \sum_{q_1 \ldots q_{2\nu}} C^{(n)}_{q_1 \ldots q_{2\nu}} \sqrt{L_{q_1} \ldots L_{q_{2\nu}}}$$

$$= P \sum_{\nu=2}^{\infty} \sum_{q_1 \ldots q_{2\nu}} C^{(n)}_{q_1 \ldots q_{2\nu}} \sqrt{L_{q_1} \ldots L_{q_{2\nu}}}$$

since the pairing operator applies to everything on its right. If we now define the quantities

$$\bar{\underset{\sim}{u}}_s \equiv \frac{1}{\sqrt{NM}} \sum_{\underset{\sim}{q}j} e^{i\underset{\sim}{q}\underset{\sim}{R}_s} \underset{\sim}{e}^j(\underset{\sim}{q}) \sqrt{L_{\underset{\sim}{q}j}} \tag{2-44}$$

and

$$\bar{V}_a \equiv \frac{1}{2} \sum_{s,\rho} \sum_{m \geqslant 3} \frac{1}{m!} (n_\rho \bar{\underset{\sim}{u}}_s \underset{\sim}{p})^m \varphi_\rho \tag{2-45}$$

the expression on the right hand side of the pairing operator P is nothing but the expansion of $\bar{V}_a^{\ n}$; therefore

$$\mu_n = \langle V_a^{\ n} \rangle_h = P \, \bar{V}_a^{\ n} \tag{2-46}$$

This equation synthetizes the computational rules involved in the calculation of moments or any harmonic mean value. A simple example may best illustrate its content. Let us evaluate $\langle \underset{\sim}{u}_s^{2\nu} \rangle_h$. Application of (2-46) together with (2-44) and, of course (2-38), (2-38a) tells us immediately that

$$\langle \underset{\sim}{u}_s^{\ 2\nu} \rangle_h = P \, \bar{\underset{\sim}{u}}_s^{\ 2\nu} = (2\nu-1)\,!! \, (P\bar{u}_s^2)^\nu = (2\nu-1)\,!! \, \langle \underset{\sim}{u}_s^{\ 2} \rangle_h^\nu$$

a result which can be directly checked in treating the case of a single Einstein oscillator. In exploiting the operator formula (2-46) we can write a compact expression for the Partition Function and thus complete a formal step of the theory, namely

$$Z = \exp(-\beta V_{st}) \, . \, Z_h \, . \left\{ \sum_{n=o}^{\infty} \frac{(-\beta)^n}{n!} \mu_n \right\}$$

$$= \exp(-\beta V_{st}) \, . \, Z_h \, . \, P \exp(-\beta \bar{V}_a) \tag{2-47}$$

The explicit calculation of the successive moments μ_1, μ_2 etc. will, however, not be performed now. We shall merely discuss one of their properties which will be relevant to the next step of the developments.

The property we are talking about concerns the dependence of the moments upon the number N of atoms in the lattice. In the preceding section, μ_1 was found to be directly proportional to N since the summation index s appeared as a dummy index. In applying to μ_2 the resolution of the identity (2-39) we split this moment into two parts, namely

$$\mu_2 = P\,\overline{V}_a^{\,2}$$

$$= \frac{1}{4} \sum_{\substack{s\,\rho\,m \geqslant 3 \\ s'\rho'm' \geqslant 3}} P \frac{1}{m!}\frac{1}{m'!} (\eta_\rho\, \bar{u}_{\underset{\sim}{s}} . \underset{\sim}{p})^m (\eta_{\rho'}\, \bar{u}_{\underset{\sim}{s'}} . \underset{\sim}{p}')^{m'} \varphi_\rho \varphi_{\rho'}$$

$$= P\,\overline{V}_a \,.\, P\,\overline{V}_a + P_L\,\overline{V}_a^{\,2}$$

Application of the pairing operator within each $\overline{V}_a$ separately makes that both s and s' become dummy indices; the first part is consequently $\sim N^2$. As to the second term, which accounts for all contributions where at least one mode of the first $\overline{V}_a$ is paired with one mode of the second $\overline{V}_a$, we find that each of the relevant linking mean values contains the factor $\exp[i\,\underset{\sim}{q}\,(\underset{\sim}{R}_s - \underset{\sim}{R}_{s'})]\,.\,L_q$, thus any product of them depends upon R_s and $R_{s'}$ only via the difference $\underset{\sim}{R}_s - \underset{\sim}{R}_{s'}$ and consequently one and only one of the lattice site indices is left as a dummy index. The contributions to the second part are therefore $\sim N$. The remaining summation over the difference $s - s' = \sigma$ is readily noticed to induce wave vector conservation at each interaction by virtue of (1-28).

From the above analysis we infer that the third and higher moments will have to be similarly resolved into parts proportional to a given power of N. A systematic decomposition can be carried out on the basis of (2-39) which we iterate. For example, if we have a product of three forms $\overline{Y}_m \,.\, \overline{Y}_{m'} \,.\, \overline{Y}_{m''}$, the resolution of the identity amounts to split the total mean value as follows

$$\langle Y_m \cdot Y_{m'} \cdot Y_{m''} \rangle_h = P\, \overline{Y}_m \cdot \overline{Y}_{m'} \cdot \overline{Y}_{m''}$$

$$\equiv P\, \overline{Y}_m \cdot P\, \overline{Y}_{m'} \cdot P\, \overline{Y}_{m''} + P\, \overline{Y}_m \cdot P_L\, \overline{Y}_{m'} \quad \overline{Y}_{m''}$$

$$+ P\, \overline{Y}_{m'} \cdot P_L\, \overline{Y}_m\, \overline{Y}_{m''} + P\, \overline{Y}_{m''} \cdot P_L\, \overline{Y}_m\, \overline{Y}_{m'}$$

$$+ P_L\, \overline{Y}_m\, \overline{Y}_{m'}\, \overline{Y}_{m''}$$

and the last term accounts for all contributions where at least two indices of any one of the forms are paired with one index of the other two. If we now set

$$\overline{V}_a = \sum_m \overline{Y}_m$$

the above identity yields the resolution of μ_3 we are seeking for, namely

$$\mu_3 = (P\overline{V}_a)^3 + 3\, P\overline{V}_a \cdot P_L\, \overline{V}_a^{\,2} + P_L\, \overline{V}_a^{\,3}$$

The first term is indeed $\sim N^3$, the second one is $\sim N^2$ and the third one is $\sim N$ since, by virtue of the linking mean values of the type discussed above, one and only one of the lattice site indices is left as a dummy index, the remaining two summations inducing again wave vector conservation at each interaction. In what follows and for uniformity of notation $P\overline{V}_a$ will also be assigned an index L, and thus be written as $P_L\, \overline{V}_a$, which is redundant of course since $\mu_1 \sim N$. This permits us to define in general by the linked part of a moment the sum of all contributions which exhaust the linear dependence of this moment upon N. We see that μ_2 and μ_3 have been resolved in terms of their linked part and of products of the linked part of lower moments, these products accounting for those contributions to

μ_2 and μ_3 which are respectively quadratic and quadratic or cubic in N . We are now ready to consider the general case and assert that the resolution of μ_n will be accomplished in summing over all possible products of linked parts $P_L \overline{V}_a^k$, with $k \leqslant n$. A representative element of such a sum can be characterized by a set of integers $r_1, r_2 \ldots r_n$, r_k designating the number of parts where k interactions are linked, that is to say a factor $(P_L \overline{V}_a^k)^{r_k}$. Needless to say no one of the V_a's within a linked part is linked to another part. Altogether the representative element will be of the form

$$\prod_{k=1}^{n} (P_L \overline{V}_a^k)^{r_k}$$

where the r_k's are subject to the restriction

$$\sum_{k=1}^{n} k\, r_k = n$$

The number of ways in which this element can be realized is again given by our familiar polynomial coefficient of degree n , namely

$$\prod_{k=1}^{n} \frac{n!}{r_k!\,(k!)^{r_k}}$$

in such a way that

$$\mu_n = \sum_{r_1 r_2 \ldots r_n}^{n} \prod_{k=1}^{n} \frac{n!}{r_k!\,(k!)^{r_k}} (P_L \overline{V}_a^k)^{r_k} \tag{2-48}$$

where the upper limit of summation is understood to convey the restriction

$$n = \sum_{k=1}^{n} kr_k$$

(2-48) represents a key formula which will help us to achieve the first purpose of this section.

We proceed indeed by inserting (2-48) in the anharmonic part of (2-47) and get

$$P \exp -\beta \overline{V}_a = \sum_{n=o}^{\infty} \frac{(-\beta)^n}{n!} \mu_n$$

$$= \sum_{n=o}^{\infty} \sum_{r_1, \ldots r_n}^{n} \prod_{k=1}^{n} \frac{1}{r_k!} \left(\frac{(-\beta)^k}{k!} P_L \overline{V}_a{}^k \right)^{r_k}$$

The summation over n permits us to lift the restriction $n = \sum_k kr_k$; we can therefore perform independent summations over the r_k's and thus obtain

$$P \exp - \beta \overline{V}_a = \langle \exp - \beta V_a \rangle_h$$

$$= \prod_{k=1}^{\infty} \sum_{r_{k=o}}^{\infty} \frac{1}{r_k!} \cdot \left(\frac{(-\beta)^k}{k!} P_L \overline{V}_a{}^k \right)^{r_k}$$

$$= \prod_{k=1}^{\infty} \exp \left(+ \frac{(-\beta)^k}{k!} P_L \overline{V}_a{}^k \right)$$

$$= \exp \sum_{k=1}^{\infty} \frac{(-\beta)^k}{k!} P_L \overline{V}_a^{\,k}$$

or

$$\ell n \ \langle \exp - \beta V_a \rangle_h = \sum_{k=1}^{\infty} \frac{(-\beta)^k}{k!} P_L \overline{V}_a^{\,k} \tag{2-49}$$

that is to say an expansion for the logarithm of the anharmonic part of the partition function. Such a logarithmic expansion is called a cumulant or semi-invariant expansion †. The cumulants $\varkappa_k$ are defined as the coefficients of $\frac{(-\beta)^k}{k!}$ on the right hand side of (2-49), that is

$$\varkappa_k \equiv P_L \overline{V}_a^{\,k} = \langle V_a^{\,k} \rangle_{h,L} \tag{2-50}$$

They are identified as the linked part of the moments. Together with (2-49) and (2-50) the fundamental perturbation series for the free energy is finally obtained and reads

$$F_\beta = V_{st} + F_{\beta h} + \sum_{k=1}^{\infty} \frac{(-\beta)^{k-1}}{k!} \varkappa_k \tag{2-51}$$

† The semi-invariants or cumulants have been introduced in Mathematical Statistics by T.N. Thiele in 1903. The background about them can be found in M.G. Kendall and A. Stuart "The Advanced Theory of Statistics" (C. Griffin & Co, London, 1958) Vol. 1, sect. 3.12. It is only in the mid fifties however that they have been introduced explicitly in Statistical Mechanics, apparently by different authors independently, although their implicit use can be traced back in the famous Ursell expansion of the Grand Partition Function for imperfect gases. Among several papers in which they are quoted nowadays let us mention R. Kubo's one entitled "Generalized Cumulant Expansion Method" (J. Phys. Soc. of Japan 17, 1100, 1962). Also they are incorporated in R. Brout and P. Carruthers Monograph ([6] section 1.1 and 2.3).

where it is understood that the $\varkappa_k$'s are given by (2-50) which synthetizes the computational rules implied in the calculation of the semi-invariants for an anharmonic crystal. This equation defines what one calls the linked cluster † expansion for the free energy, an historical designation dating from the early work of Mayer on the Statistical Theory of Imperfect Gases. Owing to the property that all $\varkappa_k$'s are proportional to N , a major feature of this expansion is to satisfy the thermodynamical requirement that F_β should be proportional to N in all order of perturbation theory. During the fifties this and related problems have been a matter of considerable concern in Statistical and Quantum Mechanics. A cornerstone in this development has been laid down in 1957 by J. Goldstone who established a linked cluster expansion for the ground state energy of an electron gas. Most directly relevant to the subject of this monograph is L.V. Hove's pioneering work on the quantum theory of interacting elastic waves in Solids. In particular, in that author's M.I.T. lectures a linked cluster expansion for the free energy of an anharmonic crystal has for the first time been established ([7], section 11) . In the classical limit this expansion goes over to (2-51), the telescopic integrals over the inverse temperature yielding the factors $\frac{1}{k!}\ \beta^k$. As mentioned in the Introduction, the quantum theory of phonon-phonon interactions will be taken up later on in this work. Here, in taking full advantage of the algebraic simplicity inherent to the classical theory our next purpose will be to tackle a problem specific to anharmonicity theory which is that each semi-invariant $\varkappa_k$ contains an infinite number of contributions owing to V_a not being truncated in our treatment. This means that the convergence of the $\varkappa_k$ themselves has to be studied which may be done by searching

† The term cluster refers, as one knows, to a diagrammatic representation of the different contributions to a given cumulant. We have so far preferred an algebraic development of the theory and intend to postpone the use of diagrams until the next section.

closed form expressions for the semi-invariants. This will enable us to analyze the temperature dependence of the general term $\beta^k \varkappa_k$ of the fundamental series

$$\ln Z_V = \ln Z_{V,h} - \beta(V_{st} + \varkappa_1) + \frac{1}{2}\beta^2 \varkappa_2 - \frac{1}{3!}\beta^3 \varkappa_3 + \dots \quad (2\text{-}52)$$

and, consequently of the anharmonic corrections to the thermodynamic quantities of interest.

2-4 CLOSED FORM EXPRESSIONS FOR THE CUMULANTS

Explicit calculation of the cumulants will be taken up in what follows. To begin with, the evaluation of $\varkappa_1 = \mu_1$ will be repeated here, with the help of the pairing operator procedure. In setting directly $m = 2\nu$, we have

$$\varkappa_1 = \mu_1 = P\,\overline{V}_a = \frac{1}{2}\sum_{s\rho}\sum_{\nu=2}^{\infty} \frac{1}{2\nu!} P\,(\eta_\rho \overline{\underset{\sim}{u}}_s \cdot \underset{\sim}{p})^{2\nu} \varphi_\rho$$

With

$$P\,(\eta_\rho \overline{\underset{\sim}{u}}_s \cdot \underset{\sim}{p})^{2\nu} = (2\nu - 1)!!\,(P(\eta_\rho \overline{\underset{\sim}{u}}_s \cdot \underset{\sim}{p})^2)^\nu$$

and

$$P\,(\eta_\rho \overline{\underset{\sim}{u}}_s)^2 \equiv \langle \eta_\rho \underset{\sim}{u}_s{}^2 \rangle_h = \lambda_\rho$$

and

$$\frac{1}{2\nu!}(2\nu - 1)!! = \frac{1}{\nu!}\,\frac{1}{2^\nu}$$

we obtain

$$\varkappa_1 = N \frac{1}{2} \sum_{\rho} \sum_{\nu=2}^{\infty} \frac{1}{\nu!} \left(\frac{1}{2} \lambda_\rho \underset{\sim}{p}^2\right)^\nu \varphi_\rho$$

$$= N \frac{1}{2} \sum_{\rho} \left(\exp \frac{1}{2} \lambda_\rho \underset{\sim}{p}^2 - 1 - \frac{1}{2} \lambda_\rho \underset{\sim}{p}^2\right) \varphi_\rho$$

$$= \langle V \rangle_h - V_{st} - \langle V_h \rangle_h \equiv \langle V_a \rangle_h$$

in agreement with the calculation made in section (2-1) . As shown there in the case where $\overline{\varphi}(0)$ exists the quantity $\beta \varkappa_1$ was found to have a bounded variation as a function of the temperature, asymptotically given by

$$\frac{3}{2} N - \frac{1}{KT} \left\{ \binom{N}{2} \frac{1}{\upsilon} \int d^3R \varphi(R) - V_{st} \right\}$$

and linear in T at low temperature.

It is obviously worth investigating the structure of the higher cumulants.

Let us consider the second cumulant

$$\varkappa_2 = P_L \overline{V}_a^{\,2} = \frac{1}{4} \sum_{\substack{s\rho \\ s'\rho'}} \sum_{\substack{m \geqslant 3 \\ m' \geqslant 3}}$$

$$P_L \frac{1}{m!} \frac{1}{m'!} (\eta_\rho \underset{\sim}{\overline{u}}_s . \underset{\sim}{p})^m (\eta_{\rho'} \underset{\sim}{\overline{u}}_{s'} . \underset{\sim}{p})^{m'} \varphi_\rho \varphi_{\rho'} \qquad (2\text{-}53)$$

Here it turns out that the calculations will be greatly facilitated if we consider the new quantity

$$P_L \; \eta_\rho \bar{\underset{\sim}{u}}_s \cdot \eta_{\rho'} \bar{\underset{\sim}{u}}_{s'} = \frac{1}{NM} \sum_{\underset{\sim}{q}j}$$

$$\times \; e^{i \underset{\sim}{q} \cdot (\underset{\sim}{R}_s - \underset{\sim}{R}_{s'})} \; \eta_\rho(\underset{\sim}{q}) \; \eta_{\rho'}(-\underset{\sim}{q}) \; \underset{\sim}{e}^j(\underset{\sim}{q}) \; \underset{\sim}{e}^j(-\underset{\sim}{q}) \cdot L_{\underset{\sim}{q}j} \tag{2-54}$$

This is again a correlation matrix which will be designated by $\lambda^{s-s'}_{\rho\,\rho'}$ as a natural generalisation of the matrix λ_ρ . This new correlation matrix assumes the equivalent definition

$$\lambda^{s-s'}_{\rho\,\rho'} \equiv \langle \eta_\rho \underset{\sim}{u}_s \; \eta_{\rho'} \underset{\sim}{u}_{s'} \rangle_h \tag{2-54a}$$

in terms of which λ_ρ becomes the special case given by $\lambda^{o}_{\rho\rho}$. In using the definition (2-24) for $L_{\underset{\sim}{q}j}$, the definition (1-75) for the coefficients $\mathcal{f}^{\underset{\sim}{q}j}_{\rho\rho'\alpha\alpha'}$ and in setting $s-s' = \sigma$, $\underset{\sim}{R}_s - \underset{\sim}{R}_{s'} = \underset{\sim}{R}_\sigma$ the matrix elements of (2-54a) can be written alternatively in the form

$$\lambda^{\sigma,\,\alpha\alpha'}_{\rho\rho'} = \frac{1}{N} \sum_{\underset{\sim}{q}j} e^{i \underset{\sim}{q} \underset{\sim}{R}_\sigma} \mathcal{f}^{\underset{\sim}{q}j}_{\rho\rho'\alpha\alpha'} \cdot \frac{KT}{\omega^2_{\underset{\sim}{q}j}} \tag{2-54b}$$

By its very definition, it is natural to call $\lambda^{\sigma}_{\rho\rho'}$ a linking correlation and to picture $\lambda^{\sigma}_{\rho\rho'\underset{\sim}{p}\underset{\sim}{p}'}$ as a link between the two interaction potentials φ_ρ and $\varphi_{\rho'}$ represented by vertices. Here we refer for the first time to a diagrammatic representation which will soon become very useful. With this preparation we are ready to calculate all contributions to the linked part of μ_2 .

The first one is obviously obtained with $m = m' = 3$. In taking advantage of the summation method discussed in the preceding section we can however sum up all contributions obtained in setting $m = 3+2\nu$ and $m' = 3+2\nu'$ which are characterized by three correlations $\lambda^{\sigma}_{\rho\,\rho'}$ linking the two vertices and ν correlations λ_ρ respectively $\nu'\lambda_{\rho'}$ being "self linked" at each vertex. Indeed the number of ways in which the corresponding numbers of modes m and m' can be paired in order to realize the above configuration is

$$\frac{m!}{(2!)^{\nu}\,\nu!\;3!}\;\cdot\;3!\;\cdot\;\frac{m'!}{(2!)^{\nu'}\,\nu'!\;3!}$$

Then, in noticing the cancellation of m! and m'! with the denominator of (2-53) the summation over ν and ν' from 0 to ∞ can be performed and we obtain

$$N\,\frac{1}{4}\sum_{\rho\rho'\sigma} e^{\frac{1}{2}\lambda_\rho : \underset{\sim}{p}\underset{\sim}{p}}\;\frac{1}{3!}\,(\lambda^{\sigma}_{\rho\rho'}\,\underset{\sim}{p}\underset{\sim}{p}')^3\;e^{\frac{1}{2}\lambda_{\rho'} : \underset{\sim}{p}'\underset{\sim}{p}'}\;\varphi_\rho\,\varphi_{\rho'}$$

This procedure can immediately be generalized to account for the contributions due to four, five etc. linking correlations. In making use of the smeared potential

$$\Phi_\rho \equiv \Phi(R_\rho, \lambda_\rho) = e^{\frac{1}{2}\lambda_\rho : \underset{\sim}{p}\underset{\sim}{p}}\;\varphi(R_\rho)$$

defined by Eq. (2-7), this set of contributions amounts to

$$N\,\frac{1}{4}\sum_{\rho\rho'\sigma}\sum_{n=3}^{\infty}\frac{1}{n!}\,(\lambda^{\sigma}_{\rho\rho'}\,pp')^n\;\Phi_\rho\,\Phi_{\rho'} \tag{2-55}$$

Yet the above result does not exhaust all contributions to $\varkappa_2$. We must consider a particular situation related to the case where $m = m' = 4$. Indeed with 8 modes the general rule tells us that there are $7!! = 105$ pairing possibilities. This number breaks down as follows : there are $(3!!)^2 = 9$ configurations arising from separate pairing at each vertex; they figure in the moment but no more in the cumulant expansion. Next, there are $4! = 24$ configurations arising from pairing all eight modes between the two interactions. This yields four linking correlations between the vertices and their contributions is taken into account by (2-55) with $n = 4$ together with the ones due to the extended configurations characterized by $4 + 2\nu$ and $4 + 2\nu'$ modes. Finally there are $\frac{4!}{2!\,2!} \cdot 2! \cdot \frac{4!}{2!\,2!} = 72$ configurations which arise from pairing four modes between and two within the vertices, thus yielding two linking correlations between the vertices and one "selflinked" at each vertex. The sum is $9 + 24 + 72 = 105$ as it should be. The last category of configurations has yet to be evaluated. Their extension is obtained in writing

$$m = 2 + 2\,(1+\nu) \qquad\qquad m' = 2 + 2\,(1+\nu')$$
$$\;\; = 2 + 2\,\nu'' \qquad\qquad\quad\;\; = 2 + 2\,\nu'''$$

the summation over ν'' and ν''' having now to be made from 1 to ∞ in such a way that this remaining contribution amounts to

$$\frac{N}{4} \sum_{\rho\rho'\sigma} \left(e^{\frac{1}{2}\lambda_{\rho}:\underset{\sim}{p}\underset{\sim}{p}} - 1\right) \frac{1}{2} \left(\lambda^{\sigma}_{\rho\rho'}:\underset{\sim}{p}\underset{\sim}{p}'\right)^2 \left(e^{\frac{1}{2}\lambda_{\rho}:\underset{\sim}{p}'\underset{\sim}{p}'} - 1\right) \varphi_{\rho}\,\varphi_{\rho'}$$

$$= \frac{N}{4} \sum_{\rho\rho'\sigma} \frac{1}{2} \left(\lambda^{\sigma}_{\rho\rho'}:\underset{\sim}{p}\underset{\sim}{p}'\right)^2 \left(\Phi_{\rho} - \varphi_{\rho}\right)\left(\Phi_{\rho'} - \varphi_{\rho'}\right) \qquad (2\text{-}56)$$

As of $m, m' > 4$ this situation does not reproduce itself[+]. All possible configurations fall in either one of the categories whose contributions are summed up by (2-55) and (2-56). For example with $m = m' = 6$ we have the following configurations characterized by

[+] For completeness let us remark that in polyatomic lattices, configurations with one linking correlation come also into play, owing to the presence of optical modes of zero wave vector. These configurations are generated out of $m = m' = 3$ in setting $m = 1 + 2 + 2\nu$, $m' = 1 + 2 + 2\nu'$.

their correlation matrices versus the equations which take care of them

$$(\lambda^{\sigma}_{\rho\rho'})^6 \qquad (2\text{-}55)$$

$$\lambda_{\rho} \; (\lambda^{\sigma}_{\rho\rho'})^4 \; \lambda_{\rho'} \qquad (2\text{-}55)$$

$$\lambda_{\rho}^{2} \; (\lambda^{\sigma}_{\rho\rho'})^2 \; \lambda_{\rho'}^{2} \qquad (2\text{-}56)$$

$$\lambda_{\rho}^{3} \cdot \lambda_{\rho'}^{3}$$ unlinked part of the moment expansion

and so on, as easily shown by induction. Together, Eqs (2-55) and (2-56) exhaust the contributions to $\varkappa_2$. It is convenient to rewrite them in an even more compact form in introducing the following operators

$$\lambda^{s_1 - s_2}_{\rho_1 \rho_2} : \underset{\sim}{p}_1 \underset{\sim}{p}_2 \equiv \underline{w}_{12} \qquad (2\text{-}57)$$

$$\lambda_{\rho_1} : \underset{\sim}{p}_1 \underset{\sim}{p}_1 = \underline{w}_{11} \equiv \underline{w}_1 \qquad (2\text{-}57a)$$

In terms of these linear operators, $\varkappa_2$ reads

$$\varkappa_2 = \frac{1}{4} \sum_{s_1\rho_1,\, s_2\rho_2} \left\{ \frac{1}{2} \underline{w}_{12}^{2} (\Phi_1 - \varphi_1)(\Phi_2 - \varphi_2) + \sum_{n \geqslant 3} \frac{1}{n!} w_{12}^{n} \, \Phi_1 \, \Phi_2 \right\} \qquad (2\text{-}58)$$

an expression easily amenable to closed form. Indeed, with

$$\sum_{n=3}^{\infty} \frac{1}{n!} \underline{w}_{12}^{n} = e^{\underline{w}_{12}} - 1 - \underline{w}_{12} - \frac{1}{2!} \underline{w}_{12}^{2}$$

we find

$$\varkappa_2 = \frac{1}{4} \sum_{1,2} \left\{ \frac{1}{2} \underline{w}_{12}^{2} \left[(\Phi_1 - \varphi_1)(\Phi_2 - \varphi_2) - \Phi_1 \cdot \Phi_2 \right] + (e^{\underline{w}_{12}} - 1) \Phi_1 \Phi_2 \right\} \tag{2-58a}$$

where the shorthand notation 1, 2 has been used for $s_1 \rho_1$, $s_2 \rho_2$ under the summation symbol. Note that the term linear in w_{12} vanishes for our Bravais lattice. Eq. (2.58a) clearly shows that all of the second anharmonic corrections to the free energy can be put into a rather compact form with the single addition of the operator $\underline{w}_{12}$ to the quantities introduced before such as the smeared potentials. Once the latter are determined from solutions of Eq. (2-9) subject to appropriate boundary conditions (the initial ones are trivial since at $T = 0$, $\Phi = \varphi$) all interesting properties of $\varkappa_2$ can be analyzed. While this is a subject of investigation per se, we shall find it instructive to discuss one property of Eq. (2-58a) in connection with its counterpart in the classical perturbation theory of imperfect gases. This means that, as in the latter theory, we temporarily consider an interatomic potential with softened hard core, and investigate the limit of $\beta^2 \varkappa_2$ as $\beta \to 0$. Let us therefore Fourier transform the relevant quantities of Eq. (2-58a) and first calculate the contributions arising from the factor $\exp(w_{12}) \Phi_1 \Phi_2$. In using the definition (2-54) for the correlation matrix and in setting $s_1 + \rho_1 = s_1'$, $s_2 + \rho_2 = s_2'$, we have

$$e^{\frac{w}{}12}\,\Phi_1\,\Phi_2$$

$$= \sum_{\underset{\sim}{k}_1\underset{\sim}{k}_2} \exp - [P_L\,(\underset{\sim}{\bar{u}}_{s_1'} - \underset{\sim}{\bar{u}}_{s_1})(\underset{\sim}{\bar{u}}_{s_2'} - \underset{\sim}{\bar{u}}_{s_2})\,\underset{\sim}{k}_1\,\underset{\sim}{k}_2$$

$$+ \frac{1}{2} P_L\,(\underset{\sim}{\bar{u}}_{s_1'} - \underset{\sim}{\bar{u}}_{s_1})^2\,\underset{\sim}{k}_1^{\,2} + \frac{1}{2} P_L\,(\underset{\sim}{\bar{u}}_{s_2'} - \underset{\sim}{\bar{u}}_{s_2})^2\,\underset{\sim}{k}_2^{\,2}$$

$$+ i\,\underset{\sim}{k}_1(R_{s_1'} - R_{s_1}) + i\,k_2(R_{s_2'} - R_{s_2})\,]\;\bar{\varphi}(k_1)\,\bar{\varphi}(k_2) \qquad (2\text{-}59)$$

If we perform the limit $\beta \to 0$, that is $L_q \to \infty$, the above expression vanishes unless

a) $\underset{\sim}{k}_1 = \underset{\sim}{k}_2 = 0$ for $s_1, s_1' \neq s_2, s_2'$

b) $\underset{\sim}{k}_1 = \begin{cases} +\underset{\sim}{k}_2 \\ -\underset{\sim}{k}_2 \end{cases}$ for $s_1, s_1' = \begin{cases} s_2', s_2 \\ s_2, s_2' \end{cases}$

In the case a)

$$\lim_{\beta \to 0} (2\text{-}59) = \bar{\varphi}(0)\,\bar{\varphi}(0) = \left(\frac{1}{\upsilon}\int d^3R\,\varphi(R)\right)^2$$

and this is exactly compensated by the contribution

$$\lim_{\beta \to 0} - \Phi_1 \cdot \Phi_2 = - \bar{\varphi}(0) \cdot \bar{\varphi}(0)$$

In the case b) we find in dropping the subscript 1 of the site indices s_1 and s_1'

$$\sum_{\underset{\sim}{k}_1\underset{\sim}{k}_2} \exp \left[- \frac{1}{2} P_L\,(\underset{\sim}{\bar{u}}_{s'} - \underset{\sim}{\bar{u}}_{s})^2 (\underset{\sim}{k}_1^{\,2} \pm 2\,\underset{\sim}{k}_1\underset{\sim}{k}_2 + \underset{\sim}{k}_2^{\,2}) \right.$$

$$+ \; i\,(\underset{\sim}{k}_1 \pm \underset{\sim}{k}_2)(\underset{\sim}{R}_{s'} - \underset{\sim}{R}_s) \Big] \; \bar{\varphi}(k_1)\,\bar{\varphi}(k_2) \qquad (2\text{-}59a)$$

and

$$\lim_{\beta \to 0} (2\text{-}59a) = \sum_{\underset{\sim}{k}} \bar{\varphi}(\underset{\sim}{k})\,\bar{\varphi}(\mp \underset{\sim}{k})$$

$$= \frac{1}{\upsilon} \int d^3R \;\; \varphi(\underset{\sim}{R}) \;\; \varphi(\pm \underset{\sim}{R}) = \overline{\varphi^2}(0)$$

since $\varphi = \varphi(|\underset{\sim}{R}|)$. Therefore

$$\lim_{\beta \to 0} \frac{1}{4} \sum_{12} (e^{-w_{12}} - 1)\, \Phi_1\, \Phi_2 = \binom{N}{2}$$

$$\times \left[\frac{1}{\upsilon} \int d^3R\,\varphi^2(R) - \left(\frac{1}{\upsilon} \int d^3R\,\varphi \right)^2 \right] \qquad (2\text{-}59b)$$

and we notice that this is exactly what one obtains in the theory of imperfect gases in the corresponding approximation. Here, however, we have other contributions to $\varkappa_2$, better said to $\beta^2 \varkappa_2$. Noticing the cancellation of the product $\Phi_1 \Phi_2$ in the first part of Eq. (2-58a), the contribution that we consider next is

$$\beta^2 \; \frac{1}{4} \sum_{12} \frac{1}{2} \; w_{12}^{\;2} \; (\varphi_1\, \Phi_2 + \Phi_1\, \varphi_2)$$

In going over to the Fourier transforms we find that

$$\lim_{\beta \to 0} \frac{1}{4} \sum_{12} \sum_{\underset{\sim}{k}_1 \underset{\sim}{k}_2} \beta^2 (\lambda_{12} \underset{\sim}{k}_1 \underset{\sim}{k}_2)^2 \, \bar{\varphi}(\underset{\sim}{k}_1)$$

$$\times \; e^{-\frac{1}{2} \lambda_2 : \underset{\sim}{k}_2 \underset{\sim}{k}_2} \, \bar{\varphi}(\underset{\sim}{k}_2) \tag{2-59c}$$

vanishes unless

$$\lim_{k_2 \to 0} \underset{\sim}{k}_2^2 \, \bar{\varphi}(k_2) \neq 0$$

If so, this corresponds to the case of long range forces which anyhow require a special treatment excluded from the present analysis. This situation is known to be remedied by Debye-Hückel and similar theories which are not our concern here. So we shall assume that (2-59c) vanishes. We are left with the following contribution, namely

$$\beta^2 \frac{1}{4} \sum_{12} \frac{1}{2} \underline{w}_{12}^2 \; \varphi_1 \, \varphi_2$$

This is a temperature independent contribution which amounts to †

$$N \frac{1}{4} \cdot \frac{1}{2} \sum_{\rho_1 \rho_2, \sigma} \frac{1}{N^2 M^2} \sum_{q_1 q_2} e^{i(\underset{\sim}{q}_1 - \underset{\sim}{q}_2)\underset{\sim}{R}_\sigma}$$

$$\times \, \eta_{\rho_1}(q_1) \, \eta_{\rho_2}(-q_1) \, \underset{\sim}{e}(q_1) \underset{\sim}{p}_1 \, \underset{\sim}{e}(-q_1) \underset{\sim}{p}_2 \, L_{q_1}$$

$$\times \, \eta_{\rho_1}(q_2) \, \eta_{\rho_2}(-q_2) \, \underset{\sim}{e}(q_2) \underset{\sim}{p}_1 \, \underset{\sim}{e}(-q_2) \underset{\sim}{p}_2 \, L_{q_2} \, \varphi_{\rho_1} \, \varphi_{\rho_2}$$

† Note that here the shorthand notation $q = (\underset{\sim}{q}, j)$, $-q = (-\underset{\sim}{q}, j)$ is used again

and, in rearranging the factors, is seen to be

$$\beta^2 \frac{1}{2} \sum_q \left(\frac{1}{2M} \sum_\rho \eta_\rho(q)\, \eta_\rho(-q)\, \underset{\sim}{e}(q)\, \underset{\sim}{e}(-q) : \underset{\sim}{\rho}\underset{\sim}{\rho}\, \varphi_\rho \right)^2 L_q^{\,2}$$

$$= \frac{1}{2} \beta^2 \sum_q \omega_q^{\,4} L_q^{\,2} = 3N'$$

Altogether we therefore find that in the case of soft core and short range interactions the high temperature limit of $\frac{1}{2} \beta^2 \varkappa_2$ is given by

$$\frac{3}{2} N' + \frac{1}{2} \beta^2 \binom{N}{2} (\overline{\varphi^2(0)} - \bar{\varphi}(0)^2)$$

After this little excursion of exploratory interest let us come back to our main task of explicitly calculating the higher terms of the series (2-52).

In order to generalize the explicit calculation of the higher cumulants, the inductive method used to calculate $\varkappa_2$ will conveniently be replaced by an alternative more synthetic one. The latter will be based upon the difference procedure already employed in section (2-1) for calculating $\ell n\, Z_1$, (see Eqs (2-16) and (2-18)), and amounts to substituting $V - V_{st} - V_h$ for V_a. Furthermore, the various contributions to a given semi-invariant will conveniently be associated to certain configurations subject to a diagrammatic representation. It is instructive to illustrate this way of doing in reconsidering $\varkappa_2$. Here we have

$$\varkappa_2 = P_L \overline{V}_a^{\,2} = P_L (\overline{V} - V_{st} - \overline{V}_h)^2$$

$$= P_L \overline{V}_h^{\,2} - 2 P_L \overline{V}_h \overline{V} + P_L \overline{V}^2$$

The first term is evaluated in using either one of the definitions of

V_h, that is

$$V_h = \frac{1}{2} \sum_{s,\rho} \frac{1}{2} (\eta_\rho \underset{\sim}{u}_s \cdot \underset{\sim}{p})^2 \varphi_\rho = \frac{1}{2} \sum_{\underset{\sim}{qj}} \omega^2_{\underset{\sim}{qj}} Q_{\underset{\sim}{qj}} Q^*_{\underset{\sim}{qj}}$$

and in applying the pairing theorem to $P_L \overline{V}_h^{\,2} = \langle V_h^2 \rangle_{hL}$, that is to say to the contraction of the products of any two components of the nuclear displacement vectors $u_{s\alpha}$ or of the modes Q_{qj}. Diagrammatically this term will be represented as follows

represents $P_L \overline{V}_h^{\,2}$

The vertices represent the interaction potentials $\varphi_j = \varphi(R_{\rho_j})$ with $j = 1, 2$ and the lines joining the vertices represent the linking correlations. The algebraic value assigned to this diagram is

$$\left(\frac{1}{2}\right)^2 \sum_{12} 2! \frac{1}{2^2} \underset{-}{w}^2_{12} \varphi_1 \varphi_2 = 2! \frac{1}{2^2} \sum_{\underset{\sim}{qj}} \omega^4_{\underset{\sim}{qj}} L^2_{\underset{\sim}{qj}}$$

$$= \frac{1}{2} \sum_{\underset{\sim}{qj}} (KT)^2 = 3\, N'(KT)^2$$

the factor 2! standing for the number of ways the linked part of $\langle V_h^2 \rangle_h$ can be made out of the two $u_{s,\alpha}$'s or $Q_{\underset{\sim}{qj}}$ at each vertex. The next term will be represented as follows

represents $P_L \overline{V}_h \overline{V} = \langle V_h V \rangle_{hL}$

The heavy dot is a symbol for the sum of the anharmonic corrections generated by the unabridged crystal potential V, namely the combinatorial factors being such as to permit the inclusion of their effects into the smeared potential Φ_ρ . Indeed, with 2ν modes, the combinatorial factor associated with the representative configuration of the above series

2ν modes

is

$$\frac{(2\nu)!}{2!\ 2^{\nu-1}(\nu-1)!}$$

and consequently, $P_L\ \bar{V}_h\ \bar{V}$ is readily seen to take the form

$$\left(\frac{1}{2}\right)^2 \sum_{12} \frac{1}{2}\ \underline{w}_{12}^2\ \varphi_1\ \Phi_2$$

The third term $P_L\ \bar{V}^2$ will be represented by the following diagram

represents $P_L\ \bar{V}^2$

The heavy line linking the heavy dots is a symbol for the sum of configurations characterized by 1, 2, ... n, ... linking correlations between the two vertices, that is

Again the combinatorial factors permit us to write the result in the compact form

$$(e^{w_{12}} - 1)\, \Phi_1\, \Phi_2 \;=\; P_L\, \overline{V}^2 \;=\; \langle V^2 \rangle_{hL}$$

In summary the diagram introduced above accounts for the following configurations

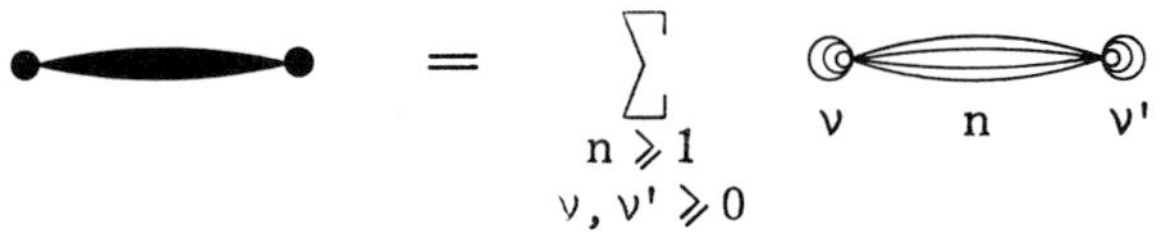

$$= \sum_{\substack{n \geqslant 1 \\ \nu, \nu' \geqslant 0}} \quad \nu \quad n \quad \nu'$$

The sum of all three terms is obviously identical with $\varkappa_2$ as given by Eq. (2-58a) which can indeed be slightly rewritten to read

$$\varkappa_2 = \frac{1}{4} \sum_{1,2} \left\{ \frac{1}{2} w_{12}^2\, \varphi_1\, \varphi_2 - w_{12}^2\, \varphi_1\, \Phi_2 \right.$$

$$\left. + \, (e^{w_{12}} - 1)\, \Phi_1\, \Phi_2 \right\} \tag{2-58b}$$

Clearly, in following this procedure we obtain much more rapidly the algebraic expressions of the $\varkappa_k$'s . Before proceeding, however, we should remark that V_{st} has dropped out of $\varkappa_2$, the linked part of μ_2 , as it will also drop from all higher semi-invariants. It is precisely for this property that the $\varkappa_k$'s have been given the name of semi-invariant (see the reference to Kendall and Stuart's book). The point is that if we add V_{st} to V_a and redefine all moments μ_n by

$$\mu'_n = \langle (V_{st} + V_a)^n \rangle_h = \langle (V - V_h)^n \rangle_h$$

then only the first cumulant $\varkappa_1$ is affected by this change and becomes $\varkappa_1' = \varkappa_1 + V_{st}$ whereas the higher ones are left unchanged. This shift in $\varkappa_1$ is precisely what we have in the second term of Eq. (2-52) and therefore we can write

$$\varkappa_1' = \varkappa_1 + V_{st} = P(\overline{V} - \overline{V}_h) = P_L(\overline{V} - \overline{V}_h)$$

$$\varkappa_2' = \varkappa_2 = P_L\,(\overline{V} - \overline{V}_h)^2$$

$$\varkappa_3' \quad \varkappa_3 = P_L\,(\overline{V} - \overline{V}_h)^3$$

$$\varkappa_k' = \varkappa_k = P_L\,(\overline{V} - \overline{V}_h)^k \tag{2-60}$$

$$\ln Z_V - \ln Z_{V,h} = \sum_{k=1}^{\infty} \frac{(-\beta)^k}{k!}\,\varkappa_k'$$

$$= P_L \exp \beta(\overline{V}_h - \overline{V}) \equiv \langle \exp \beta(V_h - V)\rangle_{hL} \tag{2-60a}$$

With the help of the diagrammatic representation introduced above we pursue our analysis with the calculation of $\varkappa_3$. Following an order of increasing complexity in the evaluation of the contributions to $\varkappa_3$, let us permute $\overline{V}$ and $\overline{V}_h$ and write

$$- \varkappa_3 = P_L\,(\overline{V}_h - \overline{V})^3 = P_L\,\overline{V}_h^{\,3} - 3\,P_L\,\overline{V}_h^{\,2}\,\overline{V}$$

$$+\ 3\,P_L\,\overline{V}_h\,\overline{V}^2 - P_L\,\overline{V}^3$$

The first term is represented by the diagram

a)  △

which symbolizes the $2.\,2^2 = 8$ equivalent configurations obtained in permuting the vertices 2 and 3 and in permuting the two modes attached to these vertices. This term amounts to

$$\left(\frac{1}{2}\right)^3 \sum_{\substack{s_1 s_2 s_3 \\ \rho_1 \rho_2 \rho_3}} 8 \, \frac{1}{2^3} \, \underline{w}_{12} \, \underline{w}_{23} \, \underline{w}_{31} \; \varphi_1 \, \varphi_2 \, \varphi_3$$

$$= \left(\frac{1}{2}\right)^3 \sum_{1,2,3} \underline{w}_{12} \, \underline{w}_{23} \, \underline{w}_{31} \; \varphi_1 \, \varphi_2 \, \varphi_3$$

It is also equal to

$$8 \, \frac{1}{2^3} \sum_{\underset{\sim}{q}j} \omega^6_{\underset{\sim}{q}j} \, L^3_{\underset{\sim}{q}j} = \sum_{\underset{\sim}{q}j} (KT)^3 = 2\times 3N'(KT)^3$$

Inspection of the second term shows that the following diagrams are representative of the possible configurations, namely

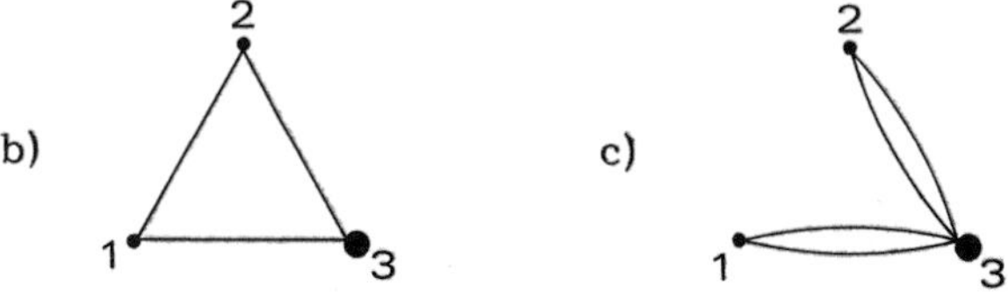

The contribution of the type b) amounts to

$$\left(\frac{1}{2}\right)^3 \sum_{1,2,3} \underline{w}_{12} \, \underline{w}_{23} \, \underline{w}_{31} \; \varphi_1 \, \varphi_2 \, \Phi_3$$

and for the type c) it is left as an exercise to show that the corresponding contribution reads

$$\left(\frac{1}{2}\right)^3 \sum_{1,2,3} \frac{1}{2} \, \underline{w}^2_{13} \, \frac{1}{2} \, \underline{w}^2_{23} \; \varphi_1 \, \varphi_2 \, \Phi_3$$

thus

$$3\, P_L\, \bar{V}_h^2\, \bar{V} = 3 \left(\frac{1}{2}\right)^3 \sum_{1,2,3} \Big\{ \underline{w}_{12}\, \underline{w}_{23}\, \underline{w}_{31}\; \varphi_1\, \varphi_2\, \Phi_3$$

$$+ \frac{1}{2}\, \underline{w}_{13}^2\, \frac{1}{2}\, \underline{w}_{23}^2\; \varphi_1\, \varphi_2\, \Phi_3 \Big\}$$

In what concerns the third term of $\varkappa_3$ one finds two possible types of diagrams which can be drawn as follows

The corresponding contributions assume the algebraic value

$$3\, P_L\, \bar{V}_h\, \bar{V}^2 = 3 \left(\frac{1}{2}\right)^3 \sum_{1,2,3} \Big\{ \underline{w}_{12}\, \underline{w}_{13}\, (e^{\underline{w}_{23}} - 1)\; \varphi_1\, \Phi_2\, \Phi_3$$

$$+ \frac{1}{2}\, \underline{w}_{13}^2\, (e^{\underline{w}_{23}} - 1)\; \varphi_1\, \Phi_2\, \Phi_3 \Big\}$$

its derivation being again left as an exercise. As to the last term of $\varkappa_3$, one readily finds that it breaks down as

f) g)

and accordingly

$$P_L\, \bar{V}^3 = \left(\frac{1}{2}\right)^3 \sum_{1,2,3} \Big\{ (e^{\underline{w}_{12}} - 1)(e^{\underline{w}_{23}} - 1)(e^{\underline{w}_{31}} - 1)$$

$$\times\, \Phi_1\, \Phi_2\, \Phi_3 + 3\, (e^{\underline{w}_{13}} - 1)(e^{\underline{w}_{23}} - 1)\; \Phi_1\, \Phi_2\, \Phi_3 \Big\}$$

It is worth making an independent check of the last result. This can be done in re-expressing the cumulant $P_L \overline{V}^3$ in terms of the moments of the potential V by inverting Eq. (2-48). This inversion yields

$$P_L \overline{V}^3 = \langle V^3 \rangle_{hL} = \langle V^3 \rangle_h - 3 \langle V^2 \rangle_h \langle V \rangle_h + 2 \langle V \rangle_h^3$$

Now

$$\langle V^3 \rangle_h = \left(\frac{1}{2}\right)^3 \sum_{1,2,3} e^{\underline{w}_{12} + \underline{w}_{23} + \underline{w}_{13}} \Phi_1 \Phi_2 \Phi_3$$

$$\equiv \left(\frac{1}{2}\right)^3 \sum_{1,2,3} \left((e^{\underline{w}_{12}}-1)+1\right)\left((e^{\underline{w}_{23}}-1)+1\right)\left((e^{\underline{w}_{31}}-1)+1\right)$$

$$\times \; \Phi_1 \Phi_2 \Phi_3$$

$$= \left(\frac{1}{2}\right)^3 \sum_{1,2,3} \Big\{ (e^{\underline{w}_{12}}-1)(e^{\underline{w}_{23}}-1)(e^{\underline{w}_{31}}-1)$$

$$+ 3(e^{\underline{w}_{12}}-1)(e^{\underline{w}_{23}}-1) + 3(e^{\underline{w}_{23}}-1) + 1 \Big\} \Phi_1 \Phi_2 \Phi_3$$

Next

$$- 3 \langle V^2 \rangle_h \langle V \rangle_h = - 3\left(\frac{1}{2}\right)^3 \sum_{1,2,3} e^{\underline{w}_{23}} \Phi_1 \Phi_2 \Phi_3$$

$$\equiv -\left(\frac{1}{2}\right)^3 \sum_{1,2,3} \left(3\,(e^{\underline{w}_{23}}-1) + 3\right) \Phi_1\, \Phi_2\, \Phi_3$$

Lastly

$$2\ \langle V\rangle_h^{\ 3} = \left(\frac{1}{2}\right)^3 \sum_{1,2,3} 2\ \Phi_1\, \Phi_2\, \Phi_3$$

and the sum is immediately seen to reproduce $\langle V^3\rangle_{hL}$ as given above. This check makes us confident in the use of diagrams and of their algebraic translation. In taking all the terms together, the complete expression for $\varkappa_3$ reads

$$\begin{aligned}\varkappa_3 = -\left(\frac{1}{2}\right)^3 \sum_{\substack{s_1 s_2 s_3\\ \rho_1\rho_2\rho_3}} \Big\{ &\underline{w}_{12}\,\underline{w}_{23}\,\underline{w}_{31}\ \varphi_1\,\varphi_2\,\varphi_3 \\ &- 3\,\underline{w}_{12}\,\underline{w}_{23}\,\underline{w}_{31}\ \varphi_1\,\varphi_2\,\Phi_3 - 3\,\frac{1}{2}\,\underline{w}_{13}^{\ 2}\ \frac{1}{2}\,\underline{w}_{23}^{\ 2}\ \varphi_1\,\varphi_2\,\Phi_3 \\ &+ 3\,\underline{w}_{12}\,\underline{w}_{13}\,(e^{\underline{w}_{23}}-1)\ \varphi_1\,\Phi_2\,\Phi_3 + 3\,\frac{1}{2}\,\underline{w}_{13}^{\ 2}\,(e^{\underline{w}_{23}}-1)\ \varphi_1\,\Phi_2\,\Phi_3 \\ &- 3\,(e^{\underline{w}_{13}}-1)(e^{\underline{w}_{23}}-1)\ \Phi_1\,\Phi_2\,\Phi_3 - (e^{\underline{w}_{12}}-1)(e^{\underline{w}_{23}}-1)(e^{\underline{w}_{31}}-1) \\ &\times \Phi_1\,\Phi_2\,\Phi_3 \Big\} \end{aligned} \tag{2-61}$$

Eq. (2-61) shows again that all of the third order anharmonic corrections to the free energy can be put into a finite number of terms which sum up a vast amount of contributions and can each be analyzed in detail. Considering in particular the instructive case of soft core and short range interactions we notice that, as $\beta \to 0, \beta^3 \varkappa_3$ saturates toward the asymptotic value of 2.3 N' originating from the first term of Eq. (2-61). Furthermore, the last two terms of $\varkappa_3$ are particularly interesting since, in the limit $\beta \to 0$, they vanish unless definite relations between the three pairs of indices $s_i, s_i' = s_i + \rho_i$ $(i = 1, 2, 3)$ are satisfied. These relations are that these pairs of indices have to be identical, that is $s_i, s_i' = s, s'$ or s', s for all i (4 ways) or "articulated", that is, for example, $s_1' = s_2$, $s_2' = s_3$, $s_3' = s_1$ (8 ways). In combining the last two terms of Eq. (2-61), we find

$$\lim_{\beta \to 0} \left(\frac{1}{2}\right)^3 \sum_{1,2,3} \left(e^{\overline{w}_{12} + w_{23} + \overline{w}_{31}} - 3\, e^{\overline{w}_{12}} + 2\right) \Phi_1 \Phi_2 \Phi_3$$

$$= \frac{1}{2} N(N-1) \left\{ \overline{\varphi^3}(0) - 3\, \overline{\varphi^2}(0) + 2\, \overline{\varphi}(0)^3 \right\}$$

$$+ N(N-1)(N-2) \sum_{\underset{\sim}{k}} \overline{\varphi}^3(\underset{\sim}{k})$$

$$= \frac{1}{2} N(N-1) \left\{ \frac{1}{\upsilon} \int d^3R\, \varphi^3(R) - 0\left(\frac{1}{\upsilon^2}\right) + 0\left(\frac{1}{\upsilon^3}\right) \right\}$$

$$+ N(N-1)(N-2) \frac{1}{\upsilon^2} \iint d^3R\, d^3R'\, \varphi(R)\, \varphi(R')\, \varphi(|\underset{\sim}{R} + \underset{\sim}{R}'|)$$

Again this is exactly a contribution that one gets in imperfect gas theory in the corresponding approximation ([6] Eq. (1-24)).

Coming back to the question of expressing the higher terms of the series (2-52) in closed form so as to gain an insight into their structure we can say that, on the basis of the experience gained up to now it seems advisable to evaluate the general semi-invariant

$$\varkappa_k = P_L (\overline{V} - \overline{V}_h)^k$$

as follows: Begin with

$$P\overline{V}^k = \langle V^k \rangle_h = \left(\frac{1}{2}\right)^k \sum_{1,2,\ldots k} \prod_{i<j} e^{\underline{w}_{ij}} \Phi_i$$

Pick out the linked part $P_L \; \overline{V}^k$ of the above mean value either by inversion of Eq. (2-48) or out of the resolution of the product of exp $\underline{w}_{ij}$ in a Mayer-like way, namely

$$\prod_{i<j} e^{\underline{w}_{ij}} \Phi_i \equiv \prod_{i<j} (1+(e^{\underline{w}_{ij}}-1)) \Phi_i$$

Draw all the diagrams associated with the linked contributions to $\langle V^k \rangle_{hL}$. Then carry out the binomial expansion of $(\overline{V}-\overline{V}_h)^k$ and draw the types of linked diagrams representing $P_L \; \overline{V}^{k-k'} \overline{V}_h^{\;k'}$ which are obtained in substituting $k' \; \overline{V}_h$ for $k' \overline{V}$.

With the general procedure given above the perturbation calculus of anharmonic effects based on the correlation functions method can be said to be completed. Exploitation of the correlation matrices λ_{ij}, has indeed made it possible to meet one of the objectives pointed out in section (1-3), at the cost, however, of explicitly losing the law of wave vector conservation which applies to any set of modes attached to a given vertex of a diagram. These correlation matrices have in addition been instrumental for revealing a link between anharmonicity theory and the theory of imperfect gases. It seems, however, that the true nature of this link is found in letting the $\lambda_{ij} \to \infty$, more so than in letting $\beta \to 0$, this being just a device for inducing the former limit, another one being indeed to let the harmonic frequencies tend to zero. If so, we describe with the same cumulant expansion which becomes a power series in $\beta = \frac{1}{KT}$ as contrasted with the power series in T of the low temperature limit, a regime of giant motional fluctuations which has nothing to do with the solid-state. We therefore strongly suspect that, although each one of the cumulants may be well behaved, over the full range of temperature or λ_{ij} variations, and thus their temperature derivative as well (which are relevant to U(T) and to $C_{\upsilon}(T)$ analysis), their sum is going to display a finite radius of convergence. For being in a position to take up this question, presumably related to the problem of the dynamical stability of the crystalline state, it is necessary that partial series of the cumulant expansion be summed up, and this is what we shall do in the next chapter.

Chapter 3

SELF-CONSISTENT EQUATIONS

The purpose of this chapter is to establish closed form expressions for $\ln Z_V$ in successive, self-consistent approximations. The method based on the so-called "ring-diagram summation" will first be employed to show how the factorization of the partition function is achieved, and also for conjecturing the form of the first order self-consistent equations which will turn out to be of particular interest for our later investigations. This conjecture will then be proved and the results generalized by using a suitable method known as the method of the "self-consistent field" .

3-1 FACTORIZATION OF THE PARTITION FUNCTION

The method we shall begin to deal with amounts to performing the summation of infinite partial series of the fundamental cumulant expansion (2-52) of $\ln Z_V$. The components of each semi-invariant $P_L \overline{V}_a^k$ as given by Eq. (2-50), which constitute the terms of the summable series are suitably picked out by considering the topology of the network formed by the correlation operators $\underline{w}_{ij}$ which link the vertices two by two in all possible ways compatible with the requirement of overall connectedness. Owing to the generally small eigenvalues of the $\underline{w}_{ij}$, the more tightly interconnected the vertices are, the higher the order of approximation will be. As we shall see and may readily anticipate, this procedure can be put on a systematic basis by starting with the least tightly connected and closed network which plays a key role in the entire development. This network is obtained when the number of linking correlations equals the number of vertices, their connections forming a closed loop, as illustrated in Fig. 1a. Although varying in the meaning of the links and vertices, this kind of loop is very common in many-body theories and is often referred to as ring diagram.

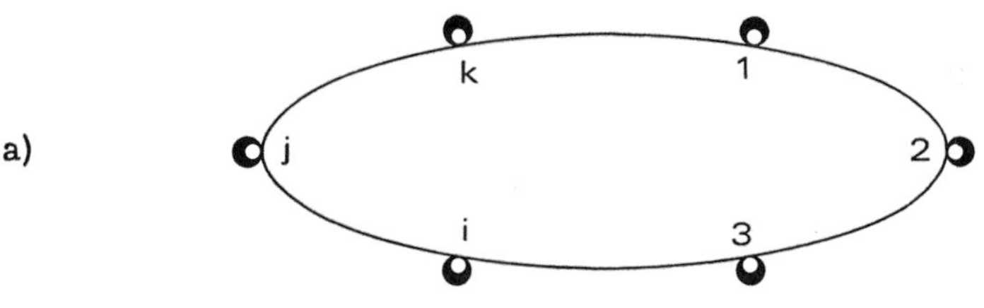

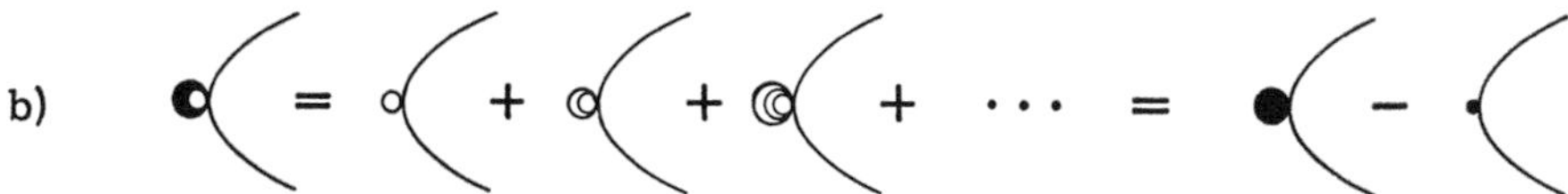

Fig. 1a. Lowest order ring diagram

1b. Definition of the vertex symbol

In the above version the links represent the correlation operator $\underline{w}_{ij}$, and the heavy dots with a small hole in them are a symbol representing the effect of the sum of the self-linked correlations $\underline{w}_j = \lambda_{\rho_j} : \underset{\sim}{p}_j \underset{\sim}{p}_j$ operating on the potential functions φ_{ρ_j}, as shown diagramatically in Fig. 1b. The function associated with each vertex is simply $\Phi_{\rho_j} - \varphi_{\rho_j}$. Indeed, since even combinations of modes only come into play and begin with the quartic term of V_a, the algebraic value of the symbol introduced above reads

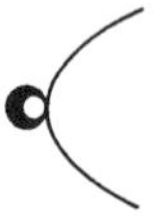

$$= \sum_{\nu \geqslant 2} \frac{1}{2\nu!} \binom{2\nu}{2} (2\nu-3)!! \, (\eta_\rho \bar{\underset{\sim}{u}}_s \cdot \underset{\sim}{p})(\lambda_\rho : \underset{\sim}{p}\underset{\sim}{p})^{\nu-1}$$

$$\times (\eta_\rho \bar{\underset{\sim}{u}}_s \cdot \underset{\sim}{p}) \, \varphi_\rho$$

$$= \frac{1}{2} (\eta_\rho \bar{\underset{\sim}{u}}_s \cdot \underset{\sim}{p}) \, (e^{\frac{1}{2}\lambda_\rho : \underset{\sim}{p}\underset{\sim}{p}} - 1) \, (\eta_\rho \bar{\underset{\sim}{u}}_s \cdot \underset{\sim}{p}) \, \varphi_\rho$$

and thus one sees how the smeared potential Φ_ρ occurs. Clearly a link is made of two "arms" $\eta_\rho \bar{\underset{\sim}{u}}_s \cdot \underset{\sim}{p}$, $\eta_{\rho'} \bar{\underset{\sim}{u}}_{s'} \cdot \underset{\sim}{p}'$ and therefore amounts to $\lambda^{s-s'}_{\rho\rho'} : \underset{\sim}{p}\underset{\sim}{p}'$ after application of the pairing operation. The next question concerns the number of ways in which such a first order ring diagram with k interactions can be drawn. Their number amounts to $(k-1)!\,2^{k-1}$ and breaks down as follows : there are $(k-1)2$ ways of pairing one mode of one of the two arms at a given vertex with one mode of any one of the two arms belonging to any one of $(k-1)$ remaining vertices, times, in brief, $(k-2)2$ for the second linking correlation times $(k-3)2$ for the third one... etc. Thus the ring diagram contribution to the semi-invariant $\varkappa_k$ reads

$$\varkappa_k(\text{ring}) = (k-1)!\,2^{k-1} \frac{1}{2^k} \sum_{1,2,..k} \frac{1}{2}\underline{w}_{12} \cdot \frac{1}{2}\underline{w}_{23} \cdot \cdots \frac{1}{2}\underline{w}_{k1}$$

$$\times (\Phi_1 - \varphi_1)(\Phi_2 - \varphi_2) \cdots (\Phi_k - \varphi_k) \qquad (3\text{-}1)$$

Next, and before proceeding to the summation over k from 2 to ∞ of these contributions properly multiplied by the factor $\frac{1}{k!}(-\beta)^k$, the form given above will be further manipulated in order to eliminate the spurious dependence of its terms upon the site indices s_1, s_2, ... s_k. This is done in going over to the normal modes representation. With Eqs (2-52) and (2-54) and slightly rearranging the order of the factors we have

$$\underline{w}_{12} = \frac{1}{NM} \sum_{\underset{\sim}{q}j} e^{i\underset{\sim}{q}(\underset{\sim}{R}_{s_1} - \underset{\sim}{R}_{s_2})} \eta_{\rho_1}(\underset{\sim}{q})\, \underset{\sim}{p}_1 \cdot \underset{\sim}{e}^j(\underset{\sim}{q}) L_{\underset{\sim}{q}j}\, \underset{\sim}{e}^j(-\underset{\sim}{q}) \cdot \underset{\sim}{p}_2$$

$$\times\, \eta_{\rho_2}(-\underset{\sim}{q})$$

and thus

$$\sum_{s_1 s_2 \ldots s_k} \frac{1}{2}\underline{w}_{12} \cdot \frac{1}{2}\underline{w}_{23} \cdots \frac{1}{2}\underline{w}_{k1} =$$

$$\frac{1}{(2M)^k} \sum_{\underset{\sim}{q}j_1 \ldots j_k} \eta_{\rho_1}(\underset{\sim}{q})\, \underset{\sim}{e}^{j_1}(\underset{\sim}{q}) \cdot \underset{\sim}{p}_1\, L_{\underset{\sim}{q}j_1}\, \underset{\sim}{e}^{j_1}(-\underset{\sim}{q}) \cdot \underset{\sim}{p}_2\, \eta_{\rho_2}(-\underset{\sim}{q})$$

$$\times\, \eta_{\rho_2}(\underset{\sim}{q})\, \underset{\sim}{e}^{j_2}(\underset{\sim}{q}) \cdot \underset{\sim}{p}_2\, L_{\underset{\sim}{q}j_2}\, \underset{\sim}{e}^{j_2}(-\underset{\sim}{q}) \cdot \underset{\sim}{p}_3\, \eta_{\rho_3}(-\underset{\sim}{q})$$

$$\times\, \ldots.$$

$$\times\, \eta_{\rho_k}(\underset{\sim}{q})\, \underset{\sim}{e}^{j_k}(\underset{\sim}{q}) \cdot \underset{\sim}{p}_k\, L_{\underset{\sim}{q}j_k}\, \underset{\sim}{e}^{j_k}(-\underset{\sim}{q}) \cdot \underset{\sim}{p}_1\, \eta_{\rho_1}(-\underset{\sim}{q})$$

Furthermore, defining a 3 x 3 matrix $\gamma_{\underset{\sim}{q}}$ by its elements

$$\gamma_{\underset{\sim}{q}jj'} \equiv \frac{1}{2}\frac{1}{M}\sum_{\rho} \underset{\sim}{e}^{j}(-\underset{\sim}{q})\cdot\underset{\sim}{\rho}\,\eta_{\rho}(-\underset{\sim}{q})\,\eta_{\rho}(\underset{\sim}{q})\,\underset{\sim}{\rho}\cdot\underset{\sim}{e}^{j'}(\underset{\sim}{q})\,(\Phi_{\rho}-\varphi_{\rho}) \tag{3-2}$$

the summation over the indices $\rho_1, \rho_2 \ldots \rho_k$ is properly accounted for and, with $L_{\underset{\sim}{q}j} = \frac{KT}{\omega^2_{\underset{\sim}{q}j}}$, Eq. (3-1) is transformed into the following form

$$\varkappa_k(\text{ring}) = \frac{1}{2}(k-1)!\,(KT)^k \sum_{\underset{\sim}{q}j_1\cdots j_k} \gamma_{\underset{\sim}{q}j_1j_2}\frac{1}{\omega^2_{\underset{\sim}{q}j_2}} \cdots$$

$$\times\, \gamma_{\underset{\sim}{q}j_kj_1}\cdot\frac{1}{\omega^2_{\underset{\sim}{q}j_1}}$$

$$= \frac{1}{2}(k-1)!\,(KT)^k \sum_{\underset{\sim}{q}} \mathrm{Tr}\,(\gamma_{\underset{\sim}{q}}\omega_{\underset{\sim}{q}}^{-2})^k \tag{3-3}$$

where Tr means the trace to be taken over the three polarization indices, $\omega^2_{\underset{\sim}{q}}$ being a diagonal matrix with elements $\omega^2_{\underset{\sim}{q}j}$. By this transformation, the ring diagram of Fig. 1a is converted into another ring diagram where the vertex functions are now given by the matrix elements $\gamma_{\underset{\sim}{q}jj'}$ and where the links represent the mean values $L_{\underset{\sim}{q}j} = \frac{KT}{\omega^2_{\underset{\sim}{q}j}}$ which are classical "propagator functions". Wave vector conservation at each vertex makes that the same wave vector $\underset{\sim}{q}$ runs through the loop whereas polarization mixing induced by the interactions $\gamma_{qjj'}$ entails that the angular frequencies may not be conserved. It is expedient to represent Eq. (3-3) by the same diagram as in Fig. 1a while keeping in mind the new interpretation of the links and vertices. The summation over k from 2 to ∞ can now easily be performed and yields

$$\sum_{k=2}^{\infty} \frac{(-\beta)^k}{k!} (k-1)! \left(\frac{1}{\beta}\right)^k \frac{1}{2} \sum_{\underset{\sim}{q}} \mathrm{Tr}\, (\gamma_{\underset{\sim}{q}} \omega_{\underset{\sim}{q}}^{-2})^k$$

$$= \frac{1}{2} \sum_{\underset{\sim}{q}} \mathrm{Tr} \sum_{k=2}^{\infty} \frac{(-1)^k}{k} (\gamma_{\underset{\sim}{q}} \omega_{\underset{\sim}{q}}^{-2})^k$$

$$= \frac{1}{2} \sum_{\underset{\sim}{q}} \mathrm{Tr}\, \gamma_{\underset{\sim}{q}} \omega_{\underset{\sim}{q}}^{-2} - \frac{1}{2} \sum_{\underset{\sim}{q}} \mathrm{Tr}\, \ell n\, (1+\gamma_{\underset{\sim}{q}} \omega_{\underset{\sim}{q}}^{-2}) \tag{3-4}$$

The noticeable feature of the above result is that a sum of logarithmic expressions has been recovered out of the originally single logarithmic expansion of the partition function†. It is proper to combine these expressions with $\ell n\, Z_{V,h}$ which is conveniently rewritten in trace form, namely

$$\ell n\, Z_{V,h} = \frac{1}{2} \sum_{\underset{\sim}{qj}} \ell n \frac{KT}{\omega_{\underset{\sim}{q}j}^2} \equiv -\frac{1}{2} \sum_{\underset{\sim}{q}} \mathrm{Tr}\, \ell n\, \beta\, \omega_{\underset{\sim}{q}}^2$$

This yields

$$-\frac{1}{2} \sum_{\underset{\sim}{q}} \mathrm{Tr}\, \ell n\, \beta\, \omega_{\underset{\sim}{q}}^2 - \frac{1}{2} \sum_{\underset{\sim}{q}} \mathrm{Tr}\, \ell n\, (1 + \gamma_{\underset{\sim}{q}} \omega_{\underset{\sim}{q}}^{-2})$$

$$= -\frac{1}{2} \sum_{\underset{\sim}{q}} \mathrm{Tr}\; \ell n\, \beta\, (\omega_{\underset{\sim}{q}}^2 + \gamma_{\underset{\sim}{q}})$$

† This feature is common to all ring diagram calculations and permits an analysis of the convergence of the link cluster expansions, whether classical or quantal. As a classical example let us mention the problem of the convergence of the cluster expansion for long range forces; here a link represents the potential $\varphi(r_{ij})$, the vertex functions turn out to be $\beta N/\upsilon$ and the ring diagram summation leads for instance to the Debye-Hückel screening of the Coulomb forces ([6], section (1-3)). In the quantum case, convergence analyses of Goldstone's expansion have been made by L. V. Hove ([8], p. 16) and A. Katz ([8], p. 199) by means of model calculations which are illustrative of the care that has to be exercised with any kind of cumulant expansion.

and means that the corresponding part of the perturbed partition function assumes the product representation

$$(KT)^{3N'} \prod_{\underset{\sim}{q}} \frac{1}{\sqrt{|\omega^2_{\underset{\sim}{q}} + \gamma_{\underset{\sim}{q}}|}}$$

where $|\omega^2_{\underset{\sim}{q}} + \gamma_{\underset{\sim}{q}}|$ is the determinant of the matrix $\omega^2_{\underset{\sim}{q}} + \gamma_{\underset{\sim}{q}}$ with elements $\omega^2_{\underset{\sim}{q}j}\,\delta_{jj'} + \gamma_{\underset{\sim}{q}jj'}$. The significance of the effect of $\gamma_{\underset{\sim}{q}jj'}$ on the harmonic eigenvalues $\omega^2_{\underset{\sim}{q}j}$ is best grasped, not in diagonalizing at this stage the 3 x 3 matrix $\omega^2_{\underset{\sim}{q}} + \gamma_{\underset{\sim}{q}}$ but in working back in the original representation of Born's dynamical matrix $D_{\underset{\sim}{q}}$. Remember that in the harmonic approximation we have

$$D_{\underset{\sim}{q}\alpha\beta} = \frac{1}{M} \sum_{\rho}{}' \left(1 - \cos \underset{\sim}{q}\,\underset{\sim}{R}_{\rho}\right) p_{\alpha}\, p_{\beta}\, \varphi_{\rho} \tag{1-31}$$

and that, in this representation, the equilibrium correlation matrix λ_{ρ} reads

$$\lambda_{\rho} = 2\,\frac{KT}{M} \cdot \frac{1}{N} \sum_{\underset{\sim}{q}}{}' \left(1 - \cos \underset{\sim}{q}\,\underset{\sim}{R}_{\rho}\right) D^{-1}_{\underset{\sim}{q}} \tag{1-82}$$

Now, the matrix elements $\gamma_{\underset{\sim}{q}jj'}$ given by Eq. (3-2) can be written as

$$\gamma_{\underset{\sim}{q}jj'} = \sum_{\alpha\beta} e^{j}_{\alpha}(-\underset{\sim}{q})\, C_{\underset{\sim}{q}\alpha\beta}\, e^{j'}_{\beta}(\underset{\sim}{q})$$

with

$$C_{\underset{\sim}{q}\alpha\beta} = \frac{1}{M} \sum_{\rho}{}' \left(1 - \cos \underset{\sim}{q}\,\underset{\sim}{R}_{\rho}\right) p_{\alpha}\, p_{\beta}\, \left(\Phi_{\rho} - \varphi_{\rho}\right) \tag{3-2a}$$

Consequently

$$\omega_{\underset{\sim}{q}}^{2} + \gamma_{\underset{\sim}{q}} = e^{+}(\underset{\sim}{q})\,(D_{\underset{\sim}{q}} + C_{\underset{\sim}{q}})\,e(\underset{\sim}{q})$$

and a new dynamical matrix

$$D_{\underset{\sim}{q}}^{(1)} = D_{\underset{\sim}{q}} + C_{\underset{\sim}{q}} \tag{3-5}$$

can accordingly be defined. The point is now that, owing to the cancellation of $D_{\underset{\sim}{q}}$ with part of $C_{\underset{\sim}{q}}$, the matrix elements of Eq. (3-5) read

$$D_{\underset{\sim}{q}\alpha\beta}^{(1)} = \frac{1}{M}\sum_{\rho}(1 - \cos \underset{\sim}{q}\,\underset{\sim}{R}_{\rho})\,p_{\alpha}\,p_{\beta}\,\Phi_{\rho} \tag{3-5a}$$

and this is a rather interesting result. Indeed, it tells us that the perturbed force constants $\Phi_{\alpha\beta}(R_{\rho}, \lambda_{\rho})$ are directly obtained from the smeared potential which already encompasses some of the effects of the motional fluctuation of the atomic nuclei at a temperature T. These effects are conveyed by the equilibrium correlation matrix λ_{ρ} calculated in terms of the elements of $D_{\underset{\sim}{q}}^{-1}$, the matrix $D_{\underset{\sim}{q}}$ being itself determined by the static force constants $\varphi_{\alpha\beta}(R\ )$. Thus Eq. (3-5a) materializes the first step toward a truly dynamical theory of crystal lattices. Before drawing the conjecture which immediatly emerges from this result we shall complete in this approximation the calculation of that part of the partition function which has been left out of the factorization. In making use of Eqs (3-2a) and (1-82) the first term of Eq. (3-4) is suitably transformed so that it can be combined with the first term of Eq. (2-60) left out by the ring diagram summation which began with $k = 2$. We have indeed

$$\frac{1}{2}\sum_{\underset{\sim}{q}} \text{Tr}\ \gamma_{\underset{\sim}{q}}\,\omega_{\underset{\sim}{q}}^{-2} = \frac{1}{2}\sum_{\underset{\sim}{q}} \text{Tr}\ C_{\underset{\sim}{q}}\,D_{\underset{\sim}{q}}^{-1} \equiv \frac{1}{2}\sum_{\underset{\sim}{q}} \text{Tr}\ D_{\underset{\sim}{q}}^{-1}\,C_{\underset{\sim}{q}}$$

$$= \frac{1}{2}\sum_{\underset{\sim}{q},\,\rho} \frac{1}{M}\,(1 - \cos \underset{\sim}{q}.\underset{\sim}{R}_{\rho})\ D_{\underset{\sim}{q}}^{-1}:\underset{\sim\sim}{pp}(\Phi_{\rho} - \varphi_{\rho})$$

$$= \frac{1}{KT}\ .\ N\ .\ \frac{1}{2}\sum_{\rho}\frac{1}{2}\,(\lambda_{\rho}:\underset{\sim\sim}{pp})\ (\Phi_{\rho} - \varphi_{\rho})$$

and furthermore, from Eq. (2-60)

$$-\ \beta\,\varkappa_1' = -\ \beta\,N\,\frac{1}{2}\sum_{\rho}\,(\Phi_{\rho} - \frac{1}{2}\,\lambda_{\rho}:\underset{\sim\sim}{pp}\,\varphi_{\rho})$$

Thus

$$-\ \beta\,\varkappa_1' + \frac{1}{2}\sum_{\underset{\sim}{q}} \text{Tr}\ \gamma_{\underset{\sim}{q}}\,\omega_{\underset{\sim}{q}}^{-2} = -\ \beta\,N\,\frac{1}{2}\sum_{\rho}\,(1 - \frac{1}{2}\,\lambda_{\rho}:\underset{\sim\sim}{pp})\,\Phi_{\rho} \qquad (3\text{-}6)$$

We notice that the static potential φ_{ρ} has disappeared from the expression, in favor of the smeared potential only. In this approximation we therefore find

$$\ell n\ Z_V^{(1)}\ (\text{ring}) = -\ \beta\,N\,\frac{1}{2}\sum_{\rho}\,(1 - \frac{1}{2}\,\lambda_{\rho}:\underset{\sim\sim}{pp})\ \Phi_{\rho}$$

$$-\ \frac{1}{2}\sum_{\underset{\sim}{q}} \text{Tr}\ \ell n\ \beta\,D_{\underset{\sim}{q}}^{(1)} \qquad (3\text{-}7)$$

The first run of ring diagram summation has produced eloquent results. They suggest that an improved correlation matrix $\lambda_{\rho}^{(1)}$ ought to be found in terms of $D_{\underset{\sim}{q}}^{(1)^{-1}}$ then fed into a new smeared potential $\Phi_\rho^{(1)}$ which in turn would lead to a new dynamical matrix, and so on. Clearly, the limit, if it exists, will be a set of first order self-consistent equations which are written below with an index I to specify the approximation, their conjectural character being marked with the conventional question mark. Furthermore and for simplicity of notation we have written the tensor product $\lambda_\rho : \underset{\sim}{p}\underset{\sim}{p}$ as $\lambda_\rho \underset{\sim}{p}^2$.

$$D_{\underset{\sim}{q}}^{(I)} \stackrel{?}{=} \frac{1}{M} \sum_\rho (1 - \cos \underset{\sim}{q}\, \underset{\sim}{R}_\rho)\, \underset{\sim}{p}^2 \quad \Phi_\rho^{(I)} \tag{3-8a}$$

$$\Phi_\rho^{(I)} \stackrel{?}{=} \exp \left[\frac{1}{2} \lambda_\rho^{(I)} \underset{\sim}{p}^2 \right] \varphi_\rho \tag{3-8b}$$

$$\lambda_\rho^{(I)} \stackrel{?}{=} 2 \frac{KT}{MN} \sum_{\underset{\sim}{q}} (1 - \cos \underset{\sim}{q}.\underset{\sim}{R}_\rho)\, D_{\underset{\sim}{q}}^{(I)^{-1}} \tag{3-8c}$$

$$\ell n\, Z_V^{(I)} \stackrel{?}{=} - \beta N \frac{1}{2} \sum_\rho (1 - \frac{1}{2} \lambda_\rho^{(I)} \underset{\sim}{p}^2)\, \Phi_\rho^{(I)} - \frac{1}{2} \sum_{\underset{\sim}{q}} \mathrm{Tr}\, \ell n\, \beta D_{\underset{\sim}{q}}^{(I)}$$

$$= - \beta N \frac{1}{2} \sum_\rho \Phi_\rho^{(I)} + \frac{3}{2} (N-1) - \frac{1}{2} \sum_{\underset{\sim}{q}} \mathrm{Tr}\, \ell n\, \beta D_{\underset{\sim}{q}}^{(I)} \tag{3-8}$$

The factor 3/2 (N-1) in the last equation expresses an interesting sum rule derived from the former equations, which reads

$$3\, KT = \mathrm{Tr} \frac{1}{2} \sum_\rho \lambda_\rho^{(I)} \underset{\sim}{p}^2\, \Phi_\rho^{(I)} \tag{3-9}$$

The procedure based on iterating ring diagram summation will, however, not be followed for establishing the set of equations conjectured above. This method is particularly cumbersome here because of the exponential relation Eq. (3-8b) which entails that an infinite set of summations has to be performed in addition to the infinite set already inherent to the method when the latter is applied to a truncated interaction $V_a = V_{4-a}$ for instance.

3-2 RENORMALIZED HARMONIC APPROXIMATION

As a suitable alternative, we shall apply what is known as the method of the self-consistent field †. Here it amounts to add and subtract from the crystal potential a potential energy W which is bilinear in the lattice wave amplitudes $u_{\underset{\sim}{q},\alpha}$ with an unknown yet positive definite dynamical matrix $\mathbf{D}_{\underset{\sim}{q}}$, namely

$$W = \frac{1}{2} \sum_{\underset{\sim}{q}\alpha\beta} M\, \mathbf{D}_{\underset{\sim}{q},\alpha\beta}\; u_{\underset{\sim}{q},\alpha}\; u^{*}_{\underset{\sim}{q},\beta} \tag{3-10}$$

and determine $\mathbf{D}_{\underset{\sim}{q}}$ by requiring that the perturbed part of the dynamical matrix obtained after summing over ring diagrams vanishes. Now instead of adding W to V_h for constituting a new "unperturbed" potential energy, and then substract W from V_a, it turns out to be more convenient to simply rewrite the crystal potential V as follows

$$V = W + V - W \tag{3-11}$$

and treat V - W as "perturbation". For clarity, let us illustrate this procedure with the trivial example provided by the case where $V = V_{st} + V_h$. $V_h - W$ being bilinear in the lattice wave amplitudes,

† An extensive and self-contained exposé of the quantum mechanical version of the method, from which our classical one is borrowed, may be found in C. Bloch, R. Balian, and C. DeDominicis series of lectures, entitled "General Perturbation Formalism of the Many-Body Problem at Non-Zero Temperature" ([8], p. 31-57, p. 139-162, p. 163-189).

the ring diagram summation carried out once exhaust the "perturbation" and we find in analogy with Eq. (3-5)

$$\mathbb{D}^{(1)}_{\underset{\sim}{q}} = \mathbb{D}_q + \mathbb{C}_{\underset{\sim}{q}}$$

with $\mathbb{C}_{\underset{\sim}{q}} = D_{\underset{\sim}{q}} - \mathbb{D}_{\underset{\sim}{q}}$

Setting

$$\mathbb{C}_{\underset{\sim}{q}} = 0$$

we recover of course the harmonic expression. The first nontrivial application of the self-consistent method will be to establish here the set of equations (3-8). For we rewrite the fundamental cumulant expansion Eq. (2-60) as follows

$$\ell n\, Z_V = \ell n\, Z_W + \sum_{k=1}^{\infty} \frac{1}{k!} (-\beta)^k\, P_L\, (\overline{V}-\overline{W})^k \tag{3-12}$$

where the mean values $L_{\underset{\sim}{q}j}$ entering the definition of the $\overline{V}$'s in Eqs (2-44), (2-45), are expressed in terms of the assumed eigenvalues of the unknown propagator matrices $KT\,\mathbb{D}^{-1}_{\underset{\sim}{q}}$. Alternatively

$$P_L\, (\overline{V}-\overline{W})^k \equiv \langle (V-W)^k \rangle_{WL} \tag{3-13}$$

the subscript W meaning that the expectation values have to be taken over the Boltzmann factor $\exp - \beta W$. We repeat now what we have done above, the perturbation $V - V_h$ being replaced by $V - W$. The algebraic value of the basic ring diagram drawn for a given term of the new expansion, Eq. (3-12), reads then

$$\frac{1}{2} \frac{(-1)^k}{k} \quad \mathrm{Tr}\,(\mathbb{C}_{\underset{\sim}{q}} \mathbb{D}_{\underset{\sim}{q}}^{-1})^k$$

with

$$\mathbb{C}_{\underset{\sim}{q},\alpha\beta} = \frac{1}{M} \sum_{\rho} (1 - \cos \underset{\sim}{q}\,\underset{\sim}{R}_{\rho})\, p_\alpha\, p_\beta\, \Phi_\rho \; - \; \mathbb{D}_{\underset{\sim}{q},\alpha\beta} \qquad (3\text{-}14a)$$

$$\Phi_\rho = \exp\left[\frac{1}{2}\lambda_\rho\, p^2\right] \varphi_\rho \qquad (3\text{-}14b)$$

$$\lambda_\rho = \frac{2KT}{M} \cdot \frac{1}{N} \sum_{\underset{\sim}{q}} (1 - \cos \underset{\sim}{q}\,\underset{\sim}{R}_{\rho})\, \mathbb{D}_{\underset{\sim}{q}}^{-1} \qquad (3\text{-}14c)$$

In performing the summation in Eq. (3-12) from $k = 2$ to ∞ and combining the result with $\ell n\, Z_W$, we find the perturbed dynamical matrix

$$\mathbb{D}_{\underset{\sim}{q}}^{(1)} = \mathbb{D}_{\underset{\sim}{q}} + \mathbb{C}_{\underset{\sim}{q}} \qquad (3\text{-}15)$$

again in analogy with Eq. (3-5), the difference being that $\mathbb{D}_q$ is not given a priori, like $D_{\underset{\sim}{q}}$ was. Now, requiring at this stage that

$$\mathbb{C}_{\underset{\sim}{q}} = 0 \qquad (3\text{-}16)$$

then via Eqs (3-14a, b, c), we produce exactly the first order self-consistent Eqs (3-8a, b, c) and accordingly

$$\mathbb{D}_q = D_{\underset{\sim}{q}}^{(I)} \qquad (3\text{-}17)$$

Furthermore, the first cumulant of Eq (3-12) reads, in this approximation

$$- \beta \langle V-W \rangle_W = - \beta N \frac{1}{2} \sum_{\rho} (1 - \frac{1}{2} \lambda_\rho \underset{\sim}{p}^2) \Phi_\rho^{(I)}$$

$$= - \beta N \frac{1}{2} \sum_{\rho} \Phi_\rho^{(I)} + \frac{3}{2} (N-1)$$

and, owing to Eq. (3-16)

$$\ell n\, Z_V^{(I)} = - \beta N \frac{1}{2} \sum_{\rho} \Phi_\rho^{(I)} + \frac{3}{2} (N-1) - \frac{1}{2} \sum_{\underset{\sim}{q}} \mathrm{Tr}\ \ell n\ \beta D_{\underset{\sim}{q}}^{(I)} \tag{3-14}$$

that is exactly Eq. (3-8). The set of Eqs (3-8a, b, c) is therefore established. Being apparently the first of their kind in lattice dynamics they have to be designated in some way. It can be said that they describe lattice dynamics in a random phase, or Hartree approximation, yet for specific designation purposes the name renormalized harmonic approximation or simply R. H. A. will be used. Several interesting features will be displayed by the solutions of Eqs (3-8). However, before limiting ourselves to a detailed investigation of the R. H. A. we shall proceed with the discussion of the self-consistent equations in second and higher order of approximation.

3-3 SECOND ORDER APPROXIMATION

Second order calculations are carried out as follows: First we consider that part of the second cumulant of Eq. (3-12) which has been left out by the first order ring diagram with $k = 2$. This means that from

$$\varkappa_2 = \langle (V-W)^2 \rangle_{WL} = \langle V^2 \rangle_{WL} - 2 \langle VW \rangle_{WL} + \langle W^2 \rangle_{WL}$$

we retain only those contributions to $\langle V^2 \rangle_{WL}$ which are characterized by three or more correlations linking the vertices. Their contributions will be said to constitute the irreducible part of $\varkappa_2$ whereas the other ones, with two linking correlations, constitute its reducible part. Thus

$$\varkappa_{2,\,ir.} = \left(\frac{1}{2}\right)^2 \sum_{1,2} \sum_{n \geqslant 3} \frac{1}{n!} (w_{12})^n \, \Phi_1 \, \Phi_2$$

and the $\sum_{n \geqslant 3}$ for a given pair of indices will be represented by the diagram shown in Fig. 2.

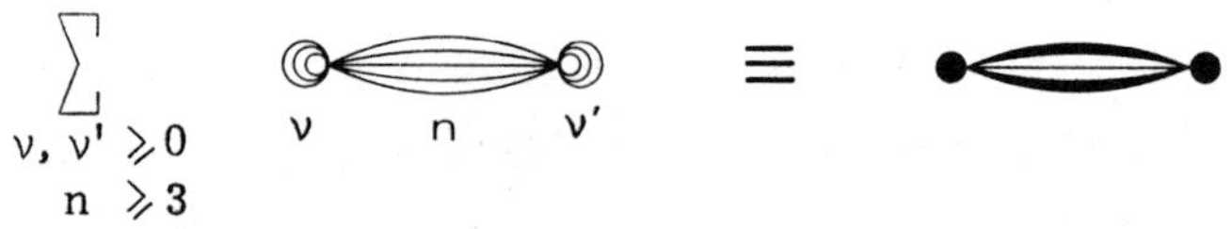

$$\sum_{\substack{\nu,\,\nu' \geqslant 0 \\ n \geqslant 3}}$$

ν n ν' ≡

Fig. 2. Irreducible part of $\varkappa_2$

Next we consider the second order irreducible components which, after suitable manipulation, are going to be inserted into ring diagrams. These components are obtained by cutting any one of the linking or self-linked correlation of the above diagram, thus providing two "arms" for inter-component linking. The result is shown in Fig. 3.

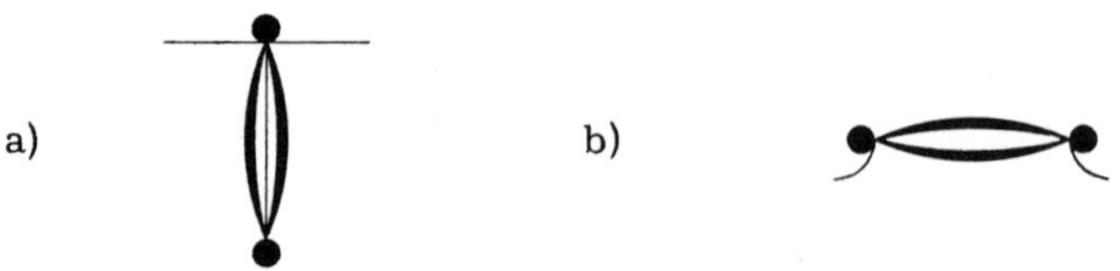

Fig. 3. Second order irreducible components

Algebraically, these components read

$$a) = 2 \cdot \frac{1}{2} \sum_{\rho' s' n \geqslant 3} \frac{1}{2} (\eta_\rho \bar{u}_{\underset{\sim}{s}} \cdot \underset{\sim}{p}) \frac{1}{n!} (\lambda_{\rho \rho'}^{s-s'} \underset{\sim\sim}{pp'})^n$$

$$\times \Phi_{\rho'} (\eta_\rho \bar{u}_{\underset{\sim}{s}} \cdot \underset{\sim}{p}) \Phi_\rho \qquad (3\text{-}19a)$$

$$b) = \sum_{n \geqslant 2} (\eta_\rho \bar{u}_{\underset{\sim}{s}} \cdot \underset{\sim}{p}) \frac{1}{n!} (\lambda_{\rho \rho'}^{s-s'} \underset{\sim\sim}{pp'})^n (\eta_{\rho'} \bar{u}_{\underset{\sim}{s'}} \cdot \underset{\sim}{p'}) \Phi_\rho \Phi_{\rho'} \qquad (3\text{-}19b)$$

the factor 2 in front of Eq. (3-19a) accounting for the permutation of the vertices 1 and 2 in the cut of a self-linked correlation. Now in linking two by two any set of first and second order components so as to form a closed loop we get our familiar correlation operator $\underline{w}_{ij}$ (without factors 1/2 as in Eq. (3-1)) which still depends upon the site indices s_i, s_j .

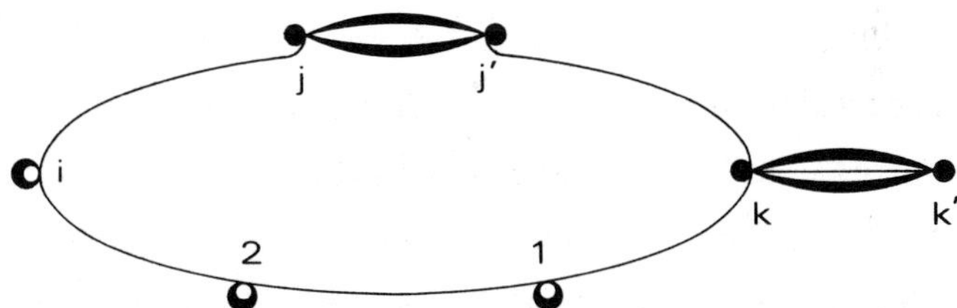

Fig. 3. Example of ring diagram with first and second order components

Here, as above, we go over to the lattice wave representation. The difference is that for the second order components there are two site indices, s, s', per component. Introducing their difference $s - s' = \sigma$ we get rid of one of them, which is necessary. The links between two components again represent elements of the propagator matrix KT $\mathbb{D}_{\underset{\sim}{q}}^{-1}$ and in analogy with the first order matrix elements Eq. (3-14a) relabelled $\mathbb{C}^{(1)}_{\underset{\sim}{q},\alpha\beta}$ we can derive from Eqs (3-19a) and (3-19b) second order matrix elements $\mathbb{C}^{(2a)}_{\underset{\sim}{q},\alpha\beta}$ and $\mathbb{C}^{(2b)}_{\underset{\sim}{q},\alpha\beta}$. For reasons of dimensional homogeneity it is convenient to multiply Eqs (3-19a) and (3-19b) by (-)1/KT. We thus find

$$\mathbb{C}^{(2)}_{\underset{\sim}{q},\alpha\beta} = \mathbb{C}^{(2a)}_{\underset{\sim}{q},\alpha\beta} + \mathbb{C}^{(2b)}_{\underset{\sim}{q},\alpha\beta}$$

$$= \frac{-1}{KT}\,\frac{1}{M}\left(\frac{1}{2}\right)^2 \sum_{\rho\rho'\,\sigma\,n\geqslant 2} \left\{ \frac{1}{(n+1)!}\,(\lambda^{\sigma}_{\rho\rho',\underset{\sim}{p}\underset{\sim}{p}'})^{n+1} \right.$$

$$\times\ \Phi_{\rho'}\,\eta_\rho(-\underset{\sim}{q})\,\eta_\rho(\underset{\sim}{q})\,p_\alpha\,p_\beta\,\Phi_\rho$$

$$+\ e^{+i\underset{\sim}{q}\underset{\sim}{R}_\sigma}\cdot\frac{1}{n!}\,(\lambda^{\sigma}_{\rho\rho',\underset{\sim}{p}\underset{\sim}{p}'})^{n}$$

$$\left.\times\ \eta_\rho(-\underset{\sim}{q})\,p_\alpha\,\Phi_\rho\,\eta_{\rho'}(\underset{\sim}{q})\,p_\beta{}'\,\Phi_{\rho'}\right\} \qquad (3\text{-}20)$$

Notice the factor $\exp{+i\underset{\sim}{q}\underset{\sim}{R}_\sigma}$ in $\mathbb{C}^{(2b)}_{\underset{\sim}{q},\alpha\beta}$ which is going to warrant wave vector conservation at the two vertices of this component if for any given n , the summation over σ is carried out. Equation (3-20) constitutes the building stone of the second order perturbation theory now developed. It is not necessary to refer specifically to any one of the subcomponents a) or b) which can be lumped together into a second order box represented by $\mathbb{C}^{(2)}_{\underset{\sim}{q}}$.

It is intructive to treat first the one dimensional case where the matrices $\mathbb{C}^{(1)}_{\underset{\sim}{q}}$, $\mathbb{C}^{(2)}_{\underset{\sim}{q}}$ and $\mathbb{D}_{\underset{\sim}{q}}$ reduce to scalar functions, since then the ordering of first order components and second order boxes in a given ring diagram is irrelevant, only their respective numbers matter. For, let a ring diagram be composed of ℓ second order boxes and of k - ℓ first order ones. The number of interactions involved being $2\ell + k - \ell = k+\ell$ the term of Eq. (3-12) from which the relevant contribution will be extracted is $\frac{1}{(k+\ell)!}(-\beta)^{k+\ell}\varkappa_{k+\ell}$. The number of ways in which such a ring diagram can be made (irrespective of the ordering) amounts to

$$\binom{k+\ell}{2\ell} \cdot \frac{(2\ell)!}{2^{\ell}.\ell!} \cdot (k-1)!\ 2^{k-1}$$

and breaks down as follows : there are $\binom{k+\ell}{2\ell}$ ways of picking out interactions for second order boxes times $\frac{(2\ell)!}{2^{\ell}\ell!}$ ways of making such boxes times $(k-1)!$ ways of linking first and second order boxes for forming the closed loop times 2^{k-1} ways of making the links with any one of the two "arms" of each box. This number is also equal to

$$\frac{1}{2}\,(k+\ell)!\ 2^{k-\ell}\,\frac{1}{k}\binom{k}{\ell}$$

The algebraic value of the corresponding contribution to the $(k+\ell)^{th}$ term of Eq. (3-12) reads then

$$\left(\frac{-1}{KT}\right)^{k+\ell} \cdot \frac{1}{(k+\ell)!} \cdot (-KT)^{\ell}\ (KT)^{k} \cdot \frac{1}{2}\,(k+\ell)!\ 2^{k-\ell}\,\frac{1}{k}\binom{k}{\ell} \cdot$$

$$\sum_{q} \left(\frac{1}{2}\,\mathbb{C}_q^{(1)}\,\mathbb{D}_q^{-1}\right)^{k-\ell} \cdot \left(\mathbb{C}_q^{(2)}\,\mathbb{D}_q^{-1}\right)^{\ell}$$

$$= \frac{1}{2}\,(-1)^{k} \sum_{q} \frac{1}{k}\binom{k}{\ell} \left(\mathbb{C}_q^{(1)}\,\mathbb{D}_q^{-1}\right)^{k-\ell} \left(\mathbb{C}_q^{(2)}\,\mathbb{D}_q^{-1}\right)^{\ell}$$

Note that the factor $(-KT)^{\ell}$ compensate the one introduced in the definition of $\mathbb{C}_q^{(2)}$ and that the factor $(KT)^{k}$ arises from the propagator functions. In summing over ℓ from o to k we find

$$\frac{1}{2}(-1)^k \cdot \frac{1}{k}\left[(\mathbb{C}_q^{(1)} + \mathbb{C}_q^{(2)})\mathbb{D}_q^{-1}\right]^k$$

and we are left with the summation over k from 2 to ∞ which yield

$$\frac{1}{2}\sum_q (\mathbb{C}_q^{(1)} + \mathbb{C}_q^{(2)})\,\mathbb{D}_q^{-1} + \frac{1}{2}\sum_q \ell n\,(1 + (\mathbb{C}_q^{(1)} + \mathbb{C}_q^{(2)})\,\mathbb{D}_q^{-1})$$

for our one dimensional case. For the three dimensional one, we readily conjecture the result

$$\frac{1}{2}\sum_{\underset{\sim}{q}} \mathrm{Tr}\,(\mathbb{C}_{\underset{\sim}{q}}^{(1)} + \mathbb{C}_{\underset{\sim}{q}}^{(2)})\,\mathbb{D}_{\underset{\sim}{q}}^{-1} + \frac{1}{2}\sum_{\underset{\sim}{q}} \mathrm{Tr}\,\ell n\,(1+(\mathbb{C}_{\underset{\sim}{q}}^{(1)} + \mathbb{C}_{\underset{\sim}{q}}^{(2)})\,\mathbb{D}_{\underset{\sim}{q}}^{-1}) \tag{3-21}$$

That this is correct is best shown in going backward, expanding the logarithmic expressions of Eq. (3-21), then the binomial products of matrices which in turn generate all possible ordering of first order and second order boxes. At this stage one identifies the different ordering of $k - \ell$ first order components and ℓ second order boxes with all possible ring diagrams which were lumped together in the one dimensional case, yielding $\binom{k}{\ell}$ possibilities.

In adding $\ell n\, Z_W$ to the logarithmic part of Eq. (3-21) we are led to introduce a perturbed dynamical matrix $\mathbb{D}_{\underset{\sim}{q}}^{(2)}$ defined by

$$\mathbb{D}_{\underset{\sim}{q}}^{(2)} = \mathbb{D}_{\underset{\sim}{q}} + \mathbb{C}_{\underset{\sim}{q}}^{(1)} + \mathbb{C}_{\underset{\sim}{q}}^{(2)} \tag{3-22}$$

in analogy with $\mathbb{D}_{\underset{\sim}{q}}^{(1)}$ given by Eq. (3-15). The self-consistent equation in second order of approximation, labelled with a roman index II, is now obtained if we require that the perturbed part of Eq. (3-22) vanishes, that is

$$\mathbb{C}^{(1)}_{\underset{\sim}{q}} + \mathbb{C}^{(2)}_{\underset{\sim}{q}} = 0$$

In introducing Eq. (3-14a) for $\mathbb{C}^{(1)}_{\underset{\sim}{q}}$ and Eq. (3-20) for $\mathbb{C}^{(2a)}_{\underset{\sim}{q}} + \mathbb{C}^{(2b)}_{\underset{\sim}{q}}$ we determine implicitly $\mathbb{D}_{\underset{\sim}{q}}$ in this approximation by

$$\mathbb{D}_{\underset{\sim}{q}\alpha\beta} = D^{(II)}_{\underset{\sim}{q}\alpha\beta}$$

$$= \frac{1}{M} \cdot \frac{1}{2} \sum_{\rho} \left\{ 1 - \frac{1}{KT} \frac{1}{2} \sum_{\rho' \sigma n \geqslant 3} \frac{1}{n!} \left(\lambda^{\sigma(II)}_{\rho\rho'} \underset{\sim}{p}\underset{\sim}{p}' \right)^{n} \right\}$$

$$\times \; \eta_{\rho}(\underset{\sim}{q}) \; \eta_{\rho}(-\underset{\sim}{q}) \; p_{\alpha} \, p_{\beta} \, \Phi^{(II)}_{\rho}$$

$$- \frac{1}{M} \frac{1}{KT} \left(\frac{1}{2} \right)^{2} \sum_{\rho\rho' \sigma \, n \geqslant 2} e^{+i \underset{\sim}{q}\underset{\sim}{R}_{\sigma}} \frac{1}{n!} \left(\lambda^{\sigma(II)}_{\rho\rho'} \underset{\sim}{p}\underset{\sim}{p}' \right)^{n}$$

$$\times \; \eta_{\rho}(\underset{\sim}{q}) \; \eta_{\rho'}(-\underset{\sim}{q}) \; p_{\alpha} \, \Phi^{(II)}_{\rho} \, p_{\beta}' \, \Phi^{(II)}_{\rho'} \tag{3-23a}$$

with

$$\Phi^{(II)}_{\rho} = \exp \left[\frac{1}{2} \lambda^{(II)}_{\rho} \underset{\sim}{p}^{2} \right] \varphi_{\rho} \tag{3-23b}$$

$$\lambda^{\sigma(II)}_{\rho\rho'} = \frac{KT}{MN} \sum_{\underset{\sim}{q}} e^{i\underset{\sim}{q}\underset{\sim}{R}_{\sigma}} \eta_{\rho}(\underset{\sim}{q}) \; \eta_{\rho'}(-\underset{\sim}{q}) \; (D^{(II)}_{\underset{\sim}{q}})^{-1} \tag{3-23c}$$

In carrying out the summation over n we find alternatively +

\+ Notice that in Eq. (3-23a) the second order component of type a) has been written as a correction to the first order component since $(1 - \cos \underset{\sim}{q}\,\underset{\sim}{R}_{\rho})\, \underset{\sim}{p}^{2}\, \Phi_{\rho}$ could be factorized.

$$D^{(II)}_{\underset{\sim}{q}\alpha\beta} = \frac{1}{M}\sum_{\rho}\left(1 - \frac{1}{KT}\frac{1}{2}\sum_{\rho'\sigma}\left[e^{\lambda^{\sigma(II)}_{\rho\rho'}\underset{\sim\sim}{pp'}} - 1 - \frac{1}{2}\left(\lambda^{\sigma(II)}_{\rho\rho'}\underset{\sim\sim}{pp'}\right)^2\right]\Phi^{(II)}_{\rho'}\right)$$

$$\times\ (1 - \cos \underset{\sim}{q}\,\underset{\sim}{R}_{\rho})\, p_{\alpha}\, p_{\beta}\, \Phi^{(II)}_{\rho}$$

$$- \frac{1}{KT}\frac{1}{M}\left(\frac{1}{2}\right)^2 \sum_{\rho\rho'\sigma} e^{+i\underset{\sim}{q}\underset{\sim}{R}_{\sigma}}\left[e^{\lambda^{\sigma(II)}_{\rho\rho'}\underset{\sim\sim}{pp'}} - \lambda^{\sigma(II)}_{\rho\rho'}\underset{\sim\sim}{pp'}\right]$$

$$\times \eta_{\rho}(\underset{\sim}{q})\, p_{\alpha}\, \eta_{\rho'}(-\underset{\sim}{q})\, p_{\beta}'\, \Phi^{(II)}_{\rho}\, \Phi^{(II)}_{\rho'} \qquad (3\text{-}23d)$$

In retaining only the irreducible cumulants of first and second order, the second order self-consistent approximation to Eq. (3-12) reads

$$\ln Z^{(II)}_{V} = \frac{3}{2}(N-1) - \beta N \frac{1}{2}\sum_{\rho}\Phi^{(II)}_{\rho}$$

$$+ \frac{1}{2}\beta^2\left(\frac{1}{2}\right)^2 N \sum_{\rho\rho'\sigma}\left[\exp\left(\lambda^{\sigma(II)}_{\rho\rho'}\underset{\sim\sim}{pp'}\right) - 1 - \frac{1}{2}\left(\lambda^{\sigma(II)}_{\rho\rho'}\underset{\sim\sim}{pp'}\right)^2\right]$$

$$\times \Phi^{(II)}_{\rho}\, \Phi^{(II)}_{\rho'}$$

$$- \frac{1}{2}\sum_{\underset{\sim}{q}} \mathrm{Tr} \ln \beta D^{(II)}_{\underset{\sim}{q}} \qquad (3\text{-}23)$$

3-4 GENERALIZED SELF-CONSISTENT EQUATIONS

The generalization of the self-consistent reduction of $\ln Z_V$ to higher order of approximation will now be taken up. This can be done in expressing mathematically the operations performed above for deriving from the irreducible parts of the cumulants the irreducible components which were inserted into ring-diagrams. These operations were and are in general 1°) to cut any one of the self-linked or linking correlation at an irreducible part of the cumulant $\varkappa_{k,ir}$ and 2°) to go over to the lattice wave representation for picking out the partial contributions $\mathbb{C}^{(k)}_{\underset{\sim}{q}}$ while eliminating the spurious inhomogeneous character of the components.

For let the $\varkappa_{k,ir}$ be expressed in terms of the correlation operators $\underline{w}_{ij}$ and $\underline{w}_i$ introduced in the preceding chapter. The $\underline{w}_{ij}$ are in turn written in terms of $\mathbb{D}_{\underset{\sim}{q}}$, later on determined by the self-consistency condition

$$\sum_{k=1}^{\infty} \mathbb{C}^{(k)}_{\underset{\sim}{q}} = 0$$

Let further

$$L_{q,\alpha\beta} = KT\,(\mathbb{D}^{-1}_{\underset{\sim}{q}})_{\alpha\beta}$$

be the elements of the propagatormatrix $L_{\underset{\sim}{q}}$ which assumed the eigenvalues $L_{\underset{\sim}{q},j}$ in the harmonic approximation. Thus

$$\underline{w}_{ij} = \frac{1}{MN} \sum_{\underset{\sim}{q},\alpha\beta} e^{i q(\underset{\sim}{R}_{\underset{\sim}{s}_i} - \underset{\sim}{R}_{\underset{\sim}{s}_j})} \eta_{\rho_i}(\underset{\sim}{q})\, \eta_{\rho_j}(-\underset{\sim}{q})\, p_{i,\alpha}\, p_{j,\beta}\, L_{\underset{\sim}{q},\alpha\beta}$$

$$\underline{w}_{i} = \frac{1}{MN} \sum_{\underset{\sim}{q},\alpha\beta} \eta_{\rho_i}(\underset{\sim}{q})\, \eta_{\rho_i}(-\underset{\sim}{q})\, p_{i,\alpha}\, p_{i,\beta}\, L_{\underset{\sim}{q},\alpha\beta}$$

Then we observe that to cut a self-linked correlation is nothing but to take the partial derivative $2\frac{\partial}{\partial \underline{w}_i}$ of any $\varkappa_{k,ir}$ (first operation) while the second operation amounts to multiply this derivative by the factor $\frac{d\,\underline{w}_i}{d\,L_{\underset{\sim}{q},\alpha\beta}}$ as readily checked with the example provided by the component $\mathbb{C}^{(1)}_{\underset{\sim}{q}}$ and $\mathbb{C}^{(2,a)}_{\underset{\sim}{q}}$. Similarly, to cut a linking correlation is to take the partial derivative $\frac{\partial}{\partial w_{ij}}$ of $\varkappa_{k,\,ir}$ while the second operation amounts to multiply this derivative by $\frac{dw_{ij}}{dL_{\underset{\sim}{q},\alpha\beta}}$. Therefore we have in general †

$$-\beta\, \mathbb{C}^{(k)}_{\underset{\sim}{q},\alpha\beta} = \frac{(-\beta)^k}{k!}$$

$$\times\ 2\left(\sum_i \frac{d\underline{w}_i}{dL_{\underset{\sim}{q},\alpha\beta}} \cdot \frac{\partial}{\partial \underline{w}_i} + \frac{1}{2}\sum_{ij} \frac{d\underline{w}_{ij}}{dL_{\underset{\sim}{q},\alpha\beta}}\ \frac{\partial}{\partial \underline{w}_{ij}}\right)\varkappa_{k,\,ir}$$

or

$$-\beta\, \mathbb{C}^{(k)}_{\underset{\sim}{q},\alpha\beta} = \frac{(-\beta)^k}{k!}$$

$$\times\ 2\ \frac{d}{dL_{\underset{\sim}{q},\alpha\beta}}\ \varkappa_{k,\,ir}\left(\{\underline{w}_i(L_{\underset{\sim}{q}'})\},\ \{\underline{w}_{ij}(L_{\underset{\sim}{q}'})\}\right) \tag{3-24}$$

since $d/dL_{\underset{\sim}{q},\alpha\beta}$ is just the quantity in the above parenthesis.

As to the evaluation of the $\varkappa_{k,\,ir}$, themselves, there is a simplification which occurs here owing to the irreducibility

---

† Notice that the w_i and w_{ij} are treated separately despite the possibility $i = j$. This is not imperative but convenient to distinguish the self-linked from the linking lines, and then nothing is wrong, if we note that

$$\underline{w}_{ij}\,\varphi_i\,\varphi_j = \lambda_{ij}\,(\underset{\sim}{p}_i\varphi)(\underset{\sim}{p}_j\varphi) = \lambda_i\,(\underset{\sim}{p}_i\varphi)^2\ /_{j=i}$$

whereas

$$\underline{w}_i\ \varphi_i\ \varphi_j = \lambda_i\,(p_i^2\,\varphi_i)\ \varphi_j = \lambda_i\,(p_i^2\,\varphi_i)\,\varphi_i\ /_{j=i}$$

in such a way that

$$\frac{1}{2}(w_i\,\varphi_i)\,\varphi_i + \underline{w}_{ii}\,\varphi_i\,\varphi_i = \frac{1}{2}\lambda_i\,(\underset{\sim}{p}_i^2\,\varphi_i)\,\varphi_i + \lambda_i\,(\underset{\sim}{p}_i\,\varphi_i)^2$$

$$= \frac{1}{2}\lambda_i\,\underset{\sim}{p}_i^2\,\varphi_i^2$$

requirement. The latter says indeed that the $\varkappa_{k,ir}$ are represented by connected diagrams with three correlation lines or more emerging from each one of the vertices and consequently, for $k > 1$

$$\varkappa_{k,ir} = P_{ir\,L} (\overline{V} - \overline{W})^k = P_{ir\,L} \overline{V}^k \equiv \langle V^k \rangle_{W,ir\,L}$$

since from the W's can only emerge two linking correlations which gave rise to reducible contributions taken care of by the ring-diagram summation. On the other hand, for $k = 1$, we have the well known expression

$$\varkappa_1' = P_L (\overline{V} - \overline{W}) = P_L \overline{V} - \frac{1}{2} \sum_{\underset{\sim}{q}} \operatorname{Tr} \mathbb{D}_{\underset{\sim}{q}} L_{\underset{\sim}{q}}$$

$$= P_L \overline{V} - \frac{3}{2} KT (N-1)$$

It is then convenient to redefine

$$\ln Z_V - \ln Z_W = 3 N' - \beta \mathcal{K} \qquad (3\text{-}25)$$

with

$$\mathcal{K} = P_L \overline{V} + \sum_{k=2}^{\infty} \frac{(-\beta)^{k-1}}{k!} P_{ir\,L} \overline{V}^k$$

$$= P_L \overline{V} + \frac{1}{\beta} P_{ir\,L} \int_0^\beta d\beta' \, \overline{V} (e^{-\beta' \overline{V}} - 1)$$

$$= \langle V \rangle_W + \frac{1}{\beta} \int_0^\beta d\beta' \, \langle V(e^{-\beta' V} - 1) \rangle_{W,ir\,L} \qquad (3\text{-}25a)$$

and finally get the set of generalised self-consistent equations

$$\frac{1}{2} D_{\underset{\sim}{q}} = \frac{d}{dL_{\underset{\sim}{q}}} \mathcal{K}\left(\left\{\underline{w}_i(L_{\underset{\sim}{q}'}),\ \underline{w}_{ij}(L_{\underset{\sim}{q}'})\right\}\right) \tag{3-26a}$$

$$\underline{w}_{ij} = \frac{1}{MN} \sum_{\underset{\sim}{q}} e^{i\underset{\sim}{q}(\underset{\sim}{R}_{s_i} - \underset{\sim}{R}_{s_j})} \eta_{\rho_i}(\underset{\sim}{q})\, \eta_{\rho_j}(-\underset{\sim}{q})\, L_{\underset{\sim}{q}}:\underset{\sim}{p}_i\underset{\sim}{p}_j \tag{3-26b}$$

$$L_{\underset{\sim}{q}} = KT\, D_{\underset{\sim}{q}}^{-1} \tag{3-26c}$$

$$\ell n\, Z = 3N' - \beta\mathcal{K} + \frac{1}{2} \sum_{\underset{\sim}{q}} \mathrm{Tr}\, \ell n \frac{KT}{\hbar^2} L_{\underset{\sim}{q}} \tag{3-26}$$

The above equations show that the classical theory of anharmonicity can be formulated entirely in terms of the correlation operators $\underline{w}_{ij} = \lambda_{ij}:\underset{\sim}{p}_i\underset{\sim}{p}_j$ together with the molecular potential function $\varphi(R)$ and the renormalized dynamical matrix $D_{\underset{\sim}{q}}$.

However instructive these equations may be, they will primarily prove useful if they permit to go beyond the lowest order approximations already established, and this at relatively low cost. In other words, since $\mathcal{K}_{ir}$ is now the fundamental series to start with, the question may be raised as to what additional summations of irreducible parts can be made so as to improve the theory if necessary. It turns out that several partial series of $\mathcal{K}_{ir}$ can be summed up and, in fact, there is hardly an end to this game. Let us give a couple of examples. One is represented graphically in Fig. 5.

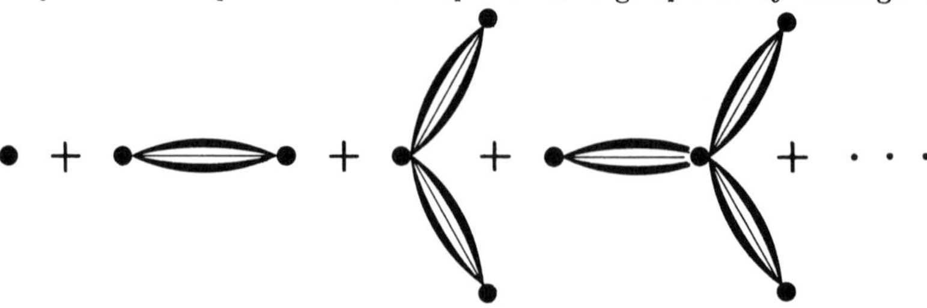

Fig. 5 Example of a summable partial series of the irreducible cumulant expansion

For this class of "star" diagrams we find in setting

$$\underline{g}_{12} \equiv e^{\underline{w}_{12}} - 1 - \frac{1}{2}\underline{w}_{12}^2$$

that the kth term of the series defining $\mathcal{K}(\text{star})$ amounts to

$$k\,\frac{1}{k!}\,(-\beta)^{k-1} \sum_{1,2,\ldots k} \underline{g}_{12}\cdot\underline{g}_{13}\cdot\ldots\,\underline{g}_{1k}\cdot\Phi_1\cdot\Phi_2\ldots\Phi_k$$

and hence that

$$\mathcal{K}(\text{star}) = \sum_1 e^{-\beta\left(\frac{1}{2}\right)\sum_2 \underline{g}_{12}\,\Phi_2}\cdot\Phi_1 \qquad (3\text{-}27)$$

$$\equiv \frac{1}{2}N\sum_\rho \exp(w^*_\rho)\cdot\varphi_\rho$$

with

$$w^*_\rho = \frac{1}{2}\lambda_\rho p^2 - \beta\,\frac{1}{2}\sum_{\rho'\sigma}\left(e^{\lambda^\sigma_{\rho\rho'}\underset{\sim\sim}{pp'}} - 1 - \frac{1}{2}\left(\lambda^\sigma_{\rho\rho'}\underset{\sim\sim}{pp'}\right)^2\right)\Phi_{\rho'}$$

(3-27a)

Inspection of the exponent (3-27a), diagramatically represented in Fig. 6, shows that the corrections to the first term are small over the entire range of temperature or λ_{ij} variations, and that the odd part of $\exp(\lambda^\sigma_{\rho\rho'}\underset{\sim\sim}{pp'})$ yield vanishing contributions for any Bravais lattice.

Fig. 6 Exponent (3-27a)

The overall boundedness of these corrections substantiate our confidence in dealing later on primarily with the simple R. H. A. Let us also remark that, by analogy, essentially the same result would be found for the corresponding corrections to the exponent of the Debye-Waller factor in X-ray scattering theory.

Another example which might sometimes be worth closer inspection is represented in Fig. 7.

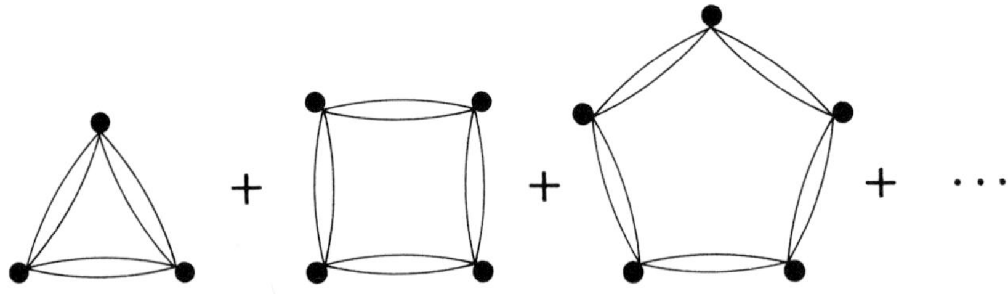

Fig. 7 Ring diagrams of the irreducible cumulant expansion

In some respects these ring diagrams are equivalent to Brueckner's diagrams in the theory of the many-fermion problem. However, we shall not deal further with them here since no detailed investigation going beyond the R. H. A. will be presented in subsequent chapters.

Let us terminate this part of the theory with a derivation of some thermodynamic quantities and general mean values which will illustrate the stationarity property $\delta \, \ell n \, Z_V / \delta \, L_{\underset{\sim}{q}} = 0$ of Eq. (3-26). For example, the internal potential energy is given by

$$U_V = - \frac{\partial}{\partial \beta} \ell n \, Z_V$$

$$= \frac{\partial}{\partial\beta} \beta \mathcal{K} - \frac{\partial}{\partial\beta} \frac{1}{2} \sum_{\underset{\sim}{q}} \operatorname{Tr} \ln L_{\underset{\sim}{q}}$$

$$= \left(\frac{\partial \beta \mathcal{K}}{\partial\beta}\right)_{L_{\underset{\sim}{q}}} + \sum_{\underset{\sim}{q}} \operatorname{Tr} \beta \frac{\partial \mathcal{K}}{\partial L_{\underset{\sim}{q}}} \quad \frac{dL_{\underset{\sim}{q}}}{d\beta}$$

$$- \frac{1}{2} \sum_{q} \operatorname{Tr} \frac{1}{L_{\underset{\sim}{q}}} \frac{dL_{\underset{\sim}{q}}}{d\beta}$$

and we notice the cancellation of the last two sums by virtue of Eqs (3-26a, b). With Eq. (3-25a) for $\mathcal{K}$ we find accordingly

$$U_V = \langle V \rangle_W + \langle V (e^{-\beta V} - 1) \rangle_{W, \text{ir } L} \tag{3-28}$$

a seemingly obvious result were it not for the meaning of the subscrip subscripts W, ir L which tell us how to compute U_V . A similar cancellation occurs in calculating the pressure. Here we have

$$P = - \frac{\partial}{\partial v} \mathcal{K} + \frac{1}{2} KT \sum_{\underset{\sim}{q}} \operatorname{Tr} \frac{\partial}{\partial v} \ln L_{\underset{\sim}{q}}$$

$$= - \left(\frac{\partial \mathcal{K}}{\partial v}\right)_{L_{\underset{\sim}{q}}} \tag{3-29}$$

In general, if we have to calculate the exact mean value 0 of a given function $0(\{u_s\})$ assumed to be differentiable, the factorization properties drawn from the pairing theorem combined with the prescriptions following the renormalization scheme tell us that

$$\langle 0 \rangle = \langle 0 \rangle_W + \langle 0(e^{-\beta V} - 1) \rangle_{W, \text{ir } L} \tag{3-30}$$

A direct proof of this equation can also be given by starting from the quantity

$$Z(\epsilon) = \int d\Omega \; e^{-\beta(H+\epsilon 0)}$$

and noticing that

$$\langle 0 \rangle = -\frac{1}{\beta} \frac{d}{d\epsilon} \ln Z(\epsilon) \Big|_{\epsilon = 0}$$

Indeed considering $V + \epsilon 0$ as a new potential energy we have

$$\ln Z(\epsilon) = \ln Z_W(\epsilon) + 3N' - \beta \mathcal{K}(\epsilon)$$

$$\langle 0 \rangle = -\frac{1}{\beta} \frac{d}{d\epsilon} \ln Z_W(\epsilon) \Big|_{\epsilon = 0} + \frac{d}{d\epsilon} \mathcal{K}(\epsilon) \Big|_{\epsilon = 0}$$

$$= \left(\frac{\partial \mathcal{K}(\epsilon)}{\partial \epsilon} \right)_{L, \underset{\sim}{q}, \; \epsilon = 0}$$

owing to the cancellation of the other partial derivatives already experienced before. From Eq. (3-25a) written in terms of $V + \epsilon 0$ we therefore find

$$\langle 0 \rangle = \langle 0 \rangle_W + \sum_{k=2}^{\infty} \frac{(-\beta)^{k-1}}{k!} \, k \, \langle 0 V^{(k-1)} \rangle_{W, \text{ir } L}$$

and thus recover Eq. (3-30). In the R.H.A. $\langle 0 \rangle$ is obtained by retaining only the first term of this equation, i.e. $\langle 0 \rangle_{R.H.A.} = \langle 0 \rangle_W$

Chapter 4

THERMAL PROPERTIES

The first two sections of this chapter are devoted to a rather extensive analysis of the first and second order derivatives of the free energy which are needed to calculate the thermodynamic quantities of interest. Then a practical scheme of evaluation of the thermal data is developed in terms of a minimum number of parameters and the scheme is tested in particular to the case of Ar. Lastly an approximate treatment of the hard core problem is given.

4-1 FIRST ORDER DERIVATIVES OF THE FREE ENERGY

To carry out the program exposed in section (1-3) it will help to consider the irreducible cumulant expansion $\mathcal{K}$ of Eq. (3-25a) as a thermodynamic potential depending upon T, υ and upon the set of propagator functions $L_{\underset{\sim}{q}\alpha\alpha'}$. The latter are regarded here as additional, though intermediate, state variables which are ultimately eliminated by means of Eqs (3-26c). This point of view is suggested by the fact that the pressure, internal potential energy and dynamical matrices are given in terms of $\mathcal{H}$ and its first order partial derivatives at fixed $T, \{L_{\underset{\sim}{q}}\}$; υ, $\{L_{\underset{\sim}{q}}\}$ and υ, T respectively.

Regarding the $L_{\underset{\sim}{q}}$'s as state variables means that if a set of values is assigned to them, it yields a set of values for the correlation functions λ_ρ and thus specifies a state of motional fluctuations of the system. It is then convenient to introduce a shorthand notation to characterize this state and designate by λ the set of values $L_{\underset{\sim}{q}\alpha\alpha'}$ devided by the mass M for reason of dimensionality, that is

$$\lambda = \left\{\frac{1}{M} L_{\underset{\sim}{q}}\right\} \equiv \left\{ \lambda_\rho \right\}$$

Functions or derivatives evaluated at fixed λ yield quantities which may be called "iso-fluctuational". In this context the temperature appears as a function $T(\lambda, \upsilon)$ determined by the mean kinetic energy equation which follows from Eq. (3-26c) and the related sum rule. In some sense, therefore, we have to deal in this chapter with a double change of variables, namely from the (λ, υ) to the (T, P) variables via the (T, υ) or (λ, P) ones.

However since $\mathcal{H}$ contains an explicit temperature dependence in all but the R. H. approximation and since the dynamical matrix is an isothermal quantity, we shall work in the overdetermined system (T, υ, λ) and impose the subsidiary condition (3-26c), which yields $L_{\underset{\sim}{q}} = L_{\underset{\sim}{q}}(\upsilon, T)$, in the course of the calculations. It is thus apparent that the $\tilde{s}$. c. equations can safely be dealt with by invoking the standard rules of thermodynamics calculus.

Alternatively, however, all quantities of practical interest can be given statistical definitions in terms of equilibrium correlation functions and of their products. This important formulation will also be given here together with some prototype applications. At this point the diagrammatic language will again be employed. An instructive comparison between the thermodynamical and statistical procedures of calculations will then be made.

In this section the thermal equation of state and internal energy will be expressed in a variety of different, though equivalent, forms which will serve different purposes. Beginning with the pressure we have found in section (3-4) that, owing to the stationarity property of $\ln Z_V$, the pressure was simply given by Eq. (3-29) or, if we use the convention of notation introduced above, by

$$P = -\left(\frac{\partial \mathcal{K}(T, \upsilon, \lambda)}{\partial \upsilon} \right)_{\lambda, T} \tag{4-1}$$

As a next formulation we wish to consider $\mathcal{K}$ as a function of υ, T and of the correlation operators $\underline{w}_{ij} = \lambda_{ij} \underset{\sim}{p}_i \underset{\sim}{p}_j$. Their eigenvalues $w_{ij} = -\lambda_{ij} \underset{\sim}{k}_i \underset{\sim}{k}_j$ constitute a set of dimensionless quantities which essentially measure the ratio of the motional fluctuation λ_ρ divided by a^2, the square of the lattice constant. The symbol w may be used to specify a state characterized by fixed values of the fluctuation parameter λ/a^2, that is

$$w = \left\{ L_{\underset{\sim}{q}}/Ma^2 \right\} = \left\{ \lambda_\rho / a^2 \right\}$$

Then with $\upsilon = Na^3$, $\frac{\partial}{\partial \upsilon} = \frac{1}{3\upsilon} a \frac{\partial}{\partial a}$ and with Eq. (3-26a) we find as a result of this change of variables

$$P = -\left(\frac{\partial \mathcal{K}}{\partial \upsilon} \right)_{T, w} - \frac{a}{3\upsilon} \sum_{\underset{\sim}{q}} \mathrm{Tr} \left(\frac{\partial \mathcal{K}}{\partial L_{\underset{\sim}{q}}/a^2} \right)_{T, \upsilon} \left(\frac{\partial L_{\underset{\sim}{q}}/a^2}{\partial a} \right)_{T, L_{\underset{\sim}{q}}}$$

$$= -\left(\frac{\partial \mathcal{K}}{\partial \upsilon} \right)_{T, w} - \frac{1}{2} \frac{1}{3\upsilon} \sum_{\underset{\sim}{q}} \mathrm{Tr}\ D_{\underset{\sim}{q}}(-2) L_{\underset{\sim}{q}}$$

or, with the subsidiary condition (3-26c) and $R = NK$

$$P = -\left(\frac{\partial \mathcal{K}(T, \upsilon, w)}{\partial \upsilon} \right)_w + \frac{RT}{\upsilon} \tag{4-2}$$

In this form the pressure equation displays an interesting feature worth mentioning. Indeed, it obviously applies to the crystalline state of matter for which $w \ll 1$ but it also applies to a state of giant motional fluctuations with $w \gg 1$, which is typical of the imperfect gas limit. Let us illustrate this property for the R. H. A. for instance. Here

$$\mathcal{K}^I = N \frac{1}{2} \sum_{\rho} e^{\frac{1}{2} \lambda_\rho \underset{\sim}{p}^2} \varphi(R_\rho) = \frac{1}{2} \sum_{1} e^{\frac{1}{2} w_1} \varphi_1$$

$$-\left(\frac{\partial \mathcal{K}^I}{\partial \upsilon} \right)_{T, w} = \frac{1}{2} \sum_{1} e^{\frac{1}{2} w_1} (-) \frac{d}{d\upsilon} \varphi_1$$

$$= N \frac{1}{2} \sum_{\rho} e^{\frac{1}{2} \lambda_\rho \underset{\sim}{p}^2} (-) \frac{d}{d\upsilon} \varphi(R_\rho) \tag{4-3}$$

Then, by going over to the Fourier transform $\bar{\varphi}(k)$ of $\varphi(R_\rho)$ and by taking the limit $\lambda_\rho \to \infty$, only the component $k = 0$ yields a non-vanishing result and we find

$$\left(-\frac{\partial \mathcal{K}}{\partial \upsilon} \right)_{T, w \to \infty} = \frac{1}{2} N \sum_{\rho} (-) \frac{d}{d\upsilon} \bar{\varphi}(0)$$

$$= \frac{1}{2} N (N-1) (-) \frac{d}{d\upsilon} \frac{1}{\upsilon} \int d^3 R \varphi(R)$$

$$= \frac{1}{2} \frac{N(N-1)}{\upsilon^2} \int d^3 R \varphi(R)$$

in such a way that Eq. (4-2) yields

$$P(w \to \infty) = \frac{RT}{\upsilon} + \frac{1}{2}\frac{N(N-1)}{\upsilon^2}\int d^3R\,\varphi(R) \tag{4-2a}$$

which is the imperfect gas limit in the same approximation. Now, in section (2-4), we have thoroughly investigated the limit for large λ_ρ of the cumulants $\kappa_1, \kappa_2, \kappa_3$. By retaining only their irreducible parts and by taking the asymptotic limit of large w we uncover that Eq. (4-2) exactly yields the series obtained in the classical theory of imperfect gases under the assumption of integrable interatomic potentials of short range. With Eq. (4-2) we thus dispose of an equation of state suitably parametrized to describe both the solid and the gaseous states of matter. The question immediately arises then to find out by which modifications of Eq. (4-2) the hard core effects can be brought out explicitly. This question will be dealt with in the last section of this chapter.

In a third formulation, better suited than the former one in dealing specifically with the solid state, we shall consider the dynamical matrices $D_{\underset{\sim}{q}}(\upsilon, T, \lambda)$ as playing a central role instead of the thermodynamic potential $\mathcal{K}(T, \upsilon, \lambda)$. For we may imagine switching on the propagator functions $L_{\underset{\sim}{q}\alpha\alpha'}$ from zero (and not from their harmonic approximation!) to their actual value and thus replacing the $L_{\underset{\sim}{q}\alpha\alpha'}$ by

$$L'_{\underset{\sim}{q}\alpha\alpha'} = s\, L_{\underset{\sim}{q}\alpha\alpha'}$$

the parameter s varying from zero to one. In other words, the entire dynamical part of $\mathcal{K}$ is switched on. The latter quantity becomes then

$$\mathcal{K}(T, \upsilon, \lambda') = \mathcal{K}(T, \upsilon, \{s\, L_{\underset{\sim}{q}}\})$$

and we have

$$\mathcal{K}(T, \upsilon, \lambda) = \mathcal{K}(T, \upsilon, 0) + \int_0^1 ds \frac{d\mathcal{K}}{ds}(T, \upsilon, \lambda')$$

$$= \mathcal{K}(T, \upsilon, 0) + \sum_{\underset{\sim}{q}} \mathrm{Tr} \int_0^1 ds \left(\frac{\partial \mathcal{K}}{\partial L'_{\underset{\sim}{q}}} \right)_{T,\upsilon} \frac{dL'_{\underset{\sim}{q}}}{ds}$$

that is, with Eq. (3-26a), with $V_{st}(\upsilon)$ for $\mathcal{K}(T, \upsilon, 0)$ and noticing that $\frac{dL'_{\underset{\sim}{q}}}{ds} = L_{\underset{\sim}{q}}$ can be placed in front of the integral, we find

$$\mathcal{K}(T, \upsilon, \lambda) = V_{st}(\upsilon) + \frac{1}{2} \sum_{\underset{\sim}{q}} \mathrm{Tr}\, L_{\underset{\sim}{q}} \int_0^1 ds\, D_{\underset{\sim}{q}}(T, \upsilon, \lambda') \tag{4-4}$$

Application of Eq. (4-1) yields next

$$P = - \frac{dV_{st}(\upsilon)}{d\upsilon} + \frac{1}{2} \sum_{\underset{\sim}{q}} \mathrm{Tr}\, L_{\underset{\sim}{q}} \int_0^1 ds \left(- \frac{\partial D_{\underset{\sim}{q}}(T, \upsilon, \lambda')}{\partial \upsilon} \right)_{T, \lambda'} \tag{4-4a}$$

We proceed by introducing some useful logarithmic derivatives. Here we define the isothermal-isofluctuational matrix elements

$$\Gamma_{\underset{\sim}{q}T\lambda\alpha\alpha''} \equiv - \frac{1}{2} \sum_{\alpha'} \left(\frac{1}{D_{\underset{\sim}{q}}} \right)_{\alpha\alpha'} \left(\frac{\partial D_{\underset{\sim}{q}\alpha'\alpha''}(T, \upsilon, \lambda)}{\partial\, \ell n\, \upsilon} \right)_{T, \lambda}$$

$$= - \frac{1}{2} \beta \upsilon \sum_{\alpha'} L_{\underset{\sim}{q}\alpha\alpha'} \left(\frac{\partial D_{\underset{\sim}{q}\alpha'\alpha''}(T, \upsilon, \lambda)}{\partial\, \ell n\, \upsilon} \right)_{T, \lambda} \tag{4-5}$$

where $L_{\underset{\sim}{q}} = KT\, D_{\underset{\sim}{q}}^{-1}$ has been inserted in the last equation, and we conversely express, in matrix form,

$$-\frac{1}{2}\left(\frac{\partial D_{\underset{\sim}{q}}}{\partial \upsilon}\right)_{T,\lambda} = \frac{1}{\upsilon} D_{\underset{\sim}{q}} \Gamma_{\underset{\sim}{q} T\lambda} \tag{4-5a}$$

In addition the static pressure is introduced as

$$P_{st} = -\frac{dV_{st}(\upsilon)}{d\upsilon}$$

Then, substituting $KT\, D_{q}^{-1}$ for $L_{\underset{\sim}{q}}$ in front of the integral in Eq. **(4-4a)** the pressure equation reads

$$P(\upsilon, T, \lambda) = P_{st}(\upsilon) + \frac{KT}{\upsilon} \sum_{\underset{\sim}{q}} \mathrm{Tr} \frac{1}{D_{\underset{\sim}{q}}(\upsilon, T, \lambda)} \times \int_{0}^{1} ds\, D_{\underset{\sim}{q}}(\upsilon, T, \lambda')\, \Gamma_{\underset{\sim}{q}\lambda' T} \tag{4-6}$$

This equation is the s. c. generalisation of the Mie-Grüneisen equation of state. The latter is obtained by neglecting the λ dependence of all relevant quantities. Thus $D_{\underset{\sim}{q}}$ becomes the harmonic matrix $D_{\underset{\sim}{q},h}$ given in terms of the static force constants $\varphi_{\alpha\alpha'}(R_\rho)$, $\Gamma_{\underset{\sim}{q}To}$ becomes the Grüneisen matrix

$$\gamma_{\underset{\sim}{q}} = -\frac{1}{2} \frac{1}{D_{\underset{\sim}{q},h}} \frac{dD_{\underset{\sim}{q},h}(\upsilon)}{d\,\ell n\, \upsilon}$$

which as the trace

$$\mathrm{Tr}\,\gamma_{\underset{\sim}{q}} = \sum_j \gamma_{\underset{\sim}{q}j} = -\sum_j \frac{d\ln\omega_{\underset{\sim}{q}j}(\upsilon)}{d\ln\upsilon}$$

and Eq. (4-6) is reduced to the form

$$P_{M.G.} = P_{st}(\upsilon) + \frac{KT}{\upsilon}\sum_{\underset{\sim}{q}j}\gamma_{\underset{\sim}{q}j}$$

$$\equiv P_{st}(\upsilon) + 3\,\frac{RT}{\upsilon}\,\gamma \qquad (4\text{-}7)$$

where γ is the Grüneisen parameter defined by

$$\gamma = \frac{1}{3N}\sum_{\underset{\sim}{q}j}\gamma_{\underset{\sim}{q}j} \qquad (4\text{-}7a)$$

With

$$\bar{\Gamma}_{\underset{\sim}{q}}(\upsilon, T, \lambda) \equiv \mathrm{Tr}\,\frac{1}{D_{\underset{\sim}{q}}(\upsilon, T, \lambda)}\int_0^1 ds\, D_{\underset{\sim}{q}}(\upsilon, T, \lambda')\,\Gamma_{\underset{\sim}{q}T\lambda'} \qquad (4\text{-}8)$$

we shall set by analogy with Eq. (4-7a)

$$\gamma_1 = \frac{1}{3N}\sum_{\underset{\sim}{q}}\bar{\Gamma}_{\underset{\sim}{q}}(\upsilon, T, \lambda) \qquad (4\text{-}9a)$$

for this first mean value, since others are going to be introduced later on, and accordingly write Eq. (4-6) as

$$P = P_{st} + 3\,\frac{RT}{\upsilon}\,\gamma_1 \qquad (4\text{-}9)$$

At this point it is proper to further manipulate the static pressure so as to prepare a, necessarily approximate, conversion of formulae from the (υ, T) to the (P, T) variables. Let $\upsilon = \upsilon_o$ at $T = 0$, $P = 0$. Clearly $P_{st}(\upsilon_o) = 0$. It is then convenient to take for $P_{st}(\upsilon)$ an expansion in density deviations expressed in terms of

$$\delta = 1 - \frac{\upsilon_o}{\upsilon} = 1 - \frac{\rho}{\rho_o}$$

whereby

$$\rho = \frac{N}{\upsilon} \qquad \rho_o = \frac{N}{\upsilon_o} \qquad \rho = \rho_o(1-\delta)$$

and to retain only the term linear in δ since this parameter does not exceed a few % up to the triple-point. Thus

$$\begin{aligned} P_{st} &= (\rho - \rho_o)\, P'_{st}(\rho_o) + 0(\delta^2) \\ &= -\delta\rho_o\, P'_{st}(\rho_o) + 0(\delta^2) \\ &= -\delta\frac{1}{\chi_o} + 0(\delta^2) \end{aligned} \tag{4-10}$$

where χ_o is the static compressibility at $\upsilon = \upsilon_o$, namely

$$\frac{1}{\chi_o} = -\left(\upsilon\frac{dP_{st}}{d\upsilon}\right)_{\upsilon=\upsilon_o} = \left(\rho\frac{dP_{st}}{d\rho}\right)_{\rho=\rho_o} = -\left(\frac{dP_{st}}{d\delta}\right)_{\delta=0}$$

With the linear approximation (4-10) Eq. (4-9) reads

$$P = -\delta\frac{1}{\chi_o} + (1-\delta)\,3\rho_o KT\gamma_1$$

and a partial conversion can be made, yielding

$$\upsilon = \upsilon_o(1+\chi_o P)^{-1}\left(1+3\rho_o\chi_o\gamma_1(\upsilon, T, \lambda)\, KT\right) \tag{4-11}$$

an expression which will be used in section (4-3). Returning to the question of the possible formulations assumed by the pressure equation, we consider now the statistical one, derived as follows.

We start with the general definition of

$$Z_V = \int d\Omega \exp -\beta V$$

We recall that the limits of integration are volume inedependent since they extend to $\pm\infty$ and we note that the crystal potential

$$V = \frac{1}{2}\sum_{s,\rho} e^{\eta_\rho \underset{\sim}{u}_s \cdot \underset{\sim}{p}}\, \varphi(R_\rho)$$

contains, through R_ρ and $\underset{\sim}{p} = \frac{\partial}{\partial \underset{\sim}{R}_\rho}$, the lattice parameter or volume dependence of the system ($\upsilon = Na^3$). Then, $Z_{K.E.}$ being volume independent,

$$P = \frac{1}{\beta}\left(\frac{\partial \ln Z_V}{\partial \upsilon}\right)_T = -\langle \frac{dV}{d\upsilon} \rangle \tag{4-12}$$

That Eq. (4-12) is equivalent to Eq. (4-1) can be checked by introducing the s. c. interaction representation according to the rules formulated by Eq. (3-30), that is

$$\langle \frac{dV}{d\upsilon} \rangle = \langle \frac{dV}{d\upsilon} \rangle_W + \langle \frac{dV}{d\upsilon}(e^{-\beta V}-1)\rangle_{W, irL}$$

$$= \langle \frac{dV}{d\upsilon}\rangle_W - \beta \langle \frac{dV}{d\upsilon} V\rangle_{W, irL} + \frac{\beta^2}{2}\langle \frac{dV}{d\upsilon} V^2\rangle_{W, irL} \cdots$$

$$= \langle \frac{dV}{d\upsilon} \rangle_W - \frac{1}{2}\beta \langle \frac{dV^2}{d\upsilon} \rangle_{W,irL} + \frac{1}{3!}\beta^2 \langle \frac{dV^3}{d\upsilon} \rangle_{W,irL} \cdots$$

Now $\frac{d}{d\upsilon}$ can be taken outside of the brackets $\langle .. \rangle$ provided that the set of $L_{\underset{\sim}{q}}$ is kept constant and that the limits of integrations of $\int d\Omega$ are volume independent. While the latter condition is fulfilled the condition $\left\{ \frac{1}{M} L_{\underset{\sim}{q}} \right\} = \lambda$ held fixed is precisely the one which applies to Eq. (4-1). Therefore

$$\langle \frac{dV}{d\upsilon} \rangle = \left(\frac{\partial}{\partial \upsilon}\right)_{T,\lambda} \Big\{ \langle V \rangle_W - \frac{1}{2}\beta \langle V^2 \rangle_{W,irL}$$

$$+ \frac{1}{3!}\beta^2 \langle V^3 \rangle_{W,irL} \cdots \Big\} \equiv \left(\frac{\partial \mathcal{K}}{\partial \upsilon} \right)_{T,\lambda}$$

Returning to Eq. (4-12) we note that the operator $\frac{dV}{d\upsilon}$ assumes the following meaning. With

$$\frac{d}{d\upsilon} = \frac{1}{3\upsilon} a \frac{d}{da} = \frac{1}{3\upsilon} \sum_{\rho\alpha} R_{\rho\alpha} \frac{\partial}{\partial R_{\rho\alpha}}$$

$$\frac{d}{d\upsilon} e^{\eta_\rho \underset{\sim}{u}_s \cdot \underset{\sim}{p}} \varphi(R_\rho) = \frac{1}{3\upsilon} \sum_{\alpha} R_{\rho\alpha} e^{\eta_\rho \underset{\sim}{u} \cdot \underset{\sim}{p}} p_\alpha \varphi(R_\rho)$$

where the precaution has been taken to leave $R_{\rho\alpha}$ in front of the displacement operator $\exp \eta_\rho \underset{\sim}{u} \cdot \underset{\sim}{p}$ since $\underset{\sim}{R}_\rho, \underset{\sim}{p}$ do not commute, $dV/d\upsilon$ becomes

$$\frac{dV}{d\upsilon} = \frac{1}{3\upsilon} \frac{1}{2} \sum_{s\rho\alpha} R_{\rho\alpha} e^{\eta_\rho \underset{\sim}{u}_s \cdot \underset{\sim}{p}} \varphi_\alpha(R_\rho)$$

It is one third of the trace of the stress tensor operator

$$\tau_{\alpha\alpha'} = \frac{1}{2\upsilon} \sum_{s\rho} R_{\rho\alpha}\, e^{\eta_\rho \underset{\sim}{u}_s \cdot \underset{\sim}{p}}\, \varphi_{\alpha'}(R_\rho) \tag{4-13}$$

and consequently

$$P = -\frac{1}{3}\,\mathrm{Tr}\ \langle\tau\rangle \tag{4-14}$$

as it should be. It is left as an exercise to check that, in the harmonic approximation, one correctly finds†

$$\frac{d(V_{st}+V_h)}{d\upsilon} = -P_{st} + \frac{1}{2} M \sum_{\underset{\sim}{q}\alpha\alpha'} \frac{dD_{\underset{\sim}{q}h,\,\alpha\alpha'}}{d\upsilon}\, u_{\underset{\sim}{q}\alpha}\, u_{-\underset{\sim}{q}\alpha'}$$

On the other hand if we note that

$$e^{\eta_\rho \underset{\sim}{u}_s \cdot \underset{\sim}{p}}\, R_{\rho\alpha} - R_{\rho\alpha}\, e^{\eta_\rho \underset{\sim}{u}_s \cdot \underset{\sim}{p}} = e^{\eta_\rho \underset{\sim}{u}_s \cdot \underset{\sim}{p}}\, \eta_\rho u_{s\alpha} \tag{4-15}$$

we get alternatively

$$\frac{dV}{d\upsilon} = \frac{1}{3\upsilon}\,\frac{1}{2} \sum_{s\rho\alpha} e^{\eta_\rho \underset{\sim}{u}_s \cdot \underset{\sim}{p}} (R_{\rho\alpha} - \eta_\rho u_{s\alpha})\, \varphi_\alpha(R_\rho)$$

and

$$P = -\frac{1}{3\upsilon}\,\frac{1}{2} \sum_{s\rho\alpha} \langle e^{\eta_\rho \underset{\sim}{u}_s \cdot \underset{\sim}{p}}\, R_{\rho\alpha}\, \varphi_\alpha\,(R_\rho)\rangle \ +$$

---

† A look at the footnote of p. 7 is helpful.

$$+ \frac{1}{3\upsilon} \frac{1}{2} \sum_{s\rho} \langle e^{\eta_\rho \underset{\sim}{u}_s \cdot \underset{\sim}{p}} \eta_\rho \underset{\sim}{u}_s \cdot \underset{\sim}{p} \rangle \varphi(R_\rho) \tag{4-16}$$

The meaning of these terms may be usefully illustrated by considering the R. H. A. for instance. Here the first term amounts to

$$- \frac{1}{3\upsilon} \frac{N}{2} \sum_{\rho\alpha} e^{\frac{1}{2}\lambda_\rho \underset{\sim}{p}^2} R_{\rho\alpha} \varphi_\alpha(R_\rho) = - \frac{N}{2} \sum_{\rho} e^{\frac{1}{2}\lambda_\rho \underset{\sim}{p}^2} \frac{d}{d\upsilon} \varphi(R_\rho)$$

that is Eq. (4-3). It represents a sum of smeared partial pressures analogous to the smeared potentials Φ_ρ of φ_ρ. The second term is very simply

$$\frac{N}{3\upsilon} \frac{1}{2} \sum_{\rho} \lambda_\rho \underset{\sim}{p}^2 \Phi(R_\rho, \lambda_\rho) = \frac{RT}{\upsilon}$$

This example indicates that Eq. (4-16) is, in the form of an expectation value, the statistical equivalent of Eq. (4-2). The transformation from fixed λ to fixed w performed above is conveyed here by the commutation relations (4-15). Lastly we wish to relate Eq. (4-12) with Eq. (4-9), namely

$$P = -\langle \frac{dV}{d\upsilon} \rangle = - \frac{dV_{st}}{d\upsilon} - \langle \frac{d}{d\upsilon}(V - V_{st}) \rangle \tag{4-12}$$

$$= P_{st} + 3 \frac{RT}{\upsilon} \gamma_1 \tag{4-9}$$

Thus, the statistical definition of the dimensionless mean quantity γ_1 of Eq. (4-9a) is

$$\gamma_1 = - \frac{\beta}{3N} \langle \frac{d(V - V_{st})}{d \ell n \, \upsilon} \rangle \tag{4-17}$$

Going over to the internal energy we have found in section (3-4) that

$$U = \frac{3}{2} NKT + \mathcal{K} - T\left(\frac{\partial \mathcal{K}(T, \upsilon, \lambda)}{\partial T} \right)_{\upsilon, \lambda} \tag{4-18}$$

This expression is already the most convenient one. The next formulation of interest is obtained by expressing $\mathcal{K}$ in terms of the parametric integration (4-4). This yields

$$U = V_{st} + \frac{3}{2} NKT$$
$$+ \frac{1}{2} \sum_{\underset{\sim}{q}} \text{Tr } L_{\underset{\sim}{q}} \int_{0}^{1} ds \left(1 - T\left(\frac{\partial}{\partial T}\right)_{\upsilon, \lambda'}\right) D_{\underset{\sim}{q}}(T, \upsilon, \lambda') \tag{4-19}$$

By defining the matrix

$$\Delta_{\underset{\sim}{q}\,\upsilon\,\lambda} = 1 - \frac{1}{D_{\underset{\sim}{q}}} \left(\frac{\partial D_{\underset{\sim}{q}}}{\partial \ell n T} \right)_{\upsilon, \lambda} \tag{4-20}$$

and

$$\bar{\Delta}_{\underset{\sim}{q}}(T, \upsilon, \lambda) = \frac{1}{D_{\underset{\sim}{q}}(T, \upsilon, \lambda)} \int_{0}^{1} ds \, D_{\underset{\sim}{q}}(T, \upsilon, \lambda') \, \Delta_{\underset{\sim}{q}\,\upsilon\,\lambda'}$$

Eq. (4-19) becomes, with $L_{\underset{\sim}{q}} = KT \, D_{\underset{\sim}{q}}^{-1}$,

$$U = V_{st} + \frac{3}{2} NKT + \frac{1}{2} KT \sum_{\underset{\sim}{q}} \text{Tr} \bar{\Delta}_{\underset{\sim}{q}}(T, \upsilon, \lambda) \tag{4-21}$$

In the harmonic approximation $\bar{\Delta}_{q\upsilon\lambda} = 1$ and the equipartition theorem is fulfilled. The extent to which this theorem is no longer satisfied here may be conveniently measured by introducing the dimensionless function

$$\gamma_2(T,\upsilon,\lambda) \equiv \frac{1}{2} + \frac{1}{3N}\frac{1}{2}\sum_{\underset{\sim}{q}}{}' \mathrm{Tr}\bar{\Delta}_{\underset{\sim}{q}}(T,\upsilon,\lambda) \qquad (4\text{-}22)$$

The temperature dependence of this quantity will be studied in greater detail in chapter 6. Lastly there is a well known statistical definition for the internal energy, namely

$$U = \frac{3}{2}RT - \left(\frac{\partial \ell n Z_V}{\partial\beta}\right)_\upsilon$$

$$= \frac{3}{2}RT + \langle V\rangle \qquad (4\text{-}23)$$

Comparison of Eqs (4-21, 4-22, 4-23) indicates that the statistical definition of γ_2 is

$$\gamma_2(T,\upsilon,\lambda) = \frac{1}{2} + \frac{\beta}{3N}\langle(V-V_{st})\rangle \qquad (4\text{-}22a)$$

Returning to Eq. (4-23), its practical evaluation is performed by applying Eq. (3-30) which tells us that

$$\langle V\rangle = \langle V\rangle_W + \langle V(e^{-\beta V}-1)\rangle_{W,\,irL} \qquad (4\text{-}23a)$$

Using the conventions of notation made in section (2-4, p. 60) we have for instance in second order of s. c. perturbation theory

$$\langle V \rangle_{II} = \frac{1}{2} \sum_{1} \Phi_1 - \beta \left(\frac{1}{2}\right)^2 \sum_{1,2} \left(e^{\underline{w}_{12}} - 1 - \frac{1}{2}\, \underline{w}_{12}{}^2 \right) \Phi_1 \Phi_2$$

By taking the asymptotic limit of large $w^{\dagger}$ and by using Eq. (2-59b) we observe again, as in the case of the pressure, that

$$U_{II}(w \sim N^{2/3}) = \frac{3}{2} RT + \left(\frac{N}{2}\right) \frac{1}{\upsilon} \int d^3R \varphi(R)$$

$$- \beta \left(\frac{N}{2}\right) \left\{ \frac{1}{\upsilon} \int d^3R \varphi^2(R) - \left(\frac{1}{\upsilon} \int d^3R \varphi(R)\right)^2 \right\}$$

yields the imperfect gas limit in the corresponding approximation. We must of course point out here that if the pressure and internal energy equations, together with the quantities derived from them, encompass both solid state and imperfect gas situations, this is not true of the entropy derived from Eq. (3-26). In a "Lattice Gas" model with full occupancy of the sites available, as we have here, the static positions of the atoms are distinguishable but the description of a regime characterized by motional fluctuations as large as the dimensions of the system clearly contradicts the starting assumption of the localizability of the particle. While this situation can be remedied in many ways, such as for instance, by considering sets of polyatomic lattices made of cells with linear dimensions $\sim \sqrt{\lambda}$ in which the atoms are not distinguishable, our purposes are restricted to dealing with the lattice dynamics of ordered systems and, in this limited context, an equation of state like Eq. (4-2) is instructive enough. Then we go on to investigate the next point of our program.

---

† More precisely the limiting procedure is made in two steps i. e. $w \sim N^{2/3}$ or $\lambda \sim \upsilon^{2/3}$ then N and $\upsilon \to \infty$ while N/υ is held fixed.

4-2 SECOND ORDER DERIVATIVES OF THE FREE ENERGY

Let us begin this section by reviewing the three fundamental quantities that one can calculate from the pressure and internal energy in the (υ, T) variables. The first one is the well-known isothermal compressibility. Its inverse is defined by

$$\frac{1}{\chi_T} = -\upsilon \left(\frac{\partial P}{\partial \upsilon}\right)_T \tag{4-24}$$

The second one is, of course, the specific heat at constant volume

$$C_\upsilon = T\left(\frac{\partial S}{\partial T}\right)_\upsilon = \left(\frac{\partial U}{\partial T}\right)_\upsilon \tag{4-25}$$

The third one is a generally much less familiar quantity designated as latent heat of expansion†

$$L_\upsilon = T\left(\frac{\partial P}{\partial T}\right)_\upsilon = P + \left(\frac{\partial U}{\partial \upsilon}\right)_T \tag{4-26}$$

Introduced in the early days of the caloric theory, L_υ is the heat necessary to increase the volume of a substance by $d\upsilon$ at constant temperature. That χ_T, C_υ and L_υ constitute a convenient set of quantities with which to deal is further confirmed by invoking the reciprocity theorem which applies to the dependent variables υ, P, T. One has indeed

$$\left(\frac{\partial \upsilon}{\partial P}\right)_T \left(\frac{\partial P}{\partial T}\right)_\upsilon \left(\frac{\partial T}{\partial \upsilon}\right)_P = -1$$

$$= (-)\upsilon\chi_T \;\frac{1}{T} L_\upsilon \;\frac{1}{\upsilon\alpha_P}$$

† See f.i. Heat, Thermodynamics and Statistical Physics, F.H. Crawford, Harcourt, Brace and World, Inc., New-York 1963, p. 121.

where α_P is the coefficient of thermal expansion, or volume expansivity

$$\alpha_P \equiv \frac{1}{\upsilon}\left(\frac{\partial \upsilon}{\partial T}\right)_P = \frac{1}{T}\chi_T L_\upsilon \tag{4-27}$$

It follows moreover that the specific heat at constant pressure $C_P = T\left(\frac{\partial S}{\partial T}\right)_P$ traditionally written as

$$C_P = C_\upsilon + \upsilon T \frac{\alpha_P^2}{\chi_T} \tag{4-28}$$

assumes the alternative form

$$C_P = C_\upsilon + \upsilon \alpha_P L_\upsilon \tag{4-28a}$$

or

$$C_P = C_\upsilon + \frac{\upsilon}{T}\chi_T L_\upsilon^2 \tag{4-28b}$$

which we prefer to use here. Lastly we should recall that the isothermal and adiabatic compressibilities are related by the equation

$$\chi_S = \frac{C_\upsilon}{C_P}\chi_T \tag{4-29}$$

It is thus clear that we must first concentrate our analysis on χ_T, C_υ and L_υ.

Following the thermodynamical procedure discussed at the beginning of this chapter we convert the definitions (4-24, 4-25, 4-26) into manageable quantities, that is

$$\frac{1}{\chi_T} = -\upsilon\left(\frac{\partial P(T,\upsilon,\lambda)}{\partial \upsilon}\right)_T$$

$$= -\upsilon\left(\frac{\partial P}{\partial \upsilon}\right)_{T,\lambda} - \upsilon \sum_{\underset{\sim}{q}} \mathrm{Tr}\left(\frac{\partial P}{\partial L_{\underset{\sim}{q}}}\right)_{T,\upsilon}\left(\frac{\partial L_{\underset{\sim}{q}}}{\partial \upsilon}\right)_T$$

$$= \upsilon\left(\frac{\partial^2 \mathcal{H}}{\partial \upsilon^2}\right)_{T,\lambda} + \upsilon \sum_{\underset{\sim}{q}} \mathrm{Tr}\left(\frac{\partial^2 \mathcal{H}}{\partial L_{\underset{\sim}{q}}\partial \upsilon}\right)_{T,\upsilon}\left(\frac{\partial L_{\underset{\sim}{q}}}{\partial \upsilon}\right)_T$$

$$= \upsilon\left(\frac{\partial^2 \mathcal{H}}{\partial \upsilon^2}\right)_{T,\lambda} + \frac{1}{2}\upsilon \sum_{\underset{\sim}{q}} \mathrm{Tr}\left(\frac{\partial D_{\underset{\sim}{q}}}{\partial \upsilon}\right)_{T,\lambda}\left(\frac{\partial L_{\underset{\sim}{q}}}{\partial \upsilon}\right)_T \qquad (4\text{-}30)$$

$$C_\upsilon = \left(\frac{\partial U(T,\upsilon,\lambda)}{\partial T}\right)_\upsilon$$

$$= \left(\frac{\partial U}{\partial T}\right)_{\upsilon,\lambda} + \sum_{\underset{\sim}{q}} \mathrm{Tr}\left(\frac{\partial U}{\partial L_{\underset{\sim}{q}}}\right)_{\upsilon,T}\left(\frac{\partial L_{\underset{\sim}{q}}}{\partial T}\right)_\upsilon$$

$$= \frac{3}{2}NK - T\left(\frac{\partial^2 \mathcal{H}}{\partial T^2}\right)_{\upsilon,\lambda}$$

$$+ \sum_{\underset{\sim}{q}} \left\{\left(\frac{\partial \mathcal{H}}{\partial L_{\underset{\sim}{q}}}\right)_{\upsilon,T} - T\left(\frac{\partial^2 \mathcal{H}}{\partial T\partial L_{\underset{\sim}{q}}}\right)_\upsilon\right\}\left(\frac{\partial L_{\underset{\sim}{q}}}{\partial T}\right)_\upsilon$$

$$= \frac{3}{2} NK - T\left(\frac{\partial^2 \mathcal{K}}{\partial T^2}\right)_{\upsilon,\lambda}$$

$$+ \frac{1}{2} \sum_{\underset{\sim}{q}} \mathrm{Tr}\left\{ D_{\underset{\sim}{q}} - T\left(\frac{\partial D_{\underset{\sim}{q}}}{\partial T}\right)_{\upsilon, L_{\underset{\sim}{q}}}\right\}\left(\frac{\partial L_{\underset{\sim}{q}}}{\partial T}\right)_{\upsilon} \tag{4-31}$$

and

$$L_{\upsilon} = T\left(\frac{\partial P(T,\upsilon,\lambda)}{\partial T}\right)_{\upsilon}$$

$$= T\left(\frac{\partial P}{\partial T}\right)_{\upsilon,\lambda} + \sum_{\underset{\sim}{q}} \mathrm{Tr}\; T\left(\frac{\partial P}{\partial L_{\underset{\sim}{q}}}\right)_{\upsilon, T}\left(\frac{\partial L_{\underset{\sim}{q}}}{\partial T}\right)_{\upsilon}$$

$$= -T\left(\frac{\partial^2 \mathcal{K}}{\partial \upsilon \partial T}\right)_{\lambda} - T \sum_{\underset{\sim}{q}} \mathrm{Tr}\left(\frac{\partial^2 \mathcal{K}}{\partial L_{\underset{\sim}{q}} \partial \upsilon}\right)_{T}\left(\frac{\partial L_{\underset{\sim}{q}}}{\partial T}\right)_{\upsilon}$$

$$= -T\left(\frac{\partial^2 \mathcal{K}}{\partial \upsilon \partial T}\right)_{\lambda} - \frac{1}{2} \sum_{\underset{\sim}{q}} \mathrm{Tr}\left(\frac{\partial D_{\underset{\sim}{q}}}{\partial \upsilon}\right)_{T,\lambda} T\left(\frac{\partial L_{\underset{\sim}{q}}}{\partial T}\right)_{\upsilon} \tag{4-32}$$

We proceed with a further manipulation of the first terms of the above equations, conveniently designated as $\frac{1}{\chi_{T\lambda}}$, $C_{\upsilon\lambda}$ and $L_{\upsilon\lambda}$. For, we introduce Eq. (4-4) for $\mathcal{K}$ and get

$$\frac{1}{\chi_{T\lambda}} \equiv \upsilon\left(\frac{\partial^2 \mathcal{K}}{\partial \upsilon^2}\right)_{T,\lambda}$$

$$= \upsilon \frac{d^2 V_{st}(\upsilon)}{d\upsilon^2} + \frac{\upsilon}{2} \sum_{\underset{\sim}{q}} \text{Tr}\, L_{\underset{\sim}{q}} \int_0^1 ds \left(\frac{\partial^2 D_{\underset{\sim}{q}}(T, \upsilon, s\lambda)}{\partial \upsilon^2} \right)_{T,\lambda} \tag{4-33}$$

The first term of this expression yields the inverse of the static compressibility

$$\frac{1}{\chi_{st}(\upsilon)} = \upsilon \frac{d^2 V(\upsilon)}{d\upsilon^2} \tag{4-33a}$$

As we did with the static pressure we shall expand $\frac{1}{\chi_{st}(\upsilon)}$ in a power series of $\delta = 1 - \rho/\rho_o$ and retain only the term linear in δ, that is

$$\frac{1}{\chi_{st}(\upsilon)} = \frac{1}{\chi_o} + (\rho - \rho_o)(-)\frac{\chi_o'}{\chi_o^2} + 0(\delta^2)$$

$$= \frac{1}{\chi_o} - (1 - \rho/\rho_o)(-)\rho_o \frac{\chi_o'}{\chi_o^2} + 0(\delta^2)$$

By defining the material constant

$$\mu = -\left(\frac{d\,\ell n\, \chi_{st}}{d\,\ell n \rho} \right)_{\rho = \rho_o} \tag{4-34}$$

we shall have†

$$\frac{1}{\chi_{st}(\upsilon)} = \frac{1}{\chi_o}(1 - \mu\delta) + 0(\delta^2) \tag{4-35}$$

$$= \frac{1}{\chi_o} + \mu P_{st} + 0(\delta^2) \tag{4-35a}$$

with P_{st} taken from Eq. (4-10). The second term of Eq. (4-33) is further transformed by repeatedly using logarithmic derivatives and the definition (4-5) of the matrices $\Gamma_{\underset{\sim}{q} T \lambda}$, that is, with

$$\frac{\partial^2}{\partial \upsilon^2} = \frac{1}{\upsilon^2}\left(1 - \frac{\partial}{\partial \ell n \upsilon}\right) (-) \frac{\partial}{\partial \ell n \upsilon}$$

we get

$$\frac{1}{2}\left(\frac{\partial^2 D_{\underset{\sim}{q}}}{\partial \upsilon^2}\right)_\lambda = \frac{1}{\upsilon^2}\left(1 - \left(\frac{\partial}{\partial \ell n \upsilon}\right)_\lambda\right) D_{\underset{\sim}{q}} \Gamma_{\underset{\sim}{q} T \lambda}$$

$$= \frac{1}{\upsilon^2}\left\{D_{\underset{\sim}{q}} \Gamma_{\underset{\sim}{q} T\lambda} + 2 D_{\underset{\sim}{q}} \Gamma^2_{\underset{\sim}{q} T \lambda} - D_{\underset{\sim}{q}} \Gamma'_{\underset{\sim}{q} T \lambda}\right\}$$

where

$$\Gamma'_{\underset{\sim}{q} T \lambda} = \left(\frac{\partial \Gamma_{\underset{\sim}{q} T \lambda}}{\partial \ell n \upsilon}\right)_{T,\lambda}$$

---

† Note that to establish (4-35) directly from $P_{st}(\upsilon)$ one must include the term $\sim\delta^2$ in Eq. (4-10). Show that, in this case, $P_{st}(\upsilon)$ would read

$$P_{st} = \frac{1}{\chi_o}\left(- \delta + \frac{1}{2}(\mu-1)\,\delta^2\right) + 0(\delta^3)$$

Therefore

$$\frac{1}{\chi_{T\lambda}} = \frac{1}{\chi_{st}} + \frac{KT}{\upsilon} \sum_{\underset{\sim}{q}} \mathrm{Tr} \frac{1}{D_{\underset{\sim}{q}}(\upsilon, T, \lambda)}$$

$$\times \int_{o}^{1} ds\, D_{\underset{\sim}{q}} (\Gamma_{\underset{\sim}{q} T \lambda'} + 2\,\Gamma^{2}_{\underset{\sim}{q} T\lambda'} - \Gamma'_{\underset{\sim}{q}\lambda'}) \tag{4-36}$$

$$= \frac{1}{\chi_{st}} + \frac{KT}{\upsilon} \sum_{\underset{\sim}{q}} \mathrm{Tr} (\bar{\Gamma}_{\underset{\sim}{q}} + 2\,\bar{\Gamma}_{\underset{\sim}{q}}^{2} - \bar{\Gamma}'_{\underset{\sim}{q}}) \tag{4-36a}$$

in a self-explained notation, or also

$$\frac{1}{\chi_{T\lambda}} = \frac{1}{\chi_{st}} + \frac{-1}{\upsilon} \left(\frac{\partial(\mathcal{K} - V_{st})}{\partial \ell n\, \upsilon} \right)_{T, \lambda}$$

$$+ \frac{1}{\upsilon} \left(\frac{\partial^{2}(\mathcal{K} - V_{st})}{\partial^{2}(\ell n\, \upsilon)^{2}} \right)_{T, \lambda} \tag{4-36b}$$

We consider next

$$C_{\upsilon\lambda} = \frac{3}{2} NK - T \left(\frac{\partial^{2} \mathcal{K}(T, \upsilon, \lambda)}{\partial T^{2}} \right)_{\upsilon, \lambda} \tag{4-37}$$

In this form, $C_{\upsilon\lambda}$ can easily be calculated. By analogy with the previous formulation, however, we can write

$$C_{\upsilon\lambda} = \frac{3}{2} NK - T \frac{1}{2} \sum_{\underset{\sim}{q}} L_{\underset{\sim}{q}} \int_{o}^{1} ds \left(\frac{\partial^{2} D_{\underset{\sim}{q}}(\upsilon, T, s\lambda)}{\partial T^{2}} \right)_{\upsilon, \lambda} \tag{4-38}$$

and with

$$\frac{\partial^2}{\partial T^2} = (-)\frac{\partial}{\partial \ell n T}\left(1 - \frac{\partial}{\partial \ell n T}\right)$$

we find, by introducing the matrix $\Delta_{\underset{\sim}{q} \upsilon \lambda}$ of Eq. (4-20)

$$C_{\upsilon\lambda} = \frac{3}{2}NK + \frac{1}{2}K \sum_{\underset{\sim}{q}} \mathrm{Tr}\, \frac{1}{D_{\underset{\sim}{q}}} \int_o^1 ds\, D_{\underset{\sim}{q}}(\lambda')$$

$$\times \left(\Delta_{\underset{\sim}{q}\upsilon\lambda'} - \Delta^2_{\underset{\sim}{q}\upsilon\lambda'} + \mathring{\Delta}_{\underset{\sim}{q}\upsilon\lambda'}\right) \tag{4-38a}$$

$$= \frac{3}{2}NK + \frac{1}{2}K \sum_{\underset{\sim}{q}} \mathrm{Tr}\left(\bar{\Delta}_{\underset{\sim}{q}} - \overline{\Delta^2_{\underset{\sim}{q}}} + \bar{\mathring{\Delta}}_{\underset{\sim}{q}}\right) \tag{4-38b}$$

where

$$\mathring{\Delta}_{\underset{\sim}{q}\upsilon\lambda} = \left(\frac{\partial \Delta_{\underset{\sim}{q}\upsilon\lambda}}{\partial \ell n T}\right)_{\upsilon,\lambda}$$

In Eqs (4-36a) and (4-38) we observe the occurrence of the parameters γ_1 and γ_2. Lastly the quantity $L_{\upsilon\lambda}$ reads

$$L_{\upsilon\lambda} = -T\left(\frac{\partial^2 \mathcal{K}(T,\upsilon,\lambda)}{\partial \upsilon \partial T}\right)_\lambda$$

$$= -\frac{T}{\upsilon}\left(\frac{\partial^2 \mathcal{K}(T,\upsilon,\lambda)}{\partial \ell n \upsilon \partial T}\right)_\lambda \tag{4-39}$$

$$= -\frac{T}{\upsilon}\frac{1}{2}\sum_{\underset{\sim}{q}} \mathrm{Tr}\, L_{\underset{\sim}{q}} \int_o^1 ds \left(\frac{\partial^2 D_{\underset{\sim}{q}}(T,\upsilon,\lambda)}{\partial \ell n \upsilon \partial T}\right)_\lambda \tag{4-40}$$

$$= \frac{KT}{\upsilon} \sum_{\underset{\sim}{q}} \operatorname{Tr} \frac{1}{D_{\underset{\sim}{q}}} \int_0^1 ds\, D_{\underset{\sim}{q}}(\lambda') \Big((1 - \Delta_{\underset{\sim}{q}\upsilon\lambda'}) \Gamma_{\underset{\sim}{q}T\lambda'} + \mathring{\Gamma}_{\underset{\sim}{q}T\lambda'} \Big) \tag{4-40a}$$

$$= \frac{KT}{\upsilon} \sum_{\underset{\sim}{q}} \operatorname{Tr} \Big(\bar{\Gamma}_{\underset{\sim}{q}} - \overline{\Delta_{\underset{\sim}{q}} \Gamma_{\underset{\sim}{q}}} + \bar{\mathring{\Gamma}}_{\underset{\sim}{q}} \Big) \tag{4-40b}$$

where

$$\mathring{\Gamma}_{\underset{\sim}{q}T\lambda} = \left(\frac{\partial \Gamma_{\underset{\sim}{q}T\lambda}}{\partial \ell n T} \right)_{\lambda}$$

Again γ_1 occurs in Eq. (4-40b) and a mixed mean value over $\Delta_{\underset{\sim}{q}T\lambda'} \times \Gamma_{\underset{\sim}{q}T\lambda'}$ which ought to be compared with the former two mean values taken over $\Delta^2_{\underset{\sim}{q}T\lambda'}$ and $\Gamma^2_{\underset{\sim}{q}T\lambda'}$.

We now proceed to inspect the second terms of Eqs (4-30, 4-31, 4-32). Continuing to make use of logarithmic derivatives we consider†

$$\left(\frac{\partial L_{\underset{\sim}{q}}}{\partial \ell n \upsilon} \frac{1}{L_{\underset{\sim}{q}}} \right)_{T,\alpha,\alpha''} = - \left(\frac{1}{D_{\underset{\sim}{q}}} \frac{\partial D_{\underset{\sim}{q}}}{\partial \ell n \upsilon} \right)_{T,\alpha,\alpha''} \tag{4-41}$$

$$= - \beta \upsilon \sum_{\alpha'} L_{\underset{\sim}{q}\alpha\alpha'} \left(\frac{\partial D_{\underset{\sim}{q}\alpha'\alpha''}}{\partial \upsilon} \right)_T \tag{4-41a}$$

and

$$\left(\frac{\partial L_{\underset{\sim}{q}}}{\partial \ell n T} \frac{1}{L_{\underset{\sim}{q}}} \right)_{\upsilon,\alpha,\alpha''} = \delta_{\alpha\alpha''} - \left(\frac{1}{D_{\underset{\sim}{q}}} \frac{\partial D_{\underset{\sim}{q}}}{\partial \ell n T} \right)_{\upsilon,\alpha,\alpha''} \tag{4-42}$$

---

† If $A(x) \cdot B(x) = 1$ then $\frac{dA}{dx} B + A \frac{dB}{dx} = 0$,

$$\frac{dA}{dx} = - A \frac{dB}{dx} A \,, \quad \frac{dA}{dx} A^{-1} = - B^{-1} \frac{dB}{dx}$$

$$= \delta_{\alpha\alpha''} - \frac{1}{K} \sum_{\alpha'} L_{\underset{\sim}{q}\alpha\alpha'} \left(\frac{\partial D_{\underset{\sim}{q}\alpha'\alpha''}}{\partial T} \right)_{\upsilon} \tag{4-42a}$$

On the r. h. s. of Eq. (4-41) we recognize, up to a factor 1/2 , an isothermal Grüneisen matrix

$$\Gamma_{\underset{\sim}{q}T} = -\frac{1}{2}\left(\frac{1}{D_{\underset{\sim}{q}}} \frac{\partial D_{\underset{\sim}{q}}}{\partial \ell n \upsilon}\right)_T = -\frac{1}{2} \frac{1}{D_{\underset{\sim}{q}}} \left(\frac{\partial D_{\underset{\sim}{q}}}{\partial \ell n \upsilon} \right)_{T,\lambda}$$

$$- \frac{1}{2} \sum_{\underset{\sim}{q}'} \left(\frac{1}{D_{\underset{\sim}{q}}} \frac{\partial D_{\underset{\sim}{q}}}{\partial L_{\underset{\sim}{q}'}} \right)_{\upsilon, T} : \left(\frac{\partial L_{\underset{\sim}{q}'}}{\partial \ell n \upsilon} \right)_T$$

$$= \Gamma_{\underset{\sim}{q}T\lambda} - \sum_{\underset{\sim}{q}'} 2\beta L_{\underset{\sim}{q}} \frac{\partial^2 \mathcal{H}}{\partial L_{\underset{\sim}{q}} \partial L_{\underset{\sim}{q}'}} : \Gamma_{\underset{\sim}{q}'T} L_{\underset{\sim}{q}'}$$

Designating by the superscript + the operation of matrix transposition, the above equation reads also

$$\Gamma_{\underset{\sim}{q}T} = \Gamma_{\underset{\sim}{q}T\lambda} - \sum_{\underset{\sim}{q}'} 2\beta L_{\underset{\sim}{q}} \frac{\partial^2 \mathcal{H}}{\partial L_{\underset{\sim}{q}} \partial L_{\underset{\sim}{q}'}} L^{+}_{\underset{\sim}{q}'} : \Gamma_{\underset{\sim}{q}'T} \tag{4-43}$$

$$\equiv \Gamma_{\underset{\sim}{q}T\lambda} - \sum_{\underset{\sim}{q}'} G_{\underset{\sim}{q};\underset{\sim}{q}'} : \Gamma_{\underset{\sim}{q}'T} \tag{4-44}$$

and the tensor $G_{\underset{\sim}{q}'\underset{\sim}{q}'}$ so defined has the components

$$G_{\underset{\sim}{q}\alpha_o\alpha_2;\underset{\sim}{q}'\alpha_3\alpha_5} =$$

$$= 2\beta \sum_{\alpha_1\alpha_4} L_{\underset{\sim}{q}\alpha_0\alpha_1} \left(\frac{\partial^2 \mathcal{K}(T, \upsilon, \lambda)}{\partial L_{\underset{\sim}{q}\alpha_1\alpha_2} \partial L_{\underset{\sim}{q}'\alpha_3\alpha_4}} \right)_{T, \upsilon} L^{+}_{\underset{\sim}{q}'\alpha_4\alpha_5} \tag{4-44a}$$

By solving Eq. (4-43) for the renormalized isothermal Grüneisen matrices $\Gamma_{\underset{\sim}{q}T}$ one finds

$$\Gamma_{\underset{\sim}{q}T} = \sum_{\underset{\sim}{q}'} \left(\frac{1}{1+G} \right)_{\underset{\sim}{q};\underset{\sim}{q}'} : \Gamma_{\underset{\sim}{q}'T\lambda} = \Gamma_{\underset{\sim}{q}T\lambda} - \sum_{\underset{\sim}{q}'} G_{\underset{\sim}{q}\underset{\sim}{q}'} \Gamma_{\underset{\sim}{q}'T} \tag{4-45}$$

If we simplify the picture by defining the mean values

$$\Gamma_{T\lambda} = \frac{1}{3N} \sum_{\underset{\sim}{q}} \operatorname{Tr} \Gamma_{\underset{\sim}{q}T\lambda} \tag{4-45a}$$

$$\Gamma_{T} = \frac{1}{3N} \sum_{\underset{\sim}{q}} \operatorname{Tr} \Gamma_{\underset{\sim}{q}T} \tag{4-45b}$$

and

$$g\Gamma_{T} = \frac{1}{3N^2} \sum_{\underset{\sim}{q}\alpha\underset{\sim}{q}'\alpha'\alpha''} G_{\underset{\sim}{q}\alpha\alpha;\underset{\sim}{q}'\alpha'\alpha''} \Gamma_{\underset{\sim}{q}'T\alpha'\alpha''} \tag{4-45c}$$

then

$$\Gamma_T = \Gamma_{T\lambda} - g\Gamma_T$$

or

$$\Gamma_T = \frac{1}{1+g} \Gamma_{T\lambda} \tag{4-45d}$$

defines a properly renormalized Grüneisen parameter. In the Mie-Grüneisen scheme there is no difference between the isothermal Γ_T and the isothermal-isofluctuational $\Gamma_{T\lambda}$ and γ_1 parameters. Yet Γ_T

is the proper measure of the rate of change of observed (renormalized) frequencies with respect to the volume at constant temperature. It should thus appear in the exponent of Paskin's equation† obtained for a Debye-model with a characteristic Debye temperature $\Theta\,(T, \upsilon, \lambda(\upsilon, T))$ by a straightforward integration of

$$\Gamma_T = -\left(\frac{\partial \ln \Theta}{\partial \ln \upsilon}\right)_T$$

under the assumption that Γ_T is a constant, that is

$$\frac{\Theta(T, \upsilon, \lambda(\upsilon, T))}{\Theta(T, \upsilon_o, \lambda(\upsilon_o, T))} = \left(\frac{\upsilon_o}{\upsilon}\right)^{\Gamma_T} \tag{4-45e}$$

On the other hand it is clear that the isothermal-isofluctuational parameters $\Gamma_{\tilde{q}T\lambda}$ appear in the mean value γ_1 of the equation of state (4-9).

Returning to Eq. (4-42) we have similarly

$$\Delta_{\tilde{q}\upsilon} = \left(\frac{\partial L_{\tilde{q}}}{\partial \ln T}\right)_\upsilon \frac{1}{L_{\tilde{q}}} = 1 - \frac{1}{D_{\tilde{q}}}\left(\frac{\partial D_{\tilde{q}}}{\partial \ln T}\right)_\upsilon \tag{4-46}$$

$$= 1 - \frac{1}{D_{\tilde{q}}}\left(\frac{\partial D_{\tilde{q}}}{\partial \ln T}\right)_{\upsilon,\lambda} - \sum_{\tilde{q}'} \frac{1}{D_{\tilde{q}}}\left(\frac{\partial D_{\tilde{q}}}{\partial L_{\tilde{q}'}}\right)_{T,\upsilon} : \left(\frac{\partial L_{\tilde{q}'}}{\partial \ln T}\right)_\upsilon$$

$$= \Delta_{\tilde{q}\upsilon\lambda} - \frac{1}{D_{\tilde{q}}}\left(\frac{\partial D_{\tilde{q}}}{\partial L_{\tilde{q}'}}\right)_{T,\upsilon} : (\Delta_{\tilde{q}'\upsilon}\, L_{\tilde{q}'})$$

$$= \Delta_{\tilde{q}\upsilon\lambda} - \sum_{\tilde{q}'} G_{\tilde{q};\tilde{q};} : \Delta_{\tilde{q}'\upsilon} \tag{4-46a}$$

† Acta Cryst. 10, 667 (1957)

or

$$\underset{\sim}{\Delta}_{q\upsilon} = \sum_{\underset{\sim}{q}'} \left(\frac{1}{1+G}\right)_{\underset{\sim}{q};\underset{\sim}{q}'} : \underset{\sim}{\Delta}_{q'\upsilon\lambda} \tag{4-46b}$$

By setting

$$\frac{1}{1+G} \equiv C = 1 - G\,C \tag{4-47}$$

we shall rewrite

$$\underset{\sim}{\Gamma}_{qT} = \sum_{\underset{\sim}{q}'} C_{\underset{\sim}{q};\underset{\sim}{q}'} : \underset{\sim}{\Gamma}_{q'T\lambda} \tag{4-48}$$

$$\underset{\sim}{\Delta}_{q\upsilon} = \sum_{\underset{\sim}{q}'} C_{\underset{\sim}{q};\underset{\sim}{q}'} : \underset{\sim}{\Delta}_{q'\upsilon\lambda} \tag{4-48a}$$

With these relations we can now manipulate the second terms of Eqs (4-30, 4-31, 4-32) as follows. For $\frac{1}{\chi_T} - \frac{1}{\chi_{T\lambda}}$, we have

$$\frac{1}{2}\upsilon \sum_{\underset{\sim}{q}} \mathrm{Tr}\left(\frac{\partial \underset{\sim}{D}_q}{\partial \upsilon}\right)_{T,\lambda} \left(\frac{\partial \underset{\sim}{L}_q}{\partial \upsilon}\right)_T = -\frac{2}{\upsilon} \sum_{\underset{\sim}{q}} \mathrm{Tr}\, \underset{\sim}{D}_q \underset{\sim}{\Gamma}_{qT\lambda} \cdot \underset{\sim}{\Gamma}_{qT} \underset{\sim}{L}_q$$

$$= -\frac{2}{\upsilon} KT \sum_{\underset{\sim}{q}} \mathrm{Tr}\, \underset{\sim}{\Gamma}_{qT\lambda} \cdot \underset{\sim}{\Gamma}_{qT}$$

$$= (-)\,2\frac{KT}{\upsilon} \sum_{\underset{\sim}{q}} \underset{\sim}{\Gamma}^{+}_{qT\lambda} : \underset{\sim}{\Gamma}_{qT}$$

$$= (-)\, 2\, \frac{KT}{\upsilon} \sum_{\underset{\sim}{q}\underset{\sim}{q}'} \Gamma^{+}_{\underset{\sim}{q}T\lambda} : C_{\underset{\sim}{q};\underset{\sim}{q}'} : \Gamma_{\underset{\sim}{q}'T\lambda} \tag{4-49}$$

where $\Gamma^{+}_{\underset{\sim}{q}T\lambda}$ is the transposed matrix of $\Gamma_{\underset{\sim}{q}T\lambda}$. Here, one uses the property $D^{+}_{\underset{\sim}{q}} = D_{\underset{\sim}{q}}$. Next, with

$$\left(\frac{\partial L_{\underset{\sim}{q}}}{\partial T}\right)_{\upsilon} = \frac{1}{T}\, \Delta_{\underset{\sim}{q}\upsilon}\, L_{\underset{\sim}{q}} = K\, \Delta_{\underset{\sim}{q}\upsilon}\, \frac{1}{D_{\underset{\sim}{q}}}$$

$C_{\upsilon} - C_{\upsilon\lambda}$ becomes

$$\frac{1}{2} \sum_{\underset{\sim}{q}} \mathrm{Tr}\left(D_{\underset{\sim}{q}} \left(\frac{\partial D_{\underset{\sim}{q}}}{\partial \ell n T}\right)_{\upsilon,\lambda}\right)\left(\frac{\partial L_{\underset{\sim}{q}}}{\partial T}\right)_{\upsilon}$$

$$= \frac{1}{2} K \sum_{\underset{\sim}{q}} \mathrm{Tr}\, D_{\underset{\sim}{q}}\, \Delta_{\underset{\sim}{q}\upsilon\lambda}\, \Delta_{\underset{\sim}{q}\upsilon}\, \frac{1}{D_{\underset{\sim}{q}}} = \frac{1}{2} K \sum_{\underset{\sim}{q}} \mathrm{Tr}\, \Delta_{\underset{\sim}{q}\upsilon\lambda}\, \Delta_{\underset{\sim}{q}\upsilon}$$

$$= \frac{1}{2} K \sum_{\underset{\sim}{q}} \Delta^{+}_{\underset{\sim}{q}\upsilon\lambda} : \Delta_{\underset{\sim}{q}\upsilon} = \frac{1}{2} K \sum_{\underset{\sim}{q}'} \Delta^{+}_{\underset{\sim}{q}\upsilon\lambda} : C_{\underset{\sim}{q};\underset{\sim}{q}'} : \Delta_{\underset{\sim}{q}\upsilon\lambda} \tag{4-50}$$

Lastly, $L_{\upsilon} - L_{\upsilon\lambda}$ reads

$$-\frac{1}{2} \sum_{\underset{\sim}{q}} \mathrm{Tr}\left(\frac{\partial D_{\underset{\sim}{q}}}{\partial \upsilon}\right)_{T,\lambda}\left(\frac{\partial L_{\underset{\sim}{q}}}{\partial \ell n T}\right)_{\upsilon}$$

$$= \frac{KT}{\upsilon} \sum_{\underset{\sim}{q}} \mathrm{Tr}\, D_{\underset{\sim}{q}}\, \Gamma_{\underset{\sim}{q}T\lambda}\, \Delta_{\underset{\sim}{q}\upsilon}\, \frac{1}{D_{\underset{\sim}{q}}} = KT \sum_{\underset{\sim}{q}} \mathrm{Tr}\, \Gamma_{\underset{\sim}{q}T\lambda}\, \Delta_{\underset{\sim}{q}\upsilon}$$

$$= \frac{KT}{\upsilon} \sum_{\underset{\sim}{q}} \Gamma^{\dagger}_{\underset{\sim}{q}T\lambda} : \Delta_{\underset{\sim}{q}\upsilon}$$

$$= \frac{KT}{\upsilon} \sum_{\underset{\sim}{q}\underset{\sim}{q}'} \Gamma^{\dagger}_{\underset{\sim}{q}T\lambda} : C_{\underset{\sim}{q};\underset{\sim}{q}'} : \Delta_{\underset{\sim}{q}'\upsilon\lambda} \qquad (4\text{-}51)$$

Combining all the preceding equations we observe that χ_T^{-1}, C_υ and L_υ can be put into the forms

$$\frac{1}{\chi_T} = \frac{1}{\chi_{st}} + 3\,\frac{RT}{\upsilon}\,\gamma_{11} \qquad (4\text{-}52)$$

$$C_\upsilon = 3\,R\,\gamma_{22} \qquad (4\text{-}53)$$

$$L_\upsilon = 3\,\frac{RT}{\upsilon}\,\gamma_{12} \qquad (4\text{-}54)$$

where the three dimensionless quantities γ_{ij} read

$$\gamma_{11} = \frac{1}{3N} \sum_{\underset{\sim}{q}} \mathrm{Tr}\,(\bar{\Gamma}_{\underset{\sim}{q}} + 2\,\bar{\Gamma}^{2}_{\underset{\sim}{q}} - \bar{\Gamma}'_{\underset{\sim}{q}})$$

$$- \frac{2}{3N} \sum_{\underset{\sim}{q}\underset{\sim}{q}'} \Gamma^{+}_{\underset{\sim}{q}T\lambda} : C_{\underset{\sim}{q};\underset{\sim}{q}'} : \Gamma_{\underset{\sim}{q}'T\lambda} \qquad (4\text{-}52a)$$

$$\gamma_{22} = \frac{1}{2} - \frac{1}{3NK}\,T\,\left(\frac{\partial^2 \mathcal{K}(T,\upsilon,\lambda)}{\partial T^2}\right)_{\upsilon,\lambda} +$$

$$+ \frac{1}{3N}\frac{1}{2}\sum_{\underset{\sim}{q}\underset{\sim}{q}'} \overset{+}{\Delta}_{\underset{\sim}{q}\upsilon\lambda} : C_{\underset{\sim}{q};\underset{\sim}{q}'} : \Delta_{\underset{\sim}{q}'\upsilon\lambda} \qquad (4\text{-}53a)$$

$$\gamma_{12} = \frac{1}{3N}\sum_{\underset{\sim}{q}} \mathrm{Tr}\,(\bar{\Gamma}_{\underset{\sim}{q}T\lambda} - \overline{\Delta_{\underset{\sim}{q}\upsilon\lambda}\,\Gamma_{\underset{\sim}{q}T\lambda}} + \mathring{\bar{\Gamma}}_{\underset{\sim}{q}T\lambda})$$

$$+ \frac{1}{3N}\sum_{\underset{\sim}{q}\underset{\sim}{q}'} \overset{+}{\Gamma}_{\underset{\sim}{q}T\lambda} : C_{\underset{\sim}{q};\underset{\sim}{q}'} : \Delta_{\underset{\sim}{q}'\upsilon\lambda} \qquad (4\text{-}54a)$$

In the framework of the classical theory developed thus far these equations are exact. Given an expression for the irreducible cumulant expansion, or thermodynamic potential $\mathcal{K}(\upsilon, T, \lambda)$, and thus a form for the renormalized dynamical matrices $D_{\underset{\sim}{q}}(\upsilon, T, \lambda)$ we can construct in a clear-cut way the second order partial derivatives of the s. c. free energy with respect to υ and T with the help of the intermediate derivatives

$$\left(\frac{\partial\mathcal{K}}{\partial\upsilon}\right)_{T,\lambda} ; \left(\frac{\partial\mathcal{K}}{\partial T}\right)_{\upsilon,\lambda}$$

$$\left(\frac{\partial^2\mathcal{K}}{\partial\upsilon^2}\right)_{T,\lambda} ; \left(\frac{\partial^2\mathcal{K}}{\partial T\,\partial\upsilon}\right)_{\lambda} ; \left(\frac{\partial^2\mathcal{K}}{\partial T^2}\right)_{\upsilon,\lambda}$$

$$\left(\frac{\partial D_{\underset{\sim}{q}\alpha\alpha'}}{\partial\upsilon}\right)_{T,\lambda} ; \left(\frac{\partial D_{\underset{\sim}{q}\alpha\alpha'}}{\partial T}\right)_{\upsilon,\lambda} ; \left(\frac{\partial D_{\underset{\sim}{q}\alpha\alpha'}}{\partial L_{\underset{\sim}{q}'\alpha''\alpha'''}}\right)_{\upsilon,T}$$

where, we recall that

$$\lambda = \left\{\frac{1}{M} L_{\underset{\sim}{q}}\right\}$$

stands for the set of propagator matrices L_{g}. Although a rather tedious algebra was necessitated to establish these equations, they provide a very useful frame of reference for checking approximate calculations usually performed on the basis of the statistical method of correlation functions calculations now discussed.

Expressed in terms of expectation values of given operators, χ_T, C_υ and L_υ read as follows. We have

$$\frac{1}{\chi_T} = -\frac{\upsilon}{\beta}\left(\frac{\partial^2 \ln Z_V}{\partial \upsilon^2}\right)_T$$

$$= \upsilon \left\langle \frac{d^2 V}{d\upsilon^2} \right\rangle - \beta \upsilon \left\{ \left\langle \left(\frac{dV}{d\upsilon}\right)^2 \right\rangle - \left\langle \frac{dV}{d\upsilon} \right\rangle^2 \right\}$$

$$= \frac{1}{\chi_{st}} + \upsilon \left\langle \frac{d^2 (V - V_{st})}{d\upsilon^2} \right\rangle$$

$$- \beta\upsilon \left\{ \left\langle \left(\frac{dV}{d\upsilon}\right)^2 \right\rangle - \left\langle \frac{dV}{d\upsilon} \right\rangle^2 \right\} \qquad (4\text{-}55)$$

$$C_\upsilon = \beta^2 \left(\frac{\partial^2 \ln Z}{\partial \beta^2}\right)_\upsilon$$

$$= \frac{3}{2} R + \beta^2 \left\{ \langle V^2 \rangle - \langle V \rangle^2 \right\} \qquad (4\text{-}56)$$

and

$$L_\upsilon = P - \frac{\partial^2 \ln Z}{\partial \upsilon \partial \beta}$$

$$= -\beta \left\{ \left\langle \frac{dV}{d\upsilon} V \right\rangle - \left\langle \frac{dV}{d\upsilon} \right\rangle \langle V \rangle \right\} \qquad (4\text{-}57)$$

A great advantage of this formulation is that it clearly indicates that a knowledge of U, P, χ_T, C_υ and L_υ is related to the calculation of the three mean values and of the three correlation functions written above. Writing the dimensionless quantities γ_{ij} in terms of these functions we find

$$\gamma_{11} = \frac{-1}{3N}\beta\left\langle\frac{d(V-V_{st})}{d\ell n\upsilon}\right\rangle + \frac{1}{3N}\beta\left\langle\frac{d^2(V-V_{st})}{d(\ell n\upsilon)^2}\right\rangle$$

$$+ \frac{1}{3N}\beta^2\left\{\left\langle\frac{dV}{d\ell n\upsilon}\frac{dV}{d\ell n\upsilon}\right\rangle - \left\langle\frac{dV}{d\ell n\upsilon}\right\rangle^2\right\} \tag{4-55a}$$

$$\gamma_{22} = \frac{1}{2} + \frac{1}{3N}\beta^2\left\{\langle V^2\rangle - \langle V^2\rangle\right\} \tag{4-56a}$$

$$\gamma_{12} = \frac{1}{3N}\beta^2\left\{\left\langle\frac{(-)dV}{d\ell n\upsilon}V\right\rangle - \left\langle\frac{(-)dV}{d\ell n\upsilon}\right\rangle\langle V\rangle\right\} \tag{4-57a}$$

Let us use a few examples to illustrate how approximate expressions for these correlation functions are obtained. The procedure is based on the application of Eq. (3-30). Given two operators 0_1, 0_2 of the nuclear displacement vectors this equation tells us that

$$\langle 0_1 0_2\rangle - \langle 0_1\rangle\langle 0_2\rangle$$

$$= \langle 0_1 0_2\rangle_{W,L} + \langle 0_1 0_2 (e^{-\beta V}-1)\rangle_{W,irL}$$

$$= \langle 0_1 0_2\rangle_{W,L} + \sum_{n=1}^{\infty}\frac{(-\beta)^n}{n!}\langle 0_1 0_2 V^n\rangle_{W,irL} \tag{4-58}$$

Now it must be realized that if the concept "irL" (irreducibly linked) applies to the n vertices of $(-\beta V)^n$ among themselves and to the operator $0_1 0_2$ taken as an entity it does not apply to each one of the 0_i individually. Consequently, if the vertices assigned to 0_1 and 0_2 must be linked they may already be so with two linking lines which may be further scattered by V operators from which at least three lines emerge. For clarity this situation will be illustrated here with the help of the diagrammatic representation introduced in section (2-4, p. 65) and by considering the evaluation of the correlation functions in the R. H. A. Designating by γ_{22} (R. H. A.) the quantity associated with C_υ (T) in the R. H. A. we have

$$\gamma_{22}(\text{R. H. A.}) = \frac{1}{3NK} C_\upsilon(\text{R. H. A.})$$

$$= \frac{1}{2} + \frac{1}{3N}\beta^2 \langle V V\rangle_W$$

$$+ \frac{1}{3N}\beta^2 \sum_{n=1}^{\infty} \frac{(-\beta)^n}{n!} \langle V V^n V\rangle_{W,\,irL,\ R.H.A.} \tag{4-59}$$

Inspection of this series indicates that in the approximation considered one must retain the contributions arising from the configurations drawn in the following figure

Fig. 8 Specific heat C_υ(T) in the R. H. A.

Let us begin with the first term. According to the definition following Eq. (3-30) that $\langle 0\rangle_W = \langle 0\rangle_{R.H.A.}$ it yields the potential contribution $C_{\upsilon,R.H.A.}$ to $C_\upsilon(R.H.A.)$, that is

$$\frac{1}{3N}\beta^2 \langle VV\rangle_W = \frac{1}{3N}\beta^2 \left(\frac{1}{2}\right)^2 \sum_{s\sigma\rho\rho'} \frac{1}{2}\left(\lambda^{\sigma}_{\rho\rho',\underset{\sim}{pp'}}\right)^2 \Phi_\rho \Phi_{\rho'}$$

$$= \frac{1}{3N}\beta^2 \frac{1}{2} \sum_{\underset{\sim}{q}\alpha_1\alpha_2\alpha_3\alpha_4} \left(\frac{1}{2}\right)^2 \sum_{\rho\rho'}$$

$$\times \frac{1}{M}\eta_\rho(\underset{\sim}{q})\,\eta_{\rho'}(-\underset{\sim}{q})\, L_{\underset{\sim}{q}\alpha_1\alpha_2}\, p_{\alpha_1} p'_{\alpha_2}$$

$$\times \frac{1}{M}\eta_\rho(-\underset{\sim}{q})\,\eta_{\rho'}(\underset{\sim}{q})\, L_{\underset{\sim}{q}\alpha_3\alpha_4}\, p_{\alpha_3} p'_{\alpha_4}\, \Phi_\rho \Phi_{\rho'}$$

$$= \frac{1}{3N}\beta^2 \frac{1}{2} \sum_{\underset{\sim}{q}\alpha_1\alpha_2\alpha_3\alpha_4}$$

$$\times \left(\frac{1}{2M}\sum_\rho \eta_\rho(\underset{\sim}{q})\,\eta_\rho(-\underset{\sim}{q})\, L_{\underset{\sim}{q}\alpha_1\alpha_2}\, p_{\alpha_1} p_{\alpha_3}\Phi_\rho\right)$$

$$\times \left(\frac{1}{2M}\sum_{\rho'} \eta_{\rho'}(\underset{\sim}{q})\,\eta_{\rho'}(-\underset{\sim}{q})\, L_{\underset{\sim}{q}\alpha_3\alpha_4}\, p'_{\alpha_2} p'_{\alpha_4}\Phi_\rho\right)$$

$$= \frac{1}{3N}\beta^2 \frac{1}{2} \sum_{\underset{\sim}{q}\alpha_1\alpha_2\alpha_3\alpha_4} \times$$

$$\times \; L_{\underset{\sim}{q}\alpha_1\alpha_2} \; D^{(I)}_{\underset{\sim}{q}\alpha_1\alpha_3} \; L_{\underset{\sim}{q}\alpha_3\alpha_4} \; D^{(I)}_{\underset{\sim}{q}\alpha_2\alpha_4}$$

$$= \frac{1}{3N}\frac{1}{2} \sum_{\underset{\sim}{q}\alpha_2\alpha_3} \delta_{\alpha_2\alpha_3} \; \delta_{\alpha_3\alpha_2} = \frac{1}{2}$$

therefore

$$C_{\upsilon, R.H.A.} = 3\ NK \tag{4-60}$$

and consequently we find that the Dulong-Petit law remains valid in this approximation. That the corollary is true is readily proved since, in order that the second term of the series (4-59) yields $\frac{3}{2}$ NK, the dynamical matrix $D^{(I)}_{\underset{\sim}{q}}$ must satisfy the first order Dyson equation

$$D^{(I)}_{\underset{\sim}{q}} = \frac{1}{M} \sum_{\rho} (1 - \cos \underset{\sim}{q}\underset{\sim}{R}_\rho) \; e^{\frac{1}{2}\lambda^{(I)}_\rho \underset{\sim}{p}^2} \; \underset{\sim}{p}^2 \varphi(R_\rho)$$

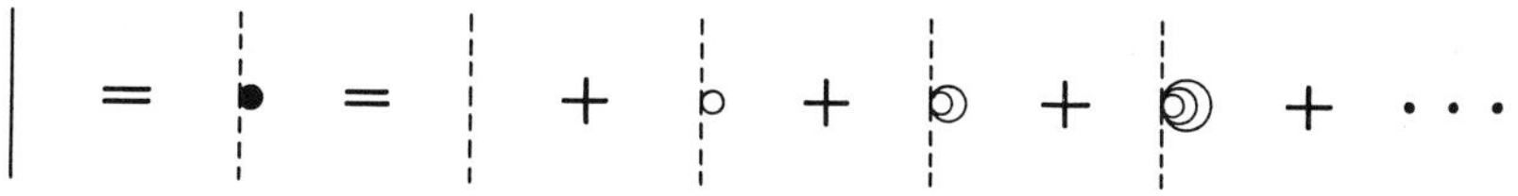

| = • = ¦ + ⦰ + ⦰ + ⦰ + . . .

This generalization of the Dulong-Petit law is a consequence of an exact cancellation occurring between two kinds of corrections respectively designated as propagator $(L_{\underset{\sim}{q}})$ and vertex $(D_{\underset{\sim}{q}})$ corrections. This property can be even further generalized by including higher order corrections to the renormalized $D_{\underset{\sim}{q}}$. Ultimately the theorem is that

$$C_\upsilon \text{(Dulong-Petit)} = 3\ NK = \frac{3}{2} NK$$

$$+ 2K\beta^2 \sum_{\underset{\sim}{q}} \operatorname{Tr} L_{\underset{\sim}{q}} \left(\frac{\partial \mathcal{K}}{\partial L_{\underset{\sim}{q}}} \right)_{\upsilon, T} L_{\underset{\sim}{q}} \left(\frac{\partial \mathcal{K}}{\partial L_{\underset{\sim}{q}}} \right)_{\upsilon, T} \tag{4-61}$$

The single, but theoretically important, difference between the usual harmonic and the above approximation to C_{υ} lies in the domain of the temperature in which they hold. We shall indeed show in chapter 6 that the renormalized $D_{\underset{\sim}{q}}$ do exist up to a limit of dynamical stability of the system, that is to say up to a limiting temperature $\bar{T}(\upsilon)$. The usual Dulong-Petit law is of course not subject to this restriction in the domain of static stability where $D_{\underset{\sim}{q},h}(\upsilon) > 0$. This theorem provides a clue to answering the question raised in section (1-3) namely, and roughly speaking, whether anharmonic effects are large or not in the (υ, T) variables. The answer is that they are less important than anticipated on the basis of a perturbation theory owing to a rather considerable number of cancellations brought about by the renormalized scheme. Let us consider next one term of the series (4-59), for example

$$\frac{1}{3N} \beta^2 \frac{(-\beta)^n}{n!} \langle V V^n V \rangle_{W,irL,\ R.H.A.} \tag{4-62}$$

The number of ways in which the configurations depicted in fig. 8 can be drawn with n intermediate vertices is $n!$. For the vertex function, designated by $A_{\underset{\sim}{q}\alpha_1\alpha_2;\underset{\sim}{q}'\alpha_3\alpha_4}$, one finds

$$A_{\underset{\sim}{q}\alpha_1\alpha_2;\underset{\sim}{q}'\alpha_3\alpha_4}$$

$$= \beta \frac{1}{2} \frac{1}{2} \frac{1}{NM^2} \sum_{\rho} \eta_\rho(\underset{\sim}{q}) \eta_\rho(-\underset{\sim}{q}) \eta_\rho(\underset{\sim}{q}') \eta_\rho(-\underset{\sim}{q}')$$

$$\times \Phi_{\alpha_1\alpha_2\alpha_3\alpha_4}(R_\rho, \lambda_\rho) \tag{4-63}$$

Furthermore by defining the tensor components

$$G_{\underset{\sim}{q}\alpha_o\alpha_2;\underset{\sim}{q}'\alpha_3\alpha_5} = \sum_{\alpha_1\alpha_4} L_{\underset{\sim}{q}\alpha_o\alpha_1} A_{\underset{\sim}{q}\alpha_1\alpha_2;\underset{\sim}{q}'\alpha_3\alpha_4} L^{+}_{\underset{\sim}{q}'\alpha_4\alpha_5}$$

and the tensor product

$$(G^n)_{\underset{\sim}{q};\underset{\sim}{q}'} = \sum_{\underset{\sim}{q}_1\cdots\underset{\sim}{q}_{n-1}} G_{\underset{\sim}{q};\underset{\sim}{q}_1} : G_{\underset{\sim}{q}_1;\underset{\sim}{q}_2} : \cdots : G_{\underset{\sim}{q}_{n-1};\underset{\sim}{q}'}$$

the value of the term considered in Eq. (4-62) is

$$\frac{1}{3N}\beta^2\frac{1}{2}\sum_{\substack{\underset{\sim}{q}\underset{\sim}{q}'\\ \alpha_o\alpha\alpha_2\alpha_3\alpha_5}} D_{\underset{\sim}{q}\alpha_o\alpha} L_{\underset{\sim}{q}\alpha\alpha_2}(-1)^n(G^n)_{\underset{\sim}{q}\alpha_o\alpha_2;\underset{\sim}{q}'\alpha_3\alpha_5}$$

$$\times L_{\underset{\sim}{q}'\alpha_5\alpha'} D_{\underset{\sim}{q}'\alpha'\alpha_3}$$

$$= \frac{(-1)^n}{3N}\frac{1}{2}\sum_{\substack{\underset{\sim}{q}\underset{\sim}{q}'\\ \alpha_o\alpha_2\alpha_3\alpha_5}} \delta_{\alpha_o\alpha_2}(G^n)_{\underset{\sim}{q}\alpha_o\alpha_2;\underset{\sim}{q}'\alpha_3\alpha_5}\delta_{\alpha_5\alpha_3}$$

$$= \frac{(-1)^n}{3N}\frac{1}{2}\sum_{\substack{\underset{\sim}{q}\underset{\sim}{q}'\\ \alpha\alpha'}} (G^n)_{\underset{\sim}{q}\alpha\alpha;\underset{\sim}{q}'\alpha'\alpha'}$$

The summation over n from 1 to ∞ can easily be performed and one finds

$$\gamma_{22}(\text{R. H. A.}) = 1 - \frac{1}{2}\frac{1}{3N} \sum_{\substack{\underset{\sim}{q}\underset{\sim}{q}'\underset{\sim}{q}'' \\ \alpha\alpha_1\alpha_2\alpha_3}} G_{\underset{\sim}{q}\alpha\alpha;\underset{\sim}{q}'\alpha_1\alpha_2}$$

$$\times \; C_{\underset{\sim}{q}'\alpha_1\alpha_2;\underset{\sim}{q}''\alpha_3\alpha_3}$$

$$= \frac{1}{2} + \frac{1}{2}\frac{1}{3N} \sum_{\substack{\underset{\sim}{q}\underset{\sim}{q}'' \\ \alpha\alpha''}} C_{\underset{\sim}{q}\alpha\alpha;\underset{\sim}{q}''\alpha''\alpha''} \tag{4-64}$$

We can check this result directly from Eq. (4-53a) evaluated in this approximation. Since, here,

$$\mathcal{H} = \mathcal{H}^{(I)} = N\frac{1}{2} \sum_{\rho} \Phi(R_\rho, \lambda_\rho)$$

does not contain the temperature explicitly the second term of Eq. (4-53a) is zero. Furthermore $\Delta_{\underset{\sim}{q}\upsilon\lambda}$ is the unit tensor and

$$2\beta \frac{\partial^2 \mathcal{H}}{\partial L_{\underset{\sim}{q}\alpha_1\alpha_2}\,\partial L_{\underset{\sim}{q}'\alpha_3\alpha_4}} = A_{\underset{\sim}{q}\alpha_1\alpha_2;\underset{\sim}{q}'\alpha_3\alpha_4}$$

of Eq. (4-63). For γ_{12} and γ_{11} calculated in the same approximation one correspondingly finds

$$\gamma_{12}(\text{R. H. A.}) = \frac{1}{3N} \sum_{\substack{\underset{\sim}{q}\underset{\sim}{q}' \\ \alpha\alpha_1\alpha_2}} \Gamma^{(I)}_{\underset{\sim}{q}\alpha\alpha_1} C_{\underset{\sim}{q}\alpha\alpha_1;\underset{\sim}{q}'\alpha_2\alpha_2} \tag{4-65}$$

$$\gamma_{11}(\text{R. H. A.}) = \frac{1}{3N} \sum_{\underset{\sim}{q}\alpha} \left(\overline{\Gamma^{(I)}_{\underset{\sim}{q}\,\alpha\alpha}} + 2\,\overline{(\Gamma^{(I)2}_{\underset{\sim}{q}})}_{\alpha\alpha} - \overline{\Gamma^{(I)'}_{\underset{\sim}{q}\,\alpha\alpha}} \right)$$

$$- \frac{2}{3N} \sum_{\substack{\underset{\sim}{q}\underset{\sim}{q}' \\ \alpha\alpha_1\alpha_2\alpha_3}} \Gamma^{(I)}_{\underset{\sim}{q}\,\alpha\alpha_1} C_{\underset{\sim}{q}\alpha\alpha_1;\underset{\sim}{q}'\alpha_2\alpha_3} \Gamma^{(I)}_{\underset{\sim}{q}'\alpha_2\alpha_3} \tag{4-66}$$

whereby

$$\Gamma^{(I)}_{\underset{\sim}{q}} = -\frac{1}{2} \frac{1}{D^{(I)}_{\underset{\sim}{q}}(\upsilon,\lambda)} \left(\frac{\partial D^{(I)}_{\underset{\sim}{q}}(\upsilon,\lambda)}{\partial \ln \upsilon} \right)_{\lambda}$$

and

$$\overline{\Gamma^{(I)}_{\underset{\sim}{q}}} = \frac{1}{D^{(I)}_{\underset{\sim}{q}}(\upsilon,\lambda)} \int_0^1 ds\, D^{(I)}_{\underset{\sim}{q}}(\upsilon,\lambda')\, \Gamma^{(I)}_{\underset{\sim}{q}}(\upsilon,\lambda')$$

It is noted that in the R. H. A. the theory can be completely formulated in terms of the (υ,λ) variables if one introduces $KT = \frac{1}{3N}\sum_{\underset{\sim}{q}} D^{(I)}_{\underset{\sim}{q}} L_{\underset{\sim}{q}}$ in the tensors $A_{\underset{\sim}{q};\underset{\sim}{q}'}$ and $G_{\underset{\sim}{q};\underset{\sim}{q}'}$. In chapter 6 we shall return to the investigation of this approximation in the dispersion free limit and also perform the transformation from the (υ,λ) to the (υ, T) variables in order to inspect the temperature dependence of the function $\gamma_{ij}(\text{R. H. A.})$ at fixed υ.

Another example of correlation function calculation that we shall briefly discuss here and leave as an exercise for detailed treatment is to consider the conventional perturbation theory based on

$$V = V_{st} + V_h + V_{3-a} + V_{4-a}$$

and to evaluate the lowest order anharmonic correction to γ_{12} and γ_{11}, thus supplementing the well-known calculation of $\gamma_{22}(T) = \frac{1}{3R} C_{\upsilon}(T)$ in the approximation dealt with in section (1-3). Inspection of Eq. (4-57a) indicates that in the lowest order of perturbation theory yielding

$$\gamma_{12}(T) = \gamma\,(1 + c_{12}\,T)$$

the contributions arising from the diagrams drawn below must be retained. Designating the operation $\frac{d}{d\ell n \upsilon}$ by the symbol * assigned to one of the vertices, this set looks as follows:

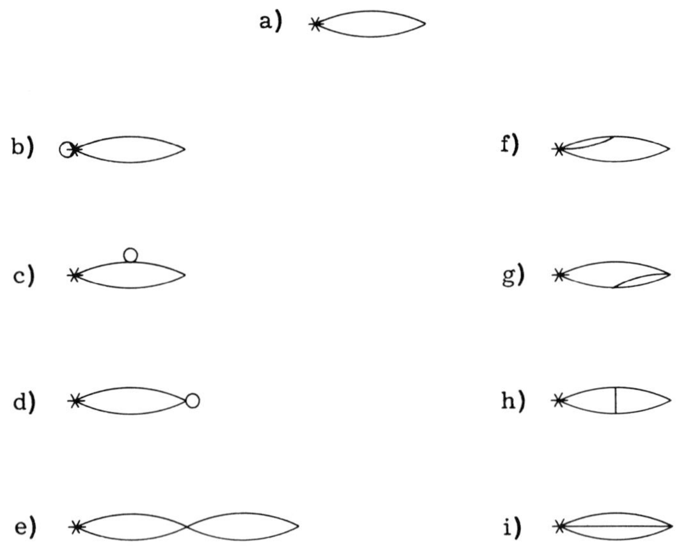

Fig. 9. Latent heat of expansion in lowest order of perturbation theory

Note that, by deleting the operation *, one obtains the set of diagrams which must be considered in calculating $\gamma_{22}(T) = 1 + c_{22}\,T$ by the method of correlation functions. In the latter case, however,

show that the contributions arising from b), c) and d) cancel one another as well as the contributions arising from f), g) and h) so that only a), e) and i) yield non-vanishing results. Returning now to the calculation of $\gamma_{12}(T)$, show that these cancellations are only partially fulfilled and that in addition to a), e) and i) some contributions from d) and g) remain. Consequently the coefficients c_{12} and c_{22} will turn out to be slightly different from one another. In order to learn more about the functions γ_{ij} introduced in this section it is however desirable now to take up the problem of converting the equations established above in the (υ, T) variables into the (P, T) ones.

4-3 EXTENSION OF THE MIE-GRÜNEISEN SCHEME

In this section we shall perform an approximate conversion of Eqs (4-52, 4-53, 4-54, 4-27, 4-28b) from the (υ, T) to the (P, T) variables with the help of the volume equation (4-11) and by making the working hypothesis that γ_1, γ_{11}, γ_{12} and γ_{22} are volume independent, that is also pressure independent and are slowly varying functions of T. This hypothesis arises from the observation made in the previous section that the Dulong-Petit law has a broader range of validity than expected from unrenormalized theories and also that the Grüneisen γ is known to be a "good" constant. Yet we make here a jump from the status of a theory which led us to introducing a set of dimensionless functions to a practical scheme of evaluation of thermal data where these functions are regarded as parameters. Thus we shall have to seek an a posteriori justification of the hypothesis by submitting the scheme proposed below to experimental tests. Gathering together the starting equations we have

$$\delta = 1 - \frac{\upsilon_o}{\upsilon}$$

$$P = -\frac{1}{\chi_o}\delta + 3\frac{RT}{\upsilon}\gamma_1 + 0(\delta^2)$$

$$\frac{1}{\chi_T} = \frac{1}{\chi_o}(1-\mu\delta) + 3\frac{RT}{\upsilon}\gamma_{11} + 0(\delta^2)$$

$$C_\upsilon = 3R\gamma_{22}$$

$$L_\upsilon = 3\frac{RT}{\upsilon}\gamma_{12}$$

$$\alpha_P = 3\frac{R}{\upsilon}\chi_T\gamma_{12}$$

$$C_P = 3R(\gamma_{22} + 3\frac{RT}{\upsilon}\gamma_{12}^2\chi_T)$$

By making the linear combination

$$\frac{1}{\chi_T} - \mu P = \frac{1}{\chi_o} - 3\frac{RT}{\upsilon}(\mu\gamma_1 - \gamma_{11})$$

by inserting

$$\upsilon = \upsilon_o\frac{1 + 3\rho_o\chi_o\gamma_1 KT}{1 + \chi_o P}$$

and setting

$$b = 3K\rho_o\chi_o = 3\frac{R}{\upsilon_o}\chi_o \tag{4-67}$$

we obtain

$$\frac{1}{\chi_T} = \frac{1}{\chi_o} + \mu P - \frac{1}{\chi_o} bT \frac{1 + \chi_o P}{1 + b\gamma_1 T}(\mu\gamma_1 - \gamma_{11}) \qquad (4\text{-}68)$$

For most practical purposes we can set $P = 0$ and thus find

$$\chi_T = \chi_o \frac{1 + b\gamma_1 T}{1 - (\mu\gamma_1 - \gamma_1 - \gamma_{11})bT} \qquad (4\text{-}68a)$$

The interesting conjecture is now that the isothermal compressibility should follow, at high temperature, a hyperbolic law with an asymptote at $T = T_1$ given by

$$T_1 = \frac{1}{(\mu-1)\gamma_1 - \gamma_{11}} \frac{1}{b} = \frac{1}{c}$$

Leaving next the C_υ equation as it stands we find for the latent heat of expansion

$$L_\upsilon = \frac{1}{\chi_o} b \gamma_{12} \frac{T}{1 + b\gamma_1 T} \qquad (4\text{-}70)$$

which has no singular behaviour toward elevated temperatures. Going over to the volume expansivity we get

$$\alpha_P = b\gamma_{12} \frac{1}{1 - cT} \qquad (4\text{-}71)$$

again a hyperbolic law. Lastly the specific heat at constant pressure reads

$$C_P = 3R(\gamma_{22} + \gamma_{12}^2 b \frac{T}{1 - cT}) \qquad (4\text{-}72)$$

the hyperlinear behaviour being stronger here than for any other quantity.

Now what is the experimental situation? Here we shall refer to the collection of data made by G. Borelius ([5]). The data for Ar, Kr, Xe, K, Na, Al, Ag, Au, Pt, Rh, and Mo all show a rather strong hyperlinear rise of $C_P(T)$ and to a lesser extent, as it should be, for $\alpha_P(T)$. A rough evaluation of these data seems to yield a qualitative support of the conjectures advanced above with ratios of T_1/T (triple point) $\cong$ 1.6 to 1.1 the higher the triple point the smaller is the ratio. However, instead of invoking the background properties of the lattice (in the sense discussed in section (1-3) p. 17), pre-melting phenomena are usually called for to produce the sharp rise of $C_P(T)$ at high T. Consequently, and in order to clarify somewhat this point, we must seek a test based on data measured with pure and monocrystalline specimens. Thanks to the reliable set of thermal data recently obtained by O. G. Peterson† for Ar a first quantitative test of the scheme proposed above is fortunately possible. We are indebted to A. Kugler‡ for setting up the table of numerical values reproduced below.

---

† Lattice constant, thermal expansion and isothermal compressibility measurements on Argon single crystals.
Ph. D. Thesis, Dept. of Physics, University of Illinois, Ill. 1965

‡ same Dept.

T (^oK)	ρ_A g/cm^3	$10^{12}\chi_T$ $cm^2/dyne$	$10^4\alpha_P$ (deg^{-1})	$\mu\gamma_1 - \gamma_{11}$ (number)	γ_{12} (number)
40	1.7348	46	10.71	26.6	2.14
45	1.7253	48	11.63	25.8	2.25
50	1.7149	51	12.54	25.7	2.30
55	1.7038	54	13.49	25.3	2.35
60	1.6919	58	14.50	25.3	2.36
65	1.6792	63	15.63	25.3	2.36
70	1.6656	68	16.98	25.6	2.40
75	1.6509	74	18.55	25.6	2.43
80	1.6349	82	20.31	25.9	2.43
83	1.6248	86	21.47	25.7	2.46

Since the principal conjecture drawn from the scheme concerns the hyperbolic law for χ_T we start directly, for $P = 0$, from

$$\frac{1}{\chi_T} = \frac{1}{\chi_o} - 3\frac{RT}{\upsilon}(\mu\gamma_1 - \gamma_{11})$$

and determine

$$\mu\gamma_1 - \gamma_{11} = \frac{\upsilon}{3RT}(\chi_T - \chi_o)\frac{1}{\chi_o\chi_T}$$

from the experimental values of T, of the mass density $\rho_A(T) = A\rho(T) = A\,N/\upsilon(T)$ with $A = 39.95$ g/mole, of χ_T and $\chi_o = 30 \cdot 10^{-12}\ cm^2\ dyne^{-1}$ determined by extrapolation. A rather astounding regularity of values lying within the experimental accuracy of 5 % around 25.6 is found for this parameter. This suggests that we inspect

$$\alpha_P^{-1}(T) = \frac{1}{b\gamma_{12}}(1 - cT) = \frac{1}{b\gamma_{12}} - \frac{1}{\gamma_{12}}(\mu\gamma_1 - \gamma_1 - \gamma_{11})\,T$$

From the data given in the table one finds indeed that eight points fall on a straight line, the points corresponding to $T = 40^{\circ}K$ and $45^{\circ}K$ lying slightly above, which is to be expected since the above theory is purely classical. The value of the slope is

$$\frac{\mu\gamma_1 - \gamma_1 - \gamma_{11}}{\gamma_{12}} = 10$$

By extrapolating the segment of straight line toward the axes one finds

$$T_1 \cong 130^{\circ} \qquad\qquad b\gamma_{12} \cong \frac{1}{1300}\,(^{\circ}K)^{-1}$$

and accordingly a ratio $T_1/T_{T\cdot P} \cong 130/84 = 1\cdot 55$. Considering next the parameter γ_{12} one determines its value with the help of the reciprocity theorem used to eliminate the latent heat of expansion that is

$$\gamma_{12} = \frac{1}{3K}\,\frac{\alpha_P}{\rho\chi_T}$$

From the values listed in the table one notices a small linear shift of $\gamma_{12}(T)$ as a function of T and finds for T varying from $40^{\circ}K$ to $80^{\circ}K$,

$$\gamma_{12}(T) = 2.40 + \frac{1}{200}\,(T - 60)$$

Again quantum effects should not be ignored here. This means that $C_\upsilon(T)/N$ is smaller than 3K and consequently that $\gamma_{22}(T)$ of the classical theory must not be analyzed here since for Ar the triple point is rather low. Yet the variation of $\gamma_{12}(T)$ is small and, choosing the value of 2.40, one finds

$$\mu\gamma_1 - \gamma_1 - \gamma_{11} = 10\,\gamma_{12} = 24$$

or

$$\gamma_1 = \mu\gamma_1 - \gamma_{11} - 10\,\gamma_{12} \cong 25.6 - 24 = 1.6$$

If this value can be trusted it would mean that the ratio

$$\frac{\gamma_1}{\gamma_{12}} \cong 0.66 < 1$$

rather than being equal to one as the Grüneisen scheme would require. It is of course premature to draw definite conclusions from a single test of a classical theory applied to Ar, a solid having a rather low triple-point. What we need is more data with pure and monocrystalline specimen of smaller $T_1/T_{T.P}$ ratio:

1°) to support the conjecture that the rise of the lattice contribution to $C_P(T)$, $\chi\,(T)$, $\alpha_P(T)$ at high temperature can be accounted for by a simple, essentially hyperbolic, law,

2°) to assert conclusively that γ_1, γ_{11}, $\Gamma_T = \frac{1}{1+g}\,\Gamma_{T\lambda}$ do differ from γ_{12} (which is actually the usual Grüneisen parameter if 3K is replaced by the true $C_\upsilon(T)/N$ in its definition) and thus reflect in their differences renormalization effects.

Incidentally we should note that the hyperbolic law is already predicted with one single parameter γ, the dominating factor being

$(\mu-2)\gamma$ where $\mu = -d \ln \chi_o / \ln \rho_o$. Dynamical corrections must be taken into account and lead us to distinguish γ_1, γ_{11}, $\Gamma_T = \frac{1}{1+g}\Gamma_{T\lambda}$ from γ_{12} . A quantitative theory of anharmonicity is therefore still to be treated. Nevertheless we hope that the scheme set up will be useful to interpret the effects observed in the (P, T) variables of the renormalized dynamical matrices $D_{\underset{\sim}{q}}(\upsilon, T, \lambda(\upsilon, T))$. There remains to extend the scheme's validity toward lower temperature, a task which will be fulfilled in the next chapter. We now turn our attention to face another problem.

4 4 THE HARD CORE PROBLEM

In a theory of anharmonicity based on a truncated form such as Eq. (1-26) for the crystal potential, the problem dealt with in this section does not arise since, together with V_{st}, a finite number of derivatives of the molecular potential function $\varphi(R)$ evaluated at the positions of static equilibrium come into play. In fact a great deal of the hard core effects is already built in that scheme. The reason why an explicit treatment of the remaining effects must be given here even if, as anticipated, they normally turn out to be small, is the following. With a trial interaction representation built up of Gaussian distribution functions for the amplitudes of the modes, non vanishing, though small, penetrations of the atoms into the core of their co-moving neighbors is permitted. This means that while calculating the effective potential function $\Phi(R_\rho, \lambda_\rho)$ with the help of the Green's function (2-10) one integrates over the core part of the bare potential function $\varphi(R)$. Now, it should be recalled here that, at very short distances, the electronic contributions to $\varphi(R)$ are bounded by the, finite, properties of the united atom limit†, while at large distances multi-

† see footnote next page

polar expansions can be used as asymptotic series to describe these contributions. The two regions must match one another by a steep portion possessing an inflexion point. Thus, inspite of the fact that the electronic part may be non analytic around $R = 0^{\dagger}$, the sum of it and of the internuclear Coulomb interaction which constitutes $\varphi(R)$ is integrable and consequently $\Phi(R_\rho, \lambda_\rho)$ does exist. Yet the role that the core repulsive forces can virtually play and the possibility that $N\bar{\varphi}(k)$, for $k = 0$ might be very large and positive may command an appropriate treatment of the said hard core effects.

This problem can be dealt with in several ways. Here, we wish to maintain the Ansatz of Gaussian distribution functions and present an approximate treatment of the hard core effects which will be valid in particular if the considerations related to the united atom limit are disregarded, as usual. For $\varphi(R)$ is resolved into two parts which will be treated by different methods of approximations, namely a normal part $\varphi_n(R)$, so designated because of the normal modes to which it gives rise, and a core part $\varphi_c(R)$ from which we demand that it practically vanishes outside a typical diameter d smaller than the nearest neighbor distance. The resolution

$$\varphi(R) = \varphi_c(R) + \varphi_n(R) \tag{4-73}$$

is certainly not unique and we shall have to consider this question more carefully later on. Here, unless otherwise specified, we shall conform to the common practice of taking $d = \sigma$, the core diameter for which $\varphi(R) = 0$, $\varphi = \varphi_c$ inside $R = \sigma$ and $\varphi = \varphi_n$ outside $R = \sigma$. Re-writing the crystal potential

† In this respect, see f.i. " Interatomic forces at very short distances" W.B. Brown, Faraday Society Meeting, September 1965, where the author presents a new approach to the calculation of the electronic part of $\varphi(R)$ based on Hellmann-Feynman theorem.

$$V = V_c + V_n \qquad (4\text{-}73a)$$

with

$$V_{c,st} = 0$$

that is

$$V_{st} = V_{n,st}$$

we proceed by splitting the Boltzmann factor

$$e^{-\beta V} = e^{-\beta V_c} e^{-\beta V_n} \equiv B_c\, e^{-\beta V_n} \qquad (4\text{-}74)$$

and formulate the hard core problem as an expectation value of B_c taken over the Boltzmann factor $\exp{-\beta V_n}$, that is by setting

$$Z_V = \langle B_c \rangle Z_{V_n} \qquad (4\text{-}75)$$

where

$$\langle B_c \rangle = \frac{\int d\Omega\, B_c\, e^{-\beta V_n}}{\int d\Omega\, e^{-\beta V_n}} \qquad (4\text{-}75a)$$

the partition function Z_{V_n} being given by Eq. (3-25) whereby $\varphi(R)$ is replaced by $\varphi_n(R) = \varphi(R) - \varphi_c(R)$. We must now evaluate $\langle B_c \rangle$ so as to extract the correct N dependence of this expectation value without having recourse to a cumulant type of expansion, and we wish to do this in a way permitting a detailed inspection of its behaviour in the two-limits of small and large values of the motional fluctuation parameter w. For this purpose let μ designate a pair of indices (s, s') whereby $s' = s + \rho > s$. Note that, the pairs being now ordered, s varies from 1 to N-1 and ρ from 1 to N-s. Furthermore, let

$$b_\mu \equiv e^{-\beta\varphi_c(r_\mu)} = e^{-\beta\varphi_c(|\underset{\sim}{R}_\rho + \eta_\rho \underset{\sim}{u}_s|)} \qquad (4\text{-}76)$$

$$\equiv 1 - f_\mu \qquad (4\text{-}76a)$$

where f_μ is (-1) times the Mayer function for the core potential

$$f_{M.c.}(r) = e^{-\beta\varphi_c(r)} - 1$$

So defined f_μ varies from one to zero in a small region around $d = \sigma$. In practice it is often represented by a step function. Then

$$B_c = \prod_\mu b_\mu = \prod_\mu (1 - f_\mu) \qquad \mu = 1, \ldots, \binom{N}{2}$$

Setting next

$$\langle b_\mu \rangle \equiv B_{1,\mu}$$

$$\langle b_\mu b_{\mu'} \rangle \equiv B_{1,\mu} B_{1,\mu'} B_{2,\mu\mu'}$$

for $\mu \neq \mu'$ and so on, we write for $\langle B_c \rangle$ the resolution of the identity

$$\langle B_c \rangle \equiv \prod_\mu B_{1,\mu} \prod_{\mu < \mu'} B_{2,\mu\mu'} \cdots B_{\binom{N}{2}, \mu, \ldots \mu_{\binom{N}{2}}} \qquad (4\text{-}77)$$

On the other hand we can write

$$\langle f_\mu \rangle \equiv F_{1,\mu}$$

$$\langle f_\mu f_{\mu'} \rangle \equiv F_{1,\mu} F_{1,\mu'} + F_{2,\mu\mu'} \tag{4-78}$$

and so on, whereby

$$F_{2,\mu\mu'} = \langle f_\mu f_{\mu'} \rangle_L$$

according to the pairing theorem. The $F_{n,\mu_1 \ldots \mu_n}$ so defined possess the familiar property of depending only upon relative indices. The dummy index left, say the starting site index s , is that which is needed to extract from $\ln \langle B_c \rangle$ its proper N dependence. Composing then the two expressions for $\langle b_\mu \rangle$, $\langle b_\mu b_{\mu'} \rangle$ etc., one finds

$$B_{1,\mu} = 1 - F_{1,\mu}$$

$$B_{2,\mu\mu'} = \frac{1}{B_{1,\mu} B_{1,\mu'}} \langle (1 - f_\mu)(1 - f_{\mu'}) \rangle$$

$$= 1 + \frac{F_{2,\mu\mu'}}{(1 - F_{1,\mu})(1 - F_{1,\mu'})}$$

and the resolution (4-72) becomes

$$\ln \langle B_c \rangle = \sum_\mu \ln(1 - F_{1,\mu}) + \sum_{\mu < \mu'} \ln\left(1 + \frac{F_{2,\mu\mu'}}{(1 - F_{1,\mu})(1 - F_{1,\mu'})}\right)$$

$$+ \ldots \tag{4-79}$$

We must next calculate the mean values (4-78). This is done in general by applying equation (3-30). To begin with, let us retain the first terms of these mean values, that is $\langle f_\mu \rangle_W$, $\langle f_\mu f_{\mu'} \rangle_{WL}$, etc. In so doing we evaluate the pure hard core part of $\ln Z_V$. For simplicity of notation let us designate in this approximation

$$\langle f_\mu \rangle_W \equiv F_\mu \equiv 1 - B_\mu$$

$$\langle f_\mu f_{\mu'} \rangle_{WL} \equiv F_{\mu\mu'} = B_\mu B_{\mu'} (B_{\mu\mu'} - 1)$$

and so on, and thus consider the series

$$\ln \langle B_c \rangle_W = \sum_\mu \ln(1 - F_\mu) + \sum_{\mu < \mu'} \ln\left(1 + \frac{F_{\mu\mu'}}{(1-F_\mu)(1-F_{\mu'})}\right)$$

$$+ \ldots \qquad (4\text{-}80)$$

Now, since $f(|\underset{\sim}{R}_\rho + \eta_\rho \underset{\sim}{u}_s|)$ is integrable we can define with $\mu = s, s+\rho$ the smeared function

$$F_\rho \equiv F(R_\rho, \lambda_\rho) = \langle f(|\underset{\sim}{R}_\rho + \eta_\rho \underset{\sim}{u}_s|) \rangle_W$$

$$= e^{\frac{1}{2}\lambda_\rho : \underset{\sim}{p}^2} f(R_\rho)$$

$$= \sum_{\underset{\sim}{k}} e^{-\frac{1}{2}\lambda_\rho : \underset{\sim}{k}^2} \cdot e^{i \underset{\sim}{k} \underset{\sim}{R}_\rho} \bar{f}(k) \qquad (4\text{-}81)$$

whereby

$$\bar{f}(k) = \frac{1}{\upsilon} \int d^3 R \, e^{-i \underset{\sim}{k} \underset{\sim}{R}_\rho} f(R)$$

and, similarly, with $\mu = s, s + \rho$; $\mu' = s', s' + \rho$ and $s - s' = \sigma$ (< 0)

$$F^{\sigma}_{\rho\rho'} = \left(e^{\lambda^{\sigma}_{\rho\rho'}:\underset{\sim}{\rho}\underset{\sim}{\rho}'} - 1 \right) F_{\rho} F_{\rho'} \tag{4-82}$$

It is apparent that the function (4-81) will play a central role in this section. Postponing for a moment the detailed inspection of its behaviour for small w values we wish first to investigate (Eq. 4-80) in the other limit: $w \gg 1$. In order to be specific the latter will be designated as the "Ordered Gas" limit. As $w \gg 1$ or $2\pi\lambda_{\rho\alpha\beta} \rightarrow \delta_{\alpha\beta}\upsilon^{2/3}$ we have

$$F_{\rho}(\text{O.G.}) = \bar{f}(0)$$

and the first contribution to Eq. (4-80) becomes

$$\begin{aligned} N\frac{1}{2} \sum_{\rho} \ln(1 - F_{\rho}(\text{O.G.})) &= \binom{N}{2} \ln(1 - \bar{f}(0)) \\ &= \binom{N}{2} \left\{ - \bar{f}(0) - \frac{1}{2}\bar{f}(0)^2 - \dots \right. \\ &= -\frac{1}{2} N (N-1) \frac{1}{\upsilon} \int d^3R \; f(R) - 0(1) \\ &= -\frac{1}{2} N\rho \int d^3R \; f(R) - 0(1) \end{aligned} \tag{4-83}$$

that is $\frac{1}{2}N\rho$ times the first irreducible cluster integral β_1 of Mayer or $-N\rho$ times the second virial coefficient of the theory of imperfect gases. To evaluate in this limit the next contribution to $\ln \langle B_c \rangle_W$ we need $F_{\mu\mu'}(\text{O.G.})$. Now we have shown in section (2-4) Eq. (2-59b) that a non-vanishing limit proportional to

$\sum_k \bar{f}(k)^2 = \overline{f^2}(0)$ exists if and only if the two pairs of indices μ and μ' are identical. But in Eq. (4-80), we have $\mu < \mu'$ which means that, at most, one index only can be the same for the two pairs. Consequently $F_{\mu\mu'} = \langle f_\mu f_{\mu'} \rangle_{WL}$ is zero in the ordered gas limit. What we find here is the reducibility rule of the imperfect gas theory. With $B_\mu(\text{O.G.}) = 1 - \bar{f}(0)$, $B_{\mu\mu'}(\text{O.G.}) = 1$ it is then rather easy to calculate the third contribution to Eq. (4-80). Deleting the intermediate steps of the calculation one finds

$$\sum_{\mu < \mu' < \mu''} \ln B_{\mu\mu'\mu''}(\text{O.G.}) =$$

$$\sum_{\mu < \mu' < \mu''} \ln \left(1 - F_{\mu\mu'\mu''}(\text{O.G.}) \left[1 + 0\left(\frac{1}{\upsilon}\right)\right]\right)$$

In section (2.4 p. 73) again it has been shown that mean values such as $F_{\mu\mu'\mu''} = \langle f_\mu f_{\mu'} f_{\mu''} \rangle_{WL}$ possess a non-vanishing imperfect gas limit provided the pairs are either identical or articulated. Since $\mu < \mu' < \mu''$ the first possibility is excluded, and since the pairs are ordered the second possibility can be realized only once. Thus

$$F_{\mu\mu'\mu''}(\text{O.G.}) = \begin{cases} \sum_{\underset{\sim}{k}} \bar{f}(k)^3 & \text{for } \mu = s, s' \;\; \mu' = s', s'' \text{ and } \mu'' = s, s'' \\ 0 & \text{otherwise} \end{cases}$$

$$\sum_{s < s' < s''} \ln \left(1 - \sum_{\underset{\sim}{k}} \bar{f}(k)^3\right) =$$

$$= \binom{N}{3}\left\{ - \sum_{k} \bar{f}(k)^3 - \frac{1}{2}\left(\sum_{k} \bar{f}(k)^3\right)^2 \cdots \right\}$$

and therefore

$$\sum_{\mu < \mu' < \mu''} \ln B_{\mu\mu'\mu''}(\text{O.G.}) =$$

$$= \frac{1}{3!} N \rho^2 \int d^3R d^3R' \left(e^{-\beta\varphi_c(R)} - 1\right)\left(e^{-\beta\varphi_c(R')} - 1\right)$$

$$\times \left(e^{-\beta\varphi_c(|R+R'|)} - 1\right) + 0(1) \qquad (4\text{-}84)$$

that is $\frac{1}{3} N\rho^2$ times the irreducible cluster integral β_2 ([6], Eq. 1-29) or $-\frac{1}{2} N\rho^2$ times the third virial coefficient. Continuing this analysis one would find that β_3 is made up of $F_{(4\mu)}(\text{O.G.})$ and of those contributions coming from $F_{(5\mu)}(\text{O.G.})$ and $F_{(6\mu)}(\text{O.G.})$ where the 4 respectively 5 and 6 pairs of indices are arranged so as to map a set of four indices s, s', s'', s''', thus yielding a total contribution $\sim \binom{N}{4} \frac{1}{\upsilon^3}$ to $\ln \langle B_c \rangle_{W,\text{O.G.}}$ These examples clearly show the connection between the familiar virial expansion of the classical theory of imperfect gases and the resolution of the identity (4-80) applicable for all w values. Let us now return to the inspection of F_ρ given by Eq. (4-81). Using the Green's function (2-10) we have

$$F(R_\rho, \lambda_\rho) = \frac{1}{(2\pi)^{3/2}} \frac{1}{\sqrt{|\lambda_\rho|}} \int d^3R\, e^{-\frac{1}{2}\lambda_\rho^{-1}:(\mathbb{R}-\mathbb{R}_\rho)^2} f(R)$$

(4-85)

In order to proceed we set

$$f(R) = \begin{cases} 1 & 0 \leqslant R \leqslant \sigma \\ 0 & R > \sigma \end{cases}$$

in which case

$$\bar{f}(k) = \frac{1}{\upsilon} \frac{4\pi}{k^3} (\sin k\sigma - k\sigma \cos k\sigma)$$

and

$$\bar{f}(0) = \frac{1}{\upsilon} \frac{4\pi}{3} \sigma^3$$

Now since $\sigma < R_\rho$ for all ρ we observe that F_ρ has no power series expansion in λ_ρ . Yet it is a perfectly well defined function of λ_ρ which enables us to make a quantitative estimate of the core repulsive effects in solids which are not included in $\varphi_n(R)$. For the purpose of illustration let us approximate the tensor λ_ρ by its diagonal, isotropic and ρ independent part, that is by setting $\lambda_{\rho\alpha\alpha'} = \delta_{\alpha\alpha'} \lambda$. Going over to polar coordinates we find

$$F(R_\rho, \lambda) = \frac{1}{(2\pi\lambda)^{3/2}} \cdot 2\pi \int_0^\sigma R^2 dR \int_0^\pi \sin\vartheta\, d\vartheta$$

$$\exp - \frac{1}{2\lambda} (R^2 + R_\rho^{\ 2} - 2RR_\rho \cos\vartheta)$$

$$= \frac{1}{\sqrt{2\pi\lambda}} \frac{1}{R_\rho} \int_0^\sigma R dR \left(\exp\left\{- \frac{(R-R_\rho)^2}{2\lambda}\right\} - \exp\left\{- \frac{(R+R_\rho)^2}{2\lambda}\right\}\right)$$

which, after some manipulations, becomes

$$F(R_\rho,\lambda) = \frac{1}{2\sqrt{\pi}}\sqrt{\frac{2\lambda}{R_\rho^2}}\left(e^{-\frac{(R_\rho+\sigma)^2}{2\lambda}} - e^{-\frac{(R_\rho-\sigma)^2}{2\lambda}}\right)$$

$$+\ \frac{1}{2}\ \mathrm{erf}\left(\frac{R_\rho+\sigma}{\sqrt{2\lambda}}\right) - \frac{1}{2}\ \mathrm{erf}\left(\frac{R_\rho-\sigma}{\sqrt{2\lambda}}\right) \qquad (4\text{-}85)$$

where

$$\mathrm{erf}(x) = \frac{2}{\sqrt{\pi}}\int_0^x dt\ e^{-t^2}$$

One sees that, for λ fixed, the step function $f(R)$ becomes smeared out and $F(R,\lambda)$ exhibits a small tail extending toward values of $R > \sigma$. Conversely, by holding $R = R_\rho$ fixed one observes that $F(R_\rho, \lambda)$ is extremely flat around $\lambda = 0$, then rises sharply, goes through an inflexion point followed by a maximum and finally decreases toward zero as $\frac{2}{3\pi}\sigma^3\lambda^{-3/2}$. In chapter 6 we shall give a detailed account of the behaviour of $F(R_\rho, \lambda)$ for various values of the parameter σ/R_ρ, and we shall show that the most important part of F extends up to its inflexion point, not up to its maximum. In the case of Neon, for example, by taking for R_ρ the nearest neighbor distance $R_1 = 3.13$ Å and for σ the value 2.75 Å, one obtains a maximum ratio $\sigma/R_1 = 0.87$, and the numerical analysis of Eq. (4-85) indicates that the inflexion point occurs at $\lambda/R_1^2 = 0.0053$ with a value of $F = 0.028$, and that the maximum of $F = 0.22$ is at $\lambda/R_1^2 = 0.11$. These facts enable us to safely expand the logarithmic functions of the resolution (4-80) in a power series of their arguments so as to find, for the first few terms for instance

$$\ell n \langle B_c \rangle_W = - \sum_{\mu} F_{\mu} - \frac{1}{2} \sum_{\mu} F_{\mu}^2 + \sum_{\mu < \mu'} F_{\mu\mu'} \cdots$$

Before proceeding, let us pose here to comment on the above expansion. By writing

$$\sum_{\mu < \mu'} F_{\mu\mu'} = \frac{1}{2} \sum_{\mu \neq \mu'} F_{\mu\mu'} = \frac{1}{2} \sum_{\mu\mu'} F_{\mu\mu'} - \frac{1}{2} \sum_{\mu} F_{\mu\mu}$$

that is by adding and subtracting $\frac{1}{2} \sum_{\mu} F_{\mu\mu}$ to the above expansion one can rearrange the terms so as to obtain

$$\ell n \langle B_c \rangle_W = - \sum_{\mu} F_{\mu} - \frac{1}{2} \sum_{\mu} (F_{\mu}^2 + F_{\mu\mu}) + \frac{1}{2} \sum_{\mu\mu'} F_{\mu\mu'} \cdots$$

$$= - \sum_{\mu} \left(F_{\mu} + \frac{1}{2} \tilde{F}_{\mu\mu} \right) + \frac{1}{2} \sum_{\mu\mu'} F_{\mu\mu'} + \ldots$$

where

$$\tilde{F}_{\mu\mu} = F_{\mu\mu} + F_{\mu}^2$$

$$= \langle f_{\mu} f_{\mu} \rangle_{WL} + \langle f_{\mu} \rangle_W^2$$

$$= \langle f_{\mu} f_{\mu} \rangle_W = \langle f_{\mu}^2 \rangle_W$$

and thus find

$$\ell n \langle B_c \rangle_W = -\sum_{\mu} \left\{ \langle f_\mu \rangle_W + \frac{1}{2} \langle f_\mu^2 \rangle_W \right\}$$

$$+ \frac{1}{2} \sum_{\mu \mu'} \langle f_\mu f_{\mu'} \rangle_{WL} + \ldots$$

One sees that these terms constitute the beginning of a cumulant expansion applied to the evaluation of

$$\langle B_c \rangle_W = \langle e^{\sum_\mu \ell n(1-f_\mu)} \rangle_W$$

$$= \langle e^{-\sum_\mu (f_\mu + \frac{1}{2} f_\mu^2 + \ldots)} \rangle_W \qquad (4\text{-}86)$$

namely

$$\ell n \langle B_c \rangle_W = \sum_{\mu} \langle \ell n(1 - f_\mu) \rangle_W$$

$$+ \frac{1}{2} \sum_{\mu \mu'} \langle \ell n(1 - f_\mu) \, \ell n(1 - f_{\mu'}) \rangle_{WL} + \ldots$$

$$= -\sum_{\mu} \left\{ \langle f_\mu \rangle_W + \frac{1}{2} \langle f_\mu^2 \rangle_W + \ldots \right\}$$

$$+ \frac{1}{2} \sum_{\mu\mu'} \left\{ \langle f_\mu f_{\mu'} \rangle_{WL} + \ldots \right\} + \ldots$$

Clearly this would represent an unjustifiable procedure of calculation since all cumulants individually diverge. For example with the step function used above for f, $f^2 = f$ and $\langle \ln(1-f) \rangle_W = \langle f \rangle_W \ln(1-1)$. However, these divergences are actually spurious and cancel with one another since, as illustrated above, they are due to the addition and subtraction of terms to the rapidly converging expansion of the logarithmic functions of the resolution (4-80). This expansion can therefore safely be used. Now the fact that, on the one hand, all the products and powers of mean values higher than the first one are extremely small in the solid state and, on the other hand, their effects vanish in the imperfect gas limit suggests that we neglect them all and retain from $\ln B_{\mu_1 \ldots \mu_n}$ its leading term $(-1)^n F_{\mu_1 \ldots \mu_n}$. The series so obtained may rightfully be designated as the virial approximation to the hard core effects in solids, that is, the index v standing for virial,

$$\ln \langle B_c \rangle_{v,W} = - \sum_{\mu} F_{\mu} + \sum_{\mu < \mu'} F_{\mu\mu'} \cdots - F_{\mu_1 \ldots \mu_{\binom{N}{2}}} \tag{4-87}$$

It is then easily seen that

$$\ln \langle B_c \rangle_{v,W} = \langle \prod_{\mu} (1 - f_{\mu}) - 1 \rangle_{W,L} \tag{4-87a}$$

Disposing now of a suitable approximation to the evaluation of the pure hard core part of $\ln \langle B_c \rangle$ we can take up the next problem of introducing these effects into the self-consistent scheme of Eqs (3-26). An efficient way of doing this is to relax Eq. (3-26a) that is to keep the interaction representation in a trial form and determine the best $\mathbb{D}_q$ by a variational procedure. Let us do that in a joint normal and core R. H. A. and discuss afterwards the implications of this method. We start from Eq. (3-26) in first order and add the first term of

Eq. (4-87), that is

$$\ell n\, Z = \frac{1}{2}\beta\sum_{\underset{\sim}{q}} \mathrm{Tr}\, \mathbb{D}_{\underset{\sim}{q}} L_{\underset{\sim}{q}} + \frac{1}{2}\sum_{\underset{\sim}{q}} \mathrm{Tr}\, \ell n \frac{KT}{\hbar^2} L_{\underset{\sim}{q}}$$

$$- \beta N \frac{1}{2}\sum_{\rho} \Phi_n(R_\rho, \lambda_\rho) - N\frac{1}{2}\sum_{\rho} F(R_\rho, \lambda_\rho) \qquad (4\text{-}88)$$

We make this expression stationary with respect to a change $\delta\mathbb{D}_{\underset{\sim}{q}}$ of $\mathbb{D}_{\underset{\sim}{q}}$ or $\delta L_{\underset{\sim}{q}}$ since $L_{\underset{\sim}{q}} = KT\, \mathbb{D}^{-1}_{\underset{\sim}{q}}$ at υ, T, fixed and find the s. c. equation

$$D_{\underset{\sim}{q}\alpha\alpha'} = N\left(\frac{\partial}{\partial L_{\underset{\sim}{q}\alpha\alpha'}}\right)_{\upsilon, T}$$

$$\times \sum_{\rho} \left\{ \Phi_n(R_\rho, \lambda_\rho) + KT\, F(R_\rho, \lambda_\rho) \right\}$$

or

$$D_{\underset{\sim}{q}\alpha\alpha'} = \frac{1}{M}\sum_{\rho} (1 - \cos \underset{\sim}{q}\, R_\rho)$$

$$\times \left\{ \Phi_{n\,\alpha\alpha'}(R_\rho, \lambda_\rho) + KT\, F_{\alpha\alpha'}(R_\rho, \lambda_\rho) \right\} \qquad (4\text{-}89)$$

We immediately notice that, in this extended R. H. A., a kind of bare pseudo-potential

$$\varphi^*(R) = \varphi_n(R) + KT\, f(R) \qquad (4\text{-}90)$$

smeared by the Green's function (2-10) to yield $\Phi^*(R_\rho, \lambda_\rho) = \Phi_n(R_\rho, \lambda_\rho) + KT\, F(R_\rho, \lambda_\rho)$ comes into play. Thus $KT\, F(R_\rho, \lambda_\rho)$

acts as a repulsive potential influencing through its tail the effective force constants by a minute amount, under normal conditions. However the non-analytic character of this effect must be kept in mind. That f(R) has been taken as (-1) times the Mayer function is now seen to be a natural choice from the solid state standpoint. In the extreme case where the entire molecular potential $\varphi(R)$ is put into f(R), the curve obtained by plotting $f_M(R)$ upside down is indeed rather suggestive, and also self-explanatory.

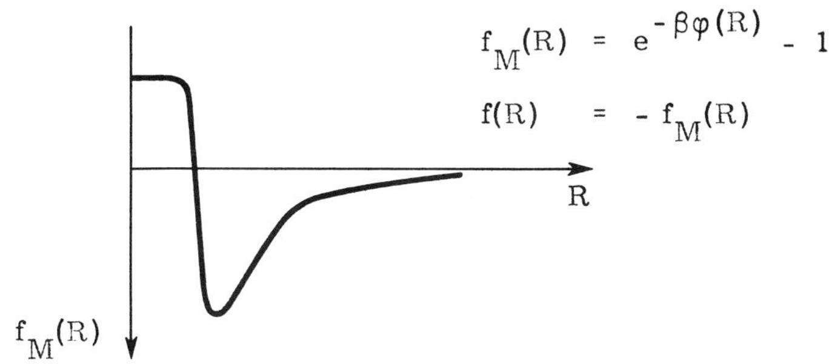

Fig. 10. Plot of $-f_M(R)$; note that its minimum coincides with that of $\varphi(R)$

In chapter 6 we shall return to the investigation of other consequences of Eq. (4-89). For this equation to be trustworthy, however, it is appropriate to understand its derivation by the thoroughly experienced method of ring diagram summations. To do this, consider the kth term of Eq. (4-87), re-write it in terms of the unordered set of indices

$$\sum_{\mu_1 < \mu_2 \ldots < \mu_n} = \frac{1}{k!} \frac{1}{2^n} \sum_{s_1 s_1' \neq s_2 s_2' \neq \ldots s_k s_k'}$$

and evaluate its ring diagram contribution as in section (3-1) with dynamical matrices $\underset{\sim}{D}_{qn}$ satisfying, here, the normal R. H. A. equations. The propagator matrices linking the vertices are KT $\underset{\sim}{D}_{qn}^{-1}$ and the vertex matrix elements read

$$G_{\underset{\sim}{q}\alpha\alpha'} = \frac{1}{M} \sum_{\rho} (1 - \cos \underset{\sim}{q} R_\rho) p_\alpha p_{\alpha'} KT F(R_\rho, \lambda_{\rho n})$$

Now since the summation over the site indices s_i is restricted to $s_1 \neq s_2 \neq \dots s_k$ the said contribution becomes

$$\sum_{\mu_1 < \dots \mu_k} (-1)^k F_{\mu_1 \dots \mu_k}(\text{ring}) =$$

$$= \frac{1}{2} \sum_{\underset{\sim}{q}} \frac{(-1)^k}{k} \frac{N(N-1)\dots(N-k+1)}{N^k} \operatorname{Tr}(G_{\underset{\sim}{q}} D^{-1}_{\underset{\sim}{q}n})^k$$

$$= \frac{1}{2} \sum_{\underset{\sim}{q}} \frac{(-1)^k}{k} \operatorname{Tr}(G_{\underset{\sim}{q}} D^{-1}_{\underset{\sim}{q}n})^k (1 - 0(\tfrac{1}{N}))$$

Next the summation over k, starting from $k = 2$ is in principle limited by $k = \binom{N}{2}$ since Eq. (4-85) is a finite series. Extending this summation to infinity one finds, up to a correction of order one, the familiar expression

$$\frac{1}{2} \sum_{\underset{\sim}{q}} \operatorname{Tr} G_{\underset{\sim}{q}} D^{-1}_{\underset{\sim}{q}n} - \frac{1}{2} \sum_{\underset{\sim}{q}} \ln(1 + G_{\underset{\sim}{q}} D^{-1}_{\underset{\sim}{q}n}) + 0(1)$$

which is known to yield a perturbed dynamical matrix $D_{\underset{\sim}{q}n} + G_{\underset{\sim}{q}}(\dots D_{\underset{\sim}{q}'n}\dots)$. Then, by using as in section (3-2) a first order s. c. field method, the same ring diagram summation produces a perturbed trial matrix $\mathbb{D}_{\underset{\sim}{q}} + \left\{ D_{\underset{\sim}{q}n}(\dots \mathbb{D}_{\underset{\sim}{q}'}\dots) + G_{\underset{\sim}{q}}(\dots \mathbb{D}_{\underset{\sim}{q}'}\dots) - \mathbb{D}_{\underset{\sim}{q}} \right\}$ and by annihilating its perturbed part one recovers Eq. (4-89) which is now seen to be valid under implicit use of the expansion (4-87) and to $0(\frac{1}{N})$. It is then rather straightforward to generalize Eqs (4-88) and (4-89) to incorporate all of the pure hard core effects in the virial approximation. It suffices to redefine $-\beta\mathcal{H}$ of Eq. (3-26) by $-\beta\mathcal{H}_n$ and to add

$$-\beta\mathcal{H}_c = -\sum_{\mu} F_{\mu} + \langle B_c - 1\rangle_{W,irL}$$

$$= -\sum_{\mu} F_{\mu} + \langle \prod_{\mu} (1-f_{\mu}) - 1\rangle_{W,irL} \tag{4-91}$$

so as to form

$$\mathcal{H} = \mathcal{H}_n + \mathcal{H}_c$$

and have

$$\frac{1}{2} D_{\underset{\sim}{q}} = \left(\frac{\partial\mathcal{H}}{\partial L_{\underset{\sim}{q}}} \right)_{\upsilon, T} \tag{4-91a}$$

So far no effect due to the interaction between the core part and the normal part of the crystal potential has been taken into account. This could be done by extending the virial approximation (4-87) to the initial resolution (4-79) that is, by retaining the series of its leading terms

$$\ln\langle B_c\rangle_v = -\sum_{\mu} F_{1\mu} + \sum_{\mu<\mu'} F_{2\mu\mu'} \cdots F_{\binom{N}{2}, \mu_1 \cdots \mu_{\binom{N}{2}}}$$

$$= \langle \prod_{\mu} (1-f_{\mu}) - 1\rangle_L$$

Then, by applying Eq. (3-30) to each of the $F_{n\,\mu_1 .. \mu_n}$, namely

$$F_{n\,\mu_1 .. \mu_n} = \langle f_{\mu_1} .. f_{\mu_n} \rangle_L$$

$$= \langle f_{\mu_1} .. f_{\mu_n} \rangle_{W,L} + \langle f_{\mu_1} .. f_{\mu_n} (e^{-\beta V} - 1) \rangle_{W,irL}$$

$$= F_{\mu_1 .. \mu_n} + \langle f_{\mu_1} .. f_{\mu_n} (e^{-\beta V} - 1) \rangle_{W,irL}$$

and by noticing that the first terms belong to $\mathcal{K}_c$, we can define in a compact way the remainder as

$$\mathcal{K}_{cn} = \langle (\prod_{\mu} (1 - f_{\mu}) - 1)(e^{-\beta V} - 1) \rangle_{W,irL} \tag{4-93}$$

and recall that these mean values are calculated according to the prescriptions given in section (4-2) under Eq. (4-58). With

$$\mathcal{K} = \mathcal{K}_n + \mathcal{K}_c + \mathcal{K}_{cn} \tag{4-94}$$

$$\frac{1}{2} D_{\underset{\sim}{q}} = \left(\frac{\partial \mathcal{K}}{\partial L_{\underset{\sim}{q}}} \right)_{v,T} \tag{4-94a}$$

and

$$\ell n\, Z = 3N' + \frac{1}{2} \sum_{\underset{\sim}{q}} \mathrm{Tr}\, \ell n \frac{KT}{\hbar^2} L_{\underset{\sim}{q}} - \beta \mathcal{K} \tag{4-94b}$$

the developments presented in the preceding sections are readily generalized. In particular it follows from this scheme where V has been splitted into $V_c + V_n$ and $\ell n \langle B_c \rangle$ approximated by $\ell n \langle B_c \rangle_v$, the series of its leading terms, that the equation of state (4-2) now reads

$$P(\upsilon, T, w) = \left(\frac{-\partial}{\partial \upsilon}\right)_{T, w} \left\{ \mathcal{H}_n + \mathcal{H}_{cn} + \mathcal{H}_c \right\} + \frac{RT}{\upsilon} \qquad (4\text{-}95)$$

So parametrized Eq. (4-95) goes over from Grüneisen's equation of state for $w = \lambda/a^2 \ll 1$ to the general equation of state of imperfect gases for $w = \lambda/a^2 \gg 1$. With this result it seems appropriate to interrupt here the analysis of the problem dealt with in this section although the subject is by no means exhausted, as other, rather extensive, investigations which need not be reported here, have indicated†.

The main conlusion to be drawn from this section is that non-analytic effects in the fluctuation parameter $w = \lambda/a^2$ are susceptible to play an important role in anharmonicity theory. We shall investigate their consequences in chapter 6, and in the mean time shall develop the quantum theoretical generalization of the classical theory treated thus far.

† For instance, instead of founding the evaluation of $\langle B_c \rangle$ on Mayer's idea of the product resolution $B_c = \prod_\mu (1 - f_\mu)$, we have expressed the hard core effects caused by all its neighbors on an atom located at a given site s, while taking care of not overcounting the total number of pairs involved in the process. This resulted in an alternative resolution of the identity suited to indicate, among other things, the conditions under which the core part of Van der Waals equation of state is obtained.

Chapter 5

QUANTUM THEORY

In the first section of this chapter the energy and position representations of the harmonic lattice in equilibrium are treated. The next section deals with the perturbation calculus of the anharmonic free energy. Compact expressions for the cumulants are obtained by introducing "temperature relaxed" correlation functions for the motional fluctuations. Next, referring to the correspondence principle, the self-consistent field method of section (3-4) is generalized, and from this the set of renormalized equations are established in the third section. The thermal properties are then studied in view of the concept that the motional fluctuations constitute internal state variables of the system. It is shown how the macroscopic thermal coefficients can be related to the microscopic parameters of the system by means of intermediate coefficients which are generalizations of the Grüneisen constant. Throughout this chapter we make the assumption (A-2a) that the bare molecular potential function can be Fourier analyzed.

5-1 INTRODUCTION

In quantum mechanics the nuclear displacement coordinates $u_{s\alpha}$ and momenta $p_{s\alpha} = M\dot{u}_{s\alpha}$ are replaced by operators which satisfy the commutation relations

$$[p_{s\alpha}, u_{s'\alpha'}] = \frac{\hbar}{i}\,\delta_{s,s'}\,\delta_{\alpha,\alpha'} \tag{5-1}$$

From these relations it follows that the lattice wave coordinates

$$u_{\underset{\sim}{q}\alpha} = \frac{1}{\sqrt{N}} \sum_s e^{-i\underset{\sim}{q}\underset{\sim}{R}_s}\, u_{s\alpha}$$

and momenta $p_{\underset{\sim}{q}\alpha} = M\dot{u}_{\underset{\sim}{q}\alpha}$ obey the commutation laws

$$[p_{\underset{\sim}{q}\alpha}, u_{\underset{\sim}{q}'\alpha'}] = \frac{\hbar}{i}\,\delta_{\underset{\sim}{q},-\underset{\sim}{q}'}\,\delta_{\alpha,\alpha'} \tag{5-1a}$$

where

$$\delta_{\underset{\sim}{q},-\underset{\sim}{q}'} = \frac{1}{N}\,\Delta(\underset{\sim}{q} + \underset{\sim}{q}')$$

Furthermore the reality condition (1-9) is replaced by

$$u_{\underset{\sim}{q}\alpha} = u^{+}_{-\underset{\sim}{q}\alpha}$$

where the superscript + means hermitian conjugation.

When dealing with the quantum theory of interacting lattice waves, the crystal Hamiltonian is usually written as

$$H = V_{st} + V_h + V_a$$

where V_{st} is the static potential energy, V_h the harmonic Hamiltonian which describes the unperturbed system and V_a the anharmonic part of the crystal potential which is considered as a perturbation. The unperturbed Hamiltonian reads

$$H_h = \frac{1}{2M} \sum_{\underset{\sim}{q}} \underset{\sim}{p}_{\underset{\sim}{q}} \underset{\sim}{p}_{-\underset{\sim}{q}} + \frac{1}{2} M \sum_{\underset{\sim}{q}} D_{\underset{\sim}{q},h} : \underset{\sim}{u}_{\underset{\sim}{q}} \underset{\sim}{u}_{-\underset{\sim}{q}} \tag{5-3}$$

where $D_{\underset{\sim}{q},h}$ is the dynamical matrix in the harmonic approximation (1-31). Its diagonalization

$$\sum_{\beta=1}^{3} D_{\underset{\sim}{q},h,\alpha\beta} \; e^j_\beta(\underset{\sim}{q}) = e^j_\alpha(\underset{\sim}{q}) \, \omega^2_{\underset{\sim}{q}j}$$

leads to the introduction of the normal mode coordinates (1-12)

$$u_{\underset{\sim}{q},\alpha} = \frac{1}{\sqrt{M}} \sum_{j=1}^{3} e^j_\alpha(\underset{\sim}{q}) \, Q_{\underset{\sim}{q}j}$$

which, in turn, are resolved in terms of the phonon amplitudes

$$Q_{\underset{\sim}{q}j} = \sqrt{\frac{\hbar}{2\omega_{\underset{\sim}{q}j}}} \left(a_{\underset{\sim}{q}j} + a^+_{-\underset{\sim}{q}j}\right)$$

The phonons are the quantized amplitudes of the classical amplitudes (1-42) $e^{i\alpha_{\underset{\sim}{q}j}} \sqrt{A_{\underset{\sim}{q}j}}$. The action integral $\int d\alpha_{\underset{\sim}{q}j} \, A_{\underset{\sim}{q}j} = 2\pi A_{\underset{\sim}{q}j}$

becomes $n_{\underset{\sim}{q}j}.h$ by Sommerfeld's quantization rule and the phase $\alpha_{\underset{\sim}{q}j}$ becomes $\frac{\hbar}{i}\frac{\partial}{\partial A_{\underset{\sim}{q}j}} = \frac{1}{i}\frac{\partial}{\partial n_{\underset{\sim}{q}j}}$ by the correspondence principle. Note that the above equation differs from Eq. (1-43) by the factor $\sqrt{\hbar}$ introduced here for making the new amplitudes dimensionless. Furthermore, one has for the momenta

$$p_{\underset{\sim}{q}\alpha} = \sqrt{M} \sum_{j} e^{j}_{\alpha}(\underset{\sim}{q})\, P_{\underset{\sim}{q}j}$$

$$iP_{\underset{\sim}{q}j} = \sqrt{\frac{\hbar}{2}\omega_{\underset{\sim}{q}j}}\,(a_{\underset{\sim}{q}j} - a^{+}_{-\underset{\sim}{q}j})$$

and the commutation relations (5-1a) read respectively

$$[P_{\underset{\sim}{q}j}, Q_{\underset{\sim}{q}'j'}] = \frac{\hbar}{i}\,\delta_{\underset{\sim}{q},-\underset{\sim}{q}'}\,\delta_{j,j'} \tag{5-1b}$$

$$[a_{\underset{\sim}{q}j}, a^{+}_{\underset{\sim}{q}'j'}] = \delta_{\underset{\sim}{q},\underset{\sim}{q}'}\,\delta_{j,j'} \tag{5-1c}$$

the quantities $a_{\underset{\sim}{q}j}$ and $i\hbar a^{+}_{\underset{\sim}{q}j}$ being canonically conjugated variables. Using the shorthand notation $q \equiv (\underset{\sim}{q}, j)$, $-q \equiv (-\underset{\sim}{q}, j)$ Eq. (5-3) becomes

$$H_h = \frac{1}{2}\sum_{q} (P_q P_{-q} + \omega_q^2 Q_q Q_{-q}) \tag{5-3a}$$

or

$$H_h = \frac{1}{2}\sum_{q} \hbar\omega_q (a_q a^{+}_q + a^{+}_{-q} a_{-q})$$

$$= \sum_q \hbar\,\omega_q(\tfrac{1}{2} + a_q^+ a_q) \tag{5-3b}$$

Quantization of Eq. (5-3b) leads to the well known energy eigenvalues

$$E(\ldots n_q \ldots) = \sum_q \hbar\omega_q(\tfrac{1}{2} + n_q) \tag{5-4}$$

where the quantum numbers n_q (= 0, 1, 2, ...) are called phonon occupation numbers. The eigenstates $\Psi(\ldots n_q \ldots)$ of

$$H_h \Psi = E\Psi$$

are factorizable as products of harmonic oscillator eigenfunctions which are designated by the symbol $|n_q)$. For a representative oscillator, one has[†]

$$|n) = \left(\frac{\hbar}{M\omega}\right)^{\frac{1}{4}} \frac{(-1)^n}{\sqrt{\sqrt{\pi}\,2^n n!}} \; e^{\frac{1}{2}\xi^2} \frac{\partial^n}{\partial\xi^n} e^{-\xi^2}$$

with

$$\xi = \sqrt{\frac{M\omega}{\hbar}}\, x = \frac{1}{\sqrt{2}}(a + a^+)$$

The familiar properties of the dipolar matrix elements

$$(n'|x|n) = \sqrt{\frac{\hbar}{2M\omega}}\,(n'|a + a^+|n)$$

† See f.i. L.I. Schiff, p. 64

$$= \begin{cases} \sqrt{\frac{\hbar}{2M\omega}}\sqrt{n} & \text{for} \quad n' = n-1 \\ \sqrt{\frac{\hbar}{2M\omega}}\sqrt{n+1} & \text{for} \quad n' = n+1 \\ 0 & \text{otherwise} \end{cases}$$

together with the momentum matrix elements $(n'|p|n) = - i\sqrt{\frac{\hbar M\omega}{2}}\,(n'|a-a^{+}|n)$ lead to identifying a and a^{+} as annihilation and creation operators in the formalism of second quantization. In this formalism, the non-vanishing matrix elements of

$$\sqrt{\frac{1}{2\hbar M\omega}}\,(M\omega x \pm ip)$$

are written in the operator form

$$a|n) = \sqrt{n}\,|n-1)$$

$$a^{+}|n) = \sqrt{n+1}\,|n+1)$$

with the hermitian conjugated expressions

$$(n|a^{+} = (n-1|\sqrt{n}$$

$$(n|a = (n+1|\sqrt{n+1}$$

In making the substitution $x \to x_q = \sqrt{\frac{\hbar}{2M\omega_q}}\,(a_q + a_q^{+})$ † one

† Note that $x_q^{+} = x_q$ while $Q_q^{+} = Q_{-q}$, but $x_q + x_{-q} = \frac{1}{\sqrt{M}}(Q_q + Q_{-q})$

correspondingly finds for any q

$$a_q |n_q) = \sqrt{n_q}\, |n_q) \tag{5-5}$$

$$a_q^+ |n_q) = \sqrt{n_q+1}\, |n_q+1) \tag{5-5a}$$

$$(n_q| a_q^+ = (n_q| \sqrt{n_q} \tag{5-5b}$$

$$(n_q+1| a_q = (n_q+1| \sqrt{n_q+1} \tag{5-5c}$$

By iterating Eq. (5-5a) one can generate a state with n_q phonons out of the state containing no phonon, the vacuum state. Indeed

$$a_q^+ |0) = \sqrt{1}\ |1)$$

$$(a_q^+)^2 |0) = \sqrt{1 \cdot 2}\, |2)$$

$$(a_q^+)^{n_q} |0) = \sqrt{n_q!}\, |n_q)$$

thus

$$|n_q) = \frac{1}{\sqrt{n_q!}} (a_q^+)^{n_q} |0) \tag{5-6}$$

and, with Eq. (5-5c) the normalization of this state is seen to be

$$(n_q|n_q) = (0| \frac{(a_q)^{n_q}(a_q^+)^{n_q}}{n!} |0) = 1 \tag{5-6a}$$

Any normalized eigenstate of H_h can therefore be written as

$$\Psi(\ldots n_q \ldots) = \prod_q \frac{(a_q^+)^{n_q}}{\sqrt{n_q!}} \,|0, \ldots, 0) \tag{5-7}$$

and these states provide a complete orthonormal set for the problem. It should be noted that, in this formalism, we maintain the individuality of the modes and thus deviate from the proper formalism of second quantization where only the total number

$$\mathcal{N} = \sum_q n_q$$

of phonons per state matters and not the set of n_q phonons per mode. For a strict application of the second quantization formalism to the anharmonic lattice problem, we wish to refer to L. Van Hove lecture notes ([7a]). Here, the representation (5-7) will turn out to be more advantageous.

Using Eq. (5-4) and introducing the shorthand notation

$$\beta_q \equiv \beta\hbar\omega_q = \beta\hbar\omega_{\underset{\sim}{q}j}$$

the partition function of the unperturbed system becomes

$$Z_h \equiv e^{-\beta F_h} = \mathrm{Tr}\, e^{-\beta H_h}$$

$$= \sum_{\ldots n_q \ldots} e^{-\beta E(\ldots n_q \ldots)} = \prod_q z_q \tag{5-8}$$

with

$$z_q = e^{-\frac{1}{2}\beta_q} \frac{1}{1-e^{-\beta_q}} = \frac{1}{2\,\mathrm{Sinh}\,\frac{1}{2}\beta_q} \tag{5-9}$$

Furthermore, the mean occupation numbers in the harmonic approximation are given by

$$\langle a_q^+ a_q \rangle_h = \langle n_q \rangle_h = \frac{1}{z_q} \sum_{n_q} n_q \, e^{-\beta_q(\frac{1}{2}+n_q)}$$

$$= \frac{e^{-\beta_q}}{1-e^{-\beta_q}} = \frac{1}{e^{\beta_q}-1} \tag{5-10}$$

and one notes that

$$\frac{1}{2} + \langle n_q \rangle_h = -\frac{d}{d\beta_q} \ln z_q$$

Lastly we have the equipartition theorem

$$\langle P_q P_{-q} \rangle_h = \omega_q^2 \langle Q_q Q_{-q} \rangle_h$$

$$= \hbar\omega_q(\frac{1}{2} + \langle n_q \rangle_h)$$

$$= \frac{1}{2}\hbar\,\omega_q \,\mathrm{Cotgh}\,\frac{1}{2}\beta_q \tag{5-10a}$$

While the phonon representation is very convenient for calculating several mean values of interest, it is nevertheless appropriate to introduce here another representation originally due to F. Bloch†, which may serve as a good alternative for dealing with the anharmonic lattice problem. Let us discuss this representation first for a one dimensional, one particle problem with a Hamiltonian $H(x, p)$ and let $\varphi_n(x)$ and E_n be the eigenfunctions and eigenvalues of

$$H\varphi = E\varphi$$

The eigenfunctions assume the orthogonality relations

$$\int dx\, \varphi_n^*(x)\, \varphi_{n'}(x) = \delta_{n,n'}$$

and the closure property

$$\sum_n \varphi_n(x)\, \varphi_n^*(x') = \delta(x-x')$$

Constructing the following function, called density matrix‡

$$K(x,\beta \mid x', 0) = \sum_n e^{-\beta E_n} \varphi_n(x)\, \varphi_n^*(x')$$

$$= e^{-\beta H(x, p)} \sum_n \varphi_n(x)\, \varphi_n^*(x')$$

$$= e^{-\beta H(x, p)}\, \delta(x-x')$$

† Zeits. Phys. 74, 295, 1932 §3

‡ As in A. H. Wilson's Theory of Metals p. 161

one notices that, formally, it is the solution of the said Bloch equation

$$- \frac{\partial}{\partial \beta} K = HK \tag{5-11}$$

which assumes the initial condition

$$K = \delta(x-x') \qquad \text{for} \qquad \beta = 0 \tag{5-12}$$

Supposing $K(x, \beta | x', 0)$ is explicitly known then the partition function is obtained as

$$Z = \int dx \, K(x, \beta \,|\, x, 0) \tag{5-13}$$

a form necessarily equivalent to the usual definition

$$Z = \sum_n e^{-\beta E_n}$$

as the above relations show. The Bloch equation is a Schrödinger-like equation where the time t has been replaced by $-i\hbar\beta$. Thus the corresponding known time dependent solutions $K(x, t| x', 0)$ can be used directly for statistical problems. These functions, designated by W. Pauli as probability amplitudes, have already been investigated in 1927 by E.H. Kennard† who constructed their explicit form for the case of a free particle, a particle under the influence of a constant force, the harmonic oscillator and a charged particle in a constant magnetic field. Twenty years later these probability amplitudes played a central role in R.P. Feynman "Space-Time Approach to

† Zur Quantenmechanik einfacher Bewegungstypen, Zeits. Phys. 44, 326, 1927

Non-Relativistic Quantum Mechanics"†. Following Feynman's work, W. Pauli has developed a practical way for calculating these functions by means of a time-dependent W.K.B. method‡. While this method furnishes in general an approximation scheme of semi-classical nature, it yields for the simple cases of Kennard and for the case of purely time dependent forces the exact result. Thus, for the harmonic oscillator problem, $K(x,t|x',0)$ assumes the form

$$K(x,t|x',0) = (2\pi i\hbar)^{-\frac{1}{2}} \sqrt{D(t)} \exp \frac{i}{\hbar} J(x,t|x',0) \tag{5-14}$$

where J is the action integral which satisfies Hamilton-Jacobi's equation

$$\frac{\partial J}{\partial t} + H\left(\frac{\partial J}{\partial x}, x\right) = 0$$

and $D(t)$ the density which satisfies the continuity equation

$$\frac{\partial D}{\partial t} + \frac{1}{M} \frac{\partial}{\partial x}\left(\frac{\partial J}{\partial x} D\right) = 0$$

the particle momentum being equal to $\frac{\partial J}{\partial x}$. These equations respectively occur as coefficients of $\hbar^o$ and $\hbar^1$ when the Ansatz (5-14) is introduced in the time-dependent Schrödinger equation and the terms ordered in ascending powers of $\hbar$. There is generally a term in $\hbar^2$ which turns out to vanish for the cases mentioned above, that is whenever the density $D(t)$ is a function of t only. Then, with

† Rev. Mod. Phys. 20, 367, 1948

‡ Ausgewählte Kapitel aus der Feldquantisierung, E.T.H. Zürich, 1951, p. 139, reprinted by Boringhieri, Turin, 1962

$$\xi(\vartheta) = x' \cos\omega\vartheta + \frac{x - x'\cos\omega t}{\sin\omega t} \sin\omega\vartheta$$

as the solution of the harmonic equation of motion with initial position x' (at $\vartheta = 0$), final position x (at $\vartheta = t$) and flight time t given (the Lagrangian boundary conditions) and with the Lagrange function

$$L = T - V = \frac{1}{2} M (\dot{\xi}^2 - \omega^2 \xi^2)$$

the action integral J can be calculated and reads

$$J(x, t | x', 0) = \int_0^t d\vartheta\, L(\dot{\xi}, \xi)$$

$$= M\omega \frac{(x^2 + x'^2)\cos\omega t - 2xx'}{2 \sin\omega t}$$

while the density can be shown to be

$$D = (-1) \frac{\partial^2 J}{\partial x \partial x'} = \frac{M\omega}{\sin\omega t}$$

Therefore

$$K(x, t | x', 0) = \sqrt{\frac{M\omega}{2\pi i \hbar \sin\omega t}} \exp \frac{i}{\hbar} M\omega \frac{(x^2 + x'^2)\cos\omega t - 2xx'}{2 \sin\omega t}$$

and, making the substitution

$$t \rightarrow -i\hbar\beta$$

the density matrix reads

$$K(x, \beta \mid x', 0) = \sqrt{\frac{M\omega}{2\pi\hbar \operatorname{Sinh} \beta\hbar\omega}}$$

$$\times \exp - \frac{M\omega}{2\hbar} \frac{(x^2 + x'^2) \operatorname{Cosh} \beta\hbar\omega - 2xx'}{\operatorname{Sinh} \beta\hbar\omega} \qquad (5\text{-}15)$$

Note that one might have considered the case of an inverted harmonic potential $V' = -\frac{1}{2} M\omega^2 x^2$ and then make the real substitution $t' = \hbar\beta$.

One easily verifies that

$$\int dx\, K(x, \beta \mid x, 0) = \frac{1}{2 \operatorname{Sinh} \frac{1}{2} \beta\hbar\omega} = z$$

of Eq. (5-9) and furthermore notes that the diagonal part of the density matrix assumes the enlightening form

$$K(x, \beta \mid x, 0) = z \sqrt{\frac{1}{\pi\lambda}} \exp - \frac{x^2}{\lambda} \qquad (5\text{-}15a)$$

with

$$\lambda = 2\langle x^2 \rangle_h = \frac{\hbar}{M\omega} \operatorname{Cotgh} \frac{1}{2} \beta\hbar\omega$$

Let us also mention that the density matrix satisfies the composition law

$$\int dx_1\, K(x\beta \mid x_1 \beta_1)\, K(x_1 \beta_1 \mid x_2 \beta_2) = K(x\beta \mid x_2 \beta_2)$$

In order to construct the density matrix for the harmonic lattice one first considers two oscillators of amplitude x, y with the same frequency ω, then one defines

$$Q = \sqrt{\frac{M}{2}}(x + iy) \qquad x = \frac{1}{\sqrt{2M}}(Q + Q^*)$$

$$Q^* = \sqrt{\frac{M}{2}}(x - iy) \qquad y = \frac{1}{i\sqrt{2M}}(Q - Q^*)$$

thus

$$dx\,dy = i\frac{1}{M}\,dQdQ^*$$

and obtains, after some manipulations

$$K(x, y, \beta \mid x', y', 0)\,dxdy = \frac{\omega}{2\pi\hbar \operatorname{Sinh}\beta\hbar\omega}$$

$$\exp\left\{-\frac{\omega}{\hbar}\frac{(QQ^*+Q'Q'^*)\operatorname{Cosh}\beta\hbar\omega - (QQ'^*+Q^*Q')}{\operatorname{Sinh}\beta\hbar\omega}\right\} idQdQ^*$$

Similarly, for the N' independent complex amplitudes Q_q, one gets

$$K_h(\ldots Q_q, \ldots \beta \mid \ldots Q'_q \ldots, 0)$$

$$= \Pi'_q \frac{\omega_q}{2\pi\hbar \operatorname{Sinh}\beta_q} \exp\left\{-\frac{\omega_q}{\hbar}\left[(Q_q Q_q^* + Q'_q Q'^*_q)\operatorname{Cosh}\beta_q - \right.\right.$$

$$\left.\left. - (Q_q Q'^*_q + Q_q^* Q'_q)\right] \frac{1}{\operatorname{Sinh}\beta_q}\right\} \qquad (5\text{-}16)$$

and the volume element reads

$$d\Omega = \prod_q{}' \, i dQ_q dQ_q^* = \prod_q{}' \, dI_q d\alpha_q$$

with

$$Q_q = \sqrt{I_q}\, e^{i\alpha_q} \tag{1-68}$$

At this point one may wonder whether there is any advantage to work in this representation of the unperturbed system. It is true that while $\exp-\beta H_h$ is diagonal in the phonon representation, K_h is not diagonal in the Q_q representation and should therefore be less easy to manipulate. However, in this representation the perturbation V_a, being a function only of the normal modes coordinates, is diagonal, whereas the phonon representation clearly destroys the symmetric character of the anharmonic lattice problem. For this reason already, the position, or Bloch representation (5-16) may be considered as the more natural one. The algebraic problem of calculating matrix elements and mean values becomes, after some exercise, rather easy owing to the bilinearity of the exponent of K_h in the amplitudes Q_q.

For the time being, however, we shall further use the more familiar phonon representation, yet, try to keep the symmetric character of the theory and shall come back later on to make use of the Bloch representation.

5-2 PERTURBATION CALCULUS

With these preliminaries the main problem of calculating the partition function of the pertubed system

$$Z = \text{Tr } e^{-\beta H}$$

in the basis (5-7) of the unperturbed system can be formulated. Writing together $V_{st} + V_a$ as V', one starts again with the Bloch equation for the density matrix $\exp-(\beta H)$ and, as in the time-dependent perturbation theory, introduces the Ansatz

$$e^{-\beta H} = e^{-\beta H_h} \cdot S$$

thus

$$-\frac{\partial}{\partial\beta} e^{-\beta H} = H_h e^{-\beta H_h} \cdot S + e^{-\beta H_h}(-)\frac{\partial}{\partial\beta} S$$

$$= H_h e^{-\beta H_h} \cdot S + V' e^{-\beta H_h} S$$

and one obtains for S the equation

$$-\frac{\partial}{\partial\beta} S = e^{\beta H_h} V' e^{-\beta H_h} S \tag{5-17}$$

in a representation designated as the interaction representation. In terms of the usual phonon picture the solution of Eq. (5-17) that one seeks satisfies the initial condition

$$S = 1 \qquad \text{for} \qquad \beta = 0 \tag{5-17a}$$

The operator acting on S is conveniently defined as

$$V'(\beta) \equiv e^{\beta H_h} V' e^{-\beta H_h} \tag{5-18}$$

and $V'(\beta)$ represents the perturbation in the interaction representation. It is of course noted that

$$[V'(\beta'), V'(\beta'')] \neq 0 \qquad \beta' \neq \beta''$$

With the initial condition (5-17a) one finds by first quadrature

$$S(\beta) = 1 - \int_0^\beta d\beta' \, V'(\beta') \, S(\beta') \tag{5-19}$$

and, consequently, by iteration

$$S(\beta) = 1 - \int_0^\beta d\beta' V'(\beta') + \int_0^\beta d\beta' \int_0^{\beta'} d\beta'' V'(\beta') \, V'(\beta'') \ldots$$

$$\ldots (-1)^n \int_0^\beta d\beta' \ldots \int_0^{\beta^{(n-1)}} d\beta^{(n)} V'(\beta') \ldots V'(\beta^{(n)}) + \ldots \tag{5-19a}$$

that is to say, an infinite series of telescopic integrals. If the perturbations $V'(\beta^{(j)})$ were to commute it would be trivial to eliminate these cumbersome integrals by extending the range of all integration variables from 0 to β and dividing the result by $n!$. Now this "if" can be materialized in annihilating the effect of the non-commutativity of the operators figuring in the integrand. This can be achieved by introducing Dyson's T ordering operator and interpreting it as a projection operator. Indeed for Bose-like excitations such as phonons this operator prescribes that given two functions $A_1(\beta')$, $A_2(\beta'')$ of the normal mode coordinates in the interaction representation

$$T\ A_1(\beta')\ A_2(\beta'') = A_1(\beta')\ A_2(\beta'') \qquad \beta' > \beta''$$

$$= A_2(\beta'')\ A_1(\beta') \qquad \beta'' > \beta' \qquad (5\text{-}20)$$

Then we observe that

$$T^2\ A_1(\beta')\ A_2(\beta'') = T\ A_1(\beta')\ A_2(\beta'')$$

and that

$$T\ [A_1(\beta'),\ A_2(\beta'')] \equiv 0$$

if

$$[A_1, A_2] = 0 \qquad \text{for} \qquad \beta' = \beta''$$

which is precisely the case for $A_1 = A_2 = V'$. Thus T can be viewed as a projection operator annihilating the effect of the non-commutativity of $V'(\beta')$, $V'(\beta'')$. Alternatively, the operation (5-20) is introduced to preserve the ordering of the perturbations $V'(\beta^{(j)})$ when a permutation of the integration variables is performed. These permutations are made to allow an extension of the range of integration of the $\beta^{(j)}$ from 0 to β. This is done by summing over all permutations and dividing the result by $n!$ since, in so doing, the value of the term has been overcounted $n!$ times. Both views are equivalent in that the preservation of ordering is equivalent to the destruction of disordering. Thus, Eq. (5-19a) assumes the form

$$S(\beta) = \sum_{n=0}^{\infty} (-1)^n \frac{1}{n!} \int_0^{\beta} d\beta' .. \int_0^{\beta} d\beta^{(n)} \; T\, V'(\beta') \ldots V'(\beta^{(n)})$$

$$= T \exp - \int_0^{\beta} d\beta' \, V(\beta') \tag{5-21}$$

From (5-21) it follows that the partition function can be written in terms of a moment expansion

$$Z = Z_h \cdot \sum_{n=0}^{\infty} \frac{(-1)^n}{n!} \bar{\mu}_n \tag{5-22}$$

with

$$\bar{\mu}_n = \frac{1}{Z_h} \int_0^{\beta} d\beta' \int_0^{\beta} d\beta^{(n)} \; \mathrm{Tr}\, e^{-\beta H_h} \; T\, V'(\beta') \ldots V'(\beta^{(n)}) \tag{5-22a}$$

The problem is now to calculate the latter quantities. Note that, in their classical limit, the $\bar{\mu}_n$ so defined differ from the μ_n of Eq. (2-42) by a factor β^n. Following the program carried out in Chapter 2, the first step consists of resolving the moment expansion into its cumulant expansion. In the classical theory this has been performed in a natural and exact way (i. e. independent of N) thanks to the pairing theorem. It turns out fortunately that the cancellation of combinatorial factors with statistical weights, which constituted a key property of classical harmonic oscillator algebra, holds in the quantum case as well, owing to a theorem established by C. Bloch and C. de Dominicis†. While the combinatorial aspect of the pairing

† Nuclear Physics 7, 459, 1958

theorem, as discussed in section (2-2), is identical in both the classical and quantum case, the algebraic aspect is less straightforward in the latter case. Here we shall establish this algebraic property in the interaction representation (5-18) and borrow from M. Gaudin† a device used by that author to provide an alternative proof of Bloch and C. de Dominicis' theorem. The natural connection between the classical and quantum version of the pairing theorem will then be shown in terms of the Bloch representation introduced in the previous section.

We begin with the perturbation in the interaction representation. Since V' is a sum of multilinear forms of the $\eta_\rho u_s$ or of the Q_q, repeated insertions of the identity $1 \equiv e^{-\beta H_h} \cdot e^{+\beta H_h}$ between the $\mathfrak{u}_s$ or the Q_q result in

$$V'(\beta) = V'(\ldots \eta_\rho u_s(\beta) \ldots) = V'(\ldots Q_q(\beta) \ldots)$$

where

$$\mathfrak{u}_s(\beta) = e^{\beta H_h} \mathfrak{u}_s e^{-\beta H_h} \tag{5-23}$$

and

$$Q_q(\beta) = e^{\beta H_h} Q_q e^{-\beta H_h} \tag{5-23a}$$

stand for the nuclear displacement vectors and normal mode coordinates in the interaction representation. Writing Eq. (5-23a) in terms of the phonon amplitudes we have further

† Nuclear Physics 15, 89, 1960

$$Q_q(\beta) = \sqrt{\frac{\hbar}{2\omega_q}}\,(a_q(\beta) + a^+_{-q}(\beta))$$

with

$$a_q(\beta) = e^{\beta H_h}\, a_q\, e^{-\beta H_h}$$

$$a^+_{-q}(\beta) = e^{\beta H_h}\, a^+_{-q}\, e^{-\beta H_h} \tag{5-23b}$$

With the help of Eqs (5-4) and (5-4a), the above definitions can be further simplified. For a representative state $|n)$ we have indeed

$$a(\beta)|n) = e^{\beta H_h}\, a\, e^{-\beta H_h}|n) = e^{\beta H_h}\, a|n)\, e^{-\beta\hbar\omega(n+\frac{1}{2})}$$

$$= e^{\beta H_h}\sqrt{n}\,|n-1)\, e^{-\beta\hbar\omega(n+\frac{1}{2})} = \sqrt{n}\,|n-1)\, e^{-\beta\hbar\omega}$$

$$= a|n)\, e^{-\beta\hbar\omega}$$

and similarly

$$a^+(\beta)\,|n) = \sqrt{n+1}\,|n+1)\, e^{+\beta\hbar\omega} = a^+|n)\, e^{+\beta\hbar\omega}$$

Since these results are independent of the state $|n)$ we can write for any q

$$a_q(\beta) = a_q\, e^{-\beta_q} \tag{5-24}$$

$$a^+_q(\beta) = a^+_q\, e^{+\beta_q} \tag{5-24a}$$

Thus

$$Q_q(\beta) = \sqrt{\frac{\hbar}{2\omega_q}} \left(a_q e^{-\beta_q} + a^+_{-q} e^{+\beta_q} \right)$$

$$= Q_q \operatorname{Cosh} \beta_q - i \frac{P_q}{\omega_q} \operatorname{Sinh} \beta_q \qquad (5\text{-}24c)$$

a form which assumes an immediate interpretation if we substitute $i\omega_q t$ for β_q since, then

$$Q_q(t) = Q_q \cos\omega_q t + \frac{P_q}{\omega_q} \sin \omega_q t$$

represents the solution of the harmonic oscillator equation of motion with given initial position and momentum (Hamiltonian formalism).

We consider next the quantum counterpart of the mean value problem (2-21) dealt with a length in section (2-2). Here it amounts to calculating the representative element

$$y_{2\nu}(1,..2\nu) = \langle Q_{q_1}(\beta')Q_{q_2}(\beta'')...Q_{q_{2\nu}}(\beta^{(2\nu)}) \rangle$$

$$= \frac{1}{Z_h} \operatorname{Tr} e^{-\beta H_h} \prod_{i=1}^{2\nu} Q_{q_i}(\beta^{(i)}) \qquad (5\text{-}26)$$

whereby

$$\beta' > \beta'' > ... > \beta^{(2\nu)}$$

no condition being imposed on the indices q_j of the modes.

For $\nu = 1$ we have

$$y_2(1,2) = \delta_{q,-q'} \frac{\hbar}{2\omega_q} \left(\langle a_q a_q^+ \rangle_h e^{-(\beta'_q - \beta''_q)} \right.$$

$$\left. + \langle a^+_{-q} a_{-q} \rangle_h e^{\beta'_q - \beta''_q} \right)$$

$$= \delta_{q,-q'} \frac{\hbar}{2\omega_q} \left(\frac{e^{\beta_q - (\beta'_q - \beta''_q)}}{e^{\beta_q} - 1} + \frac{e^{\beta'_q - \beta''_q}}{e^{\beta_q} - 1} \right)$$

$$= \delta_{q,-q'} \frac{\hbar}{2\omega_q} \frac{\operatorname{Cosh}(\frac{1}{2}\beta_q - (\beta'_q - \beta''_q))}{\operatorname{Sinh}\frac{1}{2}\beta_q} \tag{5-27}$$

To deal with $y_{2\nu}$ we shall directly use Gaudin's device in the interaction representation of the normal modes in performing step by step a clockwise rotation of $Q_{q_1}(\beta')$ up to its initial place. Using the shorthand notation

$$Q_i \equiv Q_{q_i}(\beta^{(i)})$$

one constructs the identity

$$Q_1 Q_2 \cdot\cdot Q_{2\nu} \equiv ([Q_1, Q_2] + Q_2 Q_1) Q_3 \cdot\cdot Q_{2\nu}$$

$$\equiv \sum_{i=2}^{2\nu} [Q_1, Q_i] \prod_{j \neq 1, i} Q_j + Q_2 Q_3 \cdot\cdot Q_{2\nu} Q_1$$

while noting that the commutators $[Q_1, Q_j]$ can be written in front of the remaining product of Q_j since they are functions and no longer operators. Putting this identity into (5-26) one brings back Q_1 in front of $\exp -\beta H_h$ by using the invariance property of the trace under this operation and notes that

$$Q_1 e^{-\beta H_h} \equiv Q_{q_1}(\beta') e^{-\beta H_h} = e^{-\beta H_h} e^{\beta H_h} Q_{q_1}(\beta') e^{-\beta H_h}$$

$$= e^{-\beta H_h} Q_{q_1}(\beta' + \beta) = e^{-\beta H_h} Q_1(\beta)$$

Gathering together the initial and final product of Q_i, resolving Q_1 and $Q_1(\beta)$ into phonon amplitudes and using the commutation relations (5-1b, c) one then gets the two identities

$$\left(1 - e^{-\beta\hbar\omega_{q_1}}\right)\sqrt{\frac{\hbar}{2\omega_{q_1}}} \langle a_{q_1}(\beta') Q_2 Q_3 \ldots Q_{2\nu}\rangle_h$$

$$= \sum_{i=2}^{2\nu} \frac{\hbar}{2\omega_{q_1}} e^{-\beta'\hbar\omega_{q_1} + \beta^{(i)}\hbar\omega_{q_i}} \cdot \delta_{q_1, -q_i} \langle \prod_{j \neq 1, 2} Q_j \rangle_h$$

and

$$\left(1 - e^{\beta\hbar\omega_{q_1}}\right)\sqrt{\frac{\hbar}{2\omega_{q_1}}} \langle a^+_{-q_1}(\beta') Q_2 Q_3 \ldots Q_{2\nu}\rangle_h$$

$$= \sum_{i=2}^{2\nu} \frac{(-)\hbar}{2\omega_{q_1}} e^{\beta'\hbar\omega_{q_1} - \beta^{(i)}\hbar\omega_{q_i}} \cdot \delta_{-q_1, q_i} \langle \prod_{j \neq 1, i} Q_j \rangle_h$$

Dividing the first identity by $1-\exp(-\beta\hbar\omega_{q_1})$, the second one by $1-\exp(\beta\hbar\omega_{q_1})$ and adding the resulting expressions one recovers Q_1 on the l. h. s. and one finds as factor in front of the r. h. s.

$$\frac{\hbar}{2\omega_{q_1}}\left(\frac{e^{-(\beta'-\beta^{(i)})\hbar\omega_{q_1}}}{1-e^{-\beta\hbar\omega_{q_1}}}-\frac{e^{(\beta'-\beta^{(i)}\hbar\omega_{q_1})}}{1-e^{\beta\hbar\omega_{q_1}}}\right)\delta_{q_1,-q_i}$$

$$=\frac{\hbar}{2\omega_{q_1}}\;\frac{\mathrm{Cosh}\,(\frac{1}{2}\beta-\beta'+\beta^{(i)})\hbar\omega_{q_1}}{\mathrm{Sinh}\,\frac{1}{2}\beta\hbar\omega_{q_1}}\cdot\delta_{q_1,-q_i}$$

$$=y_2(1,i)$$

therefore

$$y_{2\nu}(1,2..2\nu)=\sum_{i=2}^{2\nu}y_2(1,i)\,y_{2\nu-2}(2,\dots,i-1,i+1,..2\nu)\qquad(5\text{-}28)$$

and the ensuing factorization property of $y_{2\nu}$, which constitutes the algebraic part of the pairing theorem, is proved by iteration or induction. If, in particular

$$q_1=q_2=..=q_\nu=q\quad,\quad q_{\nu+1}=..=q_{2\nu}=-q$$

$$\beta^{(1)}=\beta^{(2)}=..=\beta^{(\nu)}=\beta'\quad,\quad\beta^{(\nu+1)}=..=\beta^{(2\nu)}=\beta''$$

Then Eq. (5-28) yields†

$$\langle Q_q^{\nu}(\beta')\, Q_{-q}^{\nu}(\beta'')\rangle_h \;=\; \nu!\; \langle Q_q(\beta')\, Q_{-q}(\beta'')\rangle_h^{\nu} \qquad (5\text{-}29)$$

and one recognizes the same feature as in the classical case in that the enhanced expectation value of this particular product exactly compensates the reduced number of configurations assumed by the system of 2ν modes when the latter are arranged into ν identical pairs (see section (2-2) p. 27-28). There is consequently always a total of $(2\nu-1)!!$ products of mean values $y_2(i,j)$, whatever may be the relations among the indices of the modes. The common root of the classical and quantum versions of the pairing theorem rests on the Gaussian character of the density matrices in both cases. This is clearly recognized by calculating for example $\langle x^{2\nu}\rangle_h$ with $K(x,\beta\,|\,x,0)$ given by (5-15a). Here we have immediately

$$\langle x^{2\nu}\rangle_h = \frac{1}{z}\int dx\, x^{2\nu}\, K(x,\beta\,|\,x,0)$$

$$= \frac{1}{\sqrt{\pi\lambda}}\int dx\, x^{2\nu}\, e^{-\frac{x^2}{\lambda}}$$

$$= (2\nu-1)!!\,\left(\frac{\lambda}{2}\right)^{\nu} = (2\nu-1)!!\,\langle x^2\rangle_h^{\nu}$$

---

† It is a good exercise to calculate this particular case directly: By introducing the phonon amplitudes, the non-vanishing mean values of the product of the two binominal expansions amount to calculating $\langle (a_q a_q^{+})^n\rangle_h$ and $\langle (a_{-q}^{+} a_{-q})^{\nu-n}\rangle_h$ which are proved, by induction, to be equal to $n!\,\langle a_q a_q^{+}\rangle_h^n$ and $(\nu-n)!\,\langle a_{-q}^{+} a_{-q}\rangle_h^{\nu-n}$.

Slightly more elaborated but equally instructive is the calculation of

$$\frac{1}{z}\int dx\,dx'\,dx''\;K(x,\beta|x',\beta')\,x'^{\nu}K(x',\beta'|x''\beta'')\,x''^{\nu}K(x''\beta''|x,0)$$

$$= (2\nu-1)!!\left(\frac{\hbar}{2\omega_q}\;\frac{\operatorname{Cosh}\left(\frac{1}{2}\beta-(\beta'-\beta'')\right)\hbar\omega}{\operatorname{Sinh}\frac{1}{2}\beta\hbar\omega}\right)^{\nu}$$

that we leave as an exercise.

A last step is required to make full use of Eq. (5-28), and this is to replace the explicit ordering of the variable $\beta^{(i)}$ by the T operation since only T products enter the definition of the moments $\bar{\mu}_n$. For $\nu = 1$ we have

$$\langle T\,Q_q(\beta')\,Q_{-q}(\beta'')\rangle_h$$

$$= \begin{cases} \dfrac{\hbar}{2\omega_q}\left(\langle a_q a_q^{+}\rangle_h\, e^{-(\beta'_q-\beta''_q)} + \langle a_{-q}^{+} a_{-q}\rangle_h\, e^{(\beta'_q-\beta''_q)}\right) & \beta' > \beta'' \\[2ex] \dfrac{\hbar}{2\omega_q}\left(\langle a_{-q} a_{-q}^{+}\rangle_h\, e^{-(\beta''_q-\beta'_q)} + \langle a_q^{+} a_q\rangle_h\, e^{(\beta''_q-\beta'_q)}\right) & \beta'' > \beta' \end{cases}$$

$$= \frac{\hbar}{2\omega_q}\;\frac{\operatorname{Cosh}\left(\frac{1}{2}\beta_q-|\beta'_q-\beta''_q|\right)}{\operatorname{Sinh}\frac{1}{2}\beta_q} \qquad (5\text{-}30)$$

since, in equilibrium, $\langle n_q\rangle = \langle n_{-q}\rangle$. By induction we obtain then the final formula

$$\langle T\, Q_1 Q_2 .. Q_{2\nu} \rangle_h = \sum_{i=1}^{2\nu} \langle T\, Q_1 Q_i \rangle_h \langle T \prod_{j \neq 1, i} Q_j \rangle_h \qquad (5\text{-}31)$$

If we now identify the set of Q_i as originating from a given set of perturbations $V'(\beta^{(i)})$ then it follows from (5-31), from the unrestricted integration over the $\beta^{(j)}$ and from the combinatorial analysis given in section (2-2), that the moments can be decomposed into sums of products of their linked parts or, in other words, into their cumulant expansion. The latter quantities are defined by

$$\bar{\varkappa}_k = \int_0^\beta d\beta^{(1)} .. \int_0^\beta d\beta^{(k)} \langle T\, V'(\beta^{(1)}) .. V'(\beta^{(k)}) \rangle_{h, L} \qquad (5\text{-}32)$$

where the subscript L stands for linked, and

$$\ln Z = \ln Z_h + \sum_{k=1}^{\infty} \frac{(-1)^k}{k!} \bar{\varkappa}_k$$

$$= \ln Z_h + \langle T \left(e^{-\int_0^\beta d\beta' V'(\beta')} - 1 \right) \rangle_{h, L}$$

$$= \ln Z_h + \langle T\, (S(\beta) - 1) \rangle_{h, L} \qquad (5\text{-}33)$$

In the classical theory, the problem of explicitly calculating the semi-invariants $\varkappa_k$ had been greatly facilitated by the introduction of the self-linked and linking correlation functions (Eqs (1-82) and (2-54a)). It is a direct consequence of the factorization theorem (5-31) that these concepts can be usefully generalized in the quantum case. For the self-linked correlation function we have simply

$$\lambda_{\rho\alpha\alpha'} = \langle \eta_\rho u_{s\alpha} \eta_\rho u_{s\alpha'} \rangle_h$$

$$= \frac{2}{MN} \sum_{\underset{\sim}{q}j} (1-\cos \underset{\sim}{q}\underset{\sim}{R}_\rho)\, e^j_\alpha(\underset{\sim}{q})\, e^j_\alpha(-\underset{\sim}{q}) \langle Q_{\underset{\sim}{q}j} Q_{-\underset{\sim}{q}j} \rangle_h \qquad (5\text{-}34)$$

with

$$\langle Q_{\underset{\sim}{q}j} Q_{-\underset{\sim}{q}j} \rangle_h = \frac{\hbar}{2\omega_{\underset{\sim}{q}j}} \operatorname{Cotgh} \frac{1}{2} \beta\hbar\omega_{\underset{\sim}{q}j} \qquad (5\text{-}34a)$$

For the linking correlation functions we introduce rather naturally the concept of "temperature relaxed" expectation values, namely

$$\lambda^{s-s'}_{\rho\rho'\alpha\alpha'}(|\beta'-\beta''|) \equiv \langle T\, \eta_\rho u_s(\beta')\, \eta_{\rho'} u_{s'}(\beta'') \rangle_h$$

$$= \frac{1}{MN} \sum_{\underset{\sim}{q}j} e^{i\underset{\sim}{q}(\underset{\sim}{R}_s - \underset{\sim}{R}_{s'})}\, \eta_\rho(\underset{\sim}{q})\, \eta_{\rho'}(-\underset{\sim}{q})\, e^j_\alpha(\underset{\sim}{q})\, e^j_{\alpha'}(-\underset{\sim}{q})$$

$$\times \langle T\, Q_{\underset{\sim}{q}j}(\beta')\, Q_{-\underset{\sim}{q}j}(\beta'') \rangle_h \qquad (5\text{-}35)$$

with

$$\langle T\, Q_{\underset{\sim}{q}j}(\beta')\, Q_{-\underset{\sim}{q}j}(\beta'') \rangle_h = \frac{\hbar}{2\omega_{\underset{\sim}{q}j}} \frac{\operatorname{Cosh}(\frac{1}{2}\beta - |\beta'-\beta''|)\hbar\omega_{\underset{\sim}{q}j}}{\operatorname{Sinh}\frac{1}{2}\beta\hbar\omega_{\underset{\sim}{q}j}} \qquad (5\text{-}35a)$$

and note that

$$\lambda^{o}_{\rho\rho}(0) = \lambda_\rho$$

Postponing for a moment the analysis of the important quantities (5-34) and (5-35) we continue with the calculation of the first two cumulants, which is already illustrative of some characteristic features of the perturbation calculus. With

$$V' = V_{st} + V_a = V - V_h$$

we have

$$\bar{\varkappa}_1 = \int_0^\beta d\beta' \langle T\, V'(\beta')\rangle_h$$

$$= \beta \langle V'\rangle_h = \beta\left(\langle V\rangle_h - \langle V_h\rangle_h\right)$$

since the diagonal elements of $V'(\beta')$ are independent of β'. Then it is again a consequence of the pairing theorem that the effects of the self-linked correlations can be summed up and yield

$$\bar{\varkappa}_1 = \beta N \frac{1}{2} \sum_\rho \left(e^{\frac{1}{2}\lambda_\rho \underset{\sim}{p}^2} - \frac{1}{2}\lambda_\rho \underset{\sim}{p}^2 \right) \varphi_\rho \tag{5-36}$$

or, in other words, that a smeared potential

$$\Phi_\rho \equiv \Phi(R_\rho, \lambda_\rho) = \langle \varphi(|R_\rho + \eta_\rho u_s|)\rangle_h$$

$$= \langle e^{\eta_\rho \underset{\sim}{u}_s \cdot \underset{\sim}{p}}\rangle_h \varphi(R_\rho) = e^{\frac{1}{2}\langle(\eta_\rho \underset{\sim}{u}_s \cdot p)^2\rangle_h} \varphi(R_\rho)$$

$$= e^{\frac{1}{2}\lambda_\rho \underset{\sim}{p}^2} \varphi_\rho \tag{5-37}$$

can be defined here in analogy with its classical counterpart (2-7). The calculation of the second cumulant

$$\bar{\varkappa}_2 = \int_0^\beta d\beta' \int_0^\beta d\beta'' \langle T(V(\beta') - V_h(\beta'))(V(\beta'') - V_h(\beta''))\rangle_{h,L}$$

can be done by closely following the procedure developed in section (2-4). The effect of the self-linked correlations, which are independent of β' and β'', can again be absorbed within the smeared potentials Φ_ρ and $\Phi_{\rho'}$. We must simply generalize the definition of the correlation operator of Eq. (2-57a) in terms of

$$\underline{w}_{12}(|\beta' - \beta''|) = \lambda_{\rho_1\rho_2}^{s_1-s_2}(|\beta' - \beta''|)\underset{\sim}{p}_1\underset{\sim}{p}_2 \tag{5-38}$$

and can take over the notation used in Eq. (2-58b). With

$$\beta' - \beta'' = \tau$$

we find

$$\bar{\varkappa}_2 = \beta\frac{1}{4}\sum_{1,2}\int_0^\beta d\tau \left\{\frac{1}{2}\underline{w}_{12}^2(|\tau|)(\Phi_1 - \varphi_1)(\Phi_2 - \varphi_2)\right.$$

$$\left. + \left(e^{\underline{w}_{12}(|\tau|)} - 1 - \frac{1}{2}\underline{w}_{12}^2(|\tau|)\right)\Phi_1\Phi_2\right\} \tag{5-39}$$

and recognize in the first product a contribution which we expect will be reducible by some appropriate means. The consequences entailed by the remaining integration over τ will most profitably be drawn once we know more about the temperature-relaxed correlation functions (5-35), which we shall learn next.

By analogy with the classical mean value

$$L_q = \frac{KT}{\omega_q^2} = \langle Q_q Q_{-q} \rangle_{h,\,class.} \tag{2-24}$$

we shall define Eq. (5-35a) as

$$L_q(|\tau|) \equiv \frac{\hbar}{2\omega_q} \frac{\mathrm{Cosh}\,(\frac{1}{2}\beta - |\tau|)\hbar\omega_q}{\mathrm{Sinh}\,\frac{1}{2}\beta\hbar\omega_q}$$

$$= \langle T\, Q_q(\tau)\ Q_{-q}(0) \rangle_h \tag{5-40}$$

$L_q(|\tau|) = L_q(|\beta' - \beta''|)$ is the temperature Green's function of the normal modes in the harmonic approximation or the unperturbed phonon propagator function. These functions play an important role in the theory of the many-body problem and we wish to refer to the book by A. A. Abrikosov, L. P. Gorkov and I. E. Dzyaloshinski, hereafter referred to as A. G. D., for an extensive presentation of the Green's function method in statistical physics ([9]). Since different authors use slightly different definitions for these basic functions, it is worth comparing Eq. (5-40) with the definitions given by L. V. Hove (V. H. [7a], Eq. (9-6), p. 60), J. R. Schrieffer (S)[†] and A. G. D. ([9], Eq. (14-8), p. 122) for example. The following relations are found

† Theory of superconductivity, J. R. Schrieffer Benjamin, 1964, Eq. (7-105b), p. 196.

$$L_q((5\text{-}40)) = \frac{\hbar}{2\omega_q} \mathscr{D}_q(\text{V. H.}) \tag{5-40a}$$

$$= -\frac{\hbar}{2\omega_q} \mathscr{D}_q(\text{S.}) \tag{5-40b}$$

$$= -\frac{\hbar}{\omega_q^2} \mathscr{D}_q(\text{A. G. D.}) \tag{5-40c}$$

While some of the above definitions may be more convenient for dealing with the problem of electron-phonon interactions, the choice of (5-40) is more or less dictated, in our case, by the fact that in constructing the quantity

$$\frac{1}{MN} \sum_{\underset{\sim}{q}j} e^{i\underset{\sim}{q}(\underset{\sim}{R}_s - \underset{\sim}{R}_{s'})} e^j_\alpha(\underset{\sim}{q})\, L_{\underset{\sim}{q}j}(|\beta' - \beta''|)\, e^j_{\alpha'}(-\underset{\sim}{q})$$

$$= \langle T\, u_{s\alpha}(\beta')\, u_{s'\alpha'}(\beta'')\rangle_h \tag{5-41}$$

one finds the temperature Green's function of the nuclear displacement coordinates in the harmonic approximation. Similar constructions based on the other $\mathscr{D}_q$'s yield certain convolution products of lesser apparent meaning. Yet, whatever definition one uses, an important property of the propagator functions, as noted by Van Hove ([7a], p. 63), is that they are symmetric about $\tau = 0$ and $\tau = \frac{1}{2}\beta$. This indicates that they are periodic in the domain $-\beta \leqslant \tau \leqslant \beta$ with period β. One can accordingly expand (5-40) in a Fourier series in the domain $0 \leqslant \tau \leqslant \beta$, that is

$$L_q(|\tau|) = \sum_{\nu=-\infty}^{+\infty} L_{q\nu}\, e^{\frac{2i\pi\nu\tau}{\beta}} \tag{5-42}$$

with

$$L_{q\nu} = \frac{1}{\beta}\int_0^\beta d\tau\; e^{-\frac{2i\pi\nu\tau}{\beta}}\, L_q(|\tau|)$$

$$= \frac{\hbar}{2\omega_q}\cdot\frac{1}{\beta}\cdot\frac{1}{2\,\mathrm{Sinh}\frac{1}{2}\beta_q}\int_0^\beta d\tau\; e^{-\frac{2i\pi\nu\tau}{\beta}}$$

$$\times\left(e^{\frac{1}{2}\beta_q - \tau\hbar\omega_q} + e^{-\frac{1}{2}\beta_q + \tau\hbar\omega_q}\right)$$

$$= \frac{h}{2\omega_q}\cdot\frac{1}{\beta}\cdot\frac{1}{\mathrm{Sinh}\frac{1}{2}\beta_q}\left(\frac{\mathrm{Sinh}\frac{1}{2}\beta_q}{\hbar\omega_q + 2i\pi\frac{\nu}{\beta}} + \frac{\mathrm{Sinh}\frac{1}{2}\beta_q}{\hbar\omega_q - 2i\pi\frac{\nu}{\beta}}\right)$$

$$= \frac{KT}{\omega_q^2 + \left(\frac{2\pi\nu}{\hbar\beta}\right)^2} \tag{5-42a}$$

One notes that L_{qo} is equal to the classical value (2-24), the only remaining component of the $L_{q\nu}$'s as $\hbar \to 0$. This property is illustrative of the principle of correspondence applying between Eqs (2-24) and (5-42a). As in the classical theory it will be convenient to work in the representation of the dynamical matrix and to then eliminate the polarization vectors $e^j(\underset{\sim}{q})$. For, one defines a propagator matrix $L_{\underset{\sim}{q}}$ with elements

$$L_{\underset{\sim}{q}\alpha\alpha'} = \sum_{j=1}^{3} e_{\alpha}^{j}(\underset{\sim}{q})\, L_{\underset{\sim}{q}j}\, e_{\alpha'}^{j}(-\underset{\sim}{q}) \tag{5-43}$$

in such a way that Eq. (5-42a) becomes, in matrix form, the factor $(2\pi\nu/\hbar\beta)^2$ being implicitly multiplied by the unit matrix

$$L_{\underset{\sim}{q}\nu} = KT\left(\left(\frac{2\pi\nu}{\hbar\beta}\right)^2 + D_{\underset{\sim}{q}h}\right)^{-1} \tag{5-39b}$$

In terms of the Fourier components $L_{\underset{\sim}{q}\nu}$, also designated as propagator matrices, the self-linked and linking correlation functions read now, also in matrix form

$$\lambda_{\rho} = \frac{1}{MN}\sum_{\underset{\sim}{q}\nu} \eta_{\rho}(\underset{\sim}{q})\,\eta_{\rho}(-\underset{\sim}{q})\,\frac{KT}{\left(\frac{2\pi\nu}{\hbar\beta}\right)^2 + D_{\underset{\sim}{q}h}} \tag{5-43}$$

and

$$\lambda_{\rho\rho'}^{\sigma}(|\tau|) = \frac{1}{MN}\sum_{\underset{\sim}{q}\nu} e^{i(\underset{\sim}{q}\underset{\sim}{R}_{\sigma} + 2\pi\nu\frac{\tau}{\beta})}\,\eta_{\rho}(\underset{\sim}{q})\,\eta_{\rho'}(-\underset{\sim}{q})$$

$$\times\ \frac{KT}{\left(\frac{2\pi\nu}{\hbar\beta}\right)^2 + D_{\underset{\sim}{q}h}} \tag{5-43a}$$

With Eq. (5-43a) we can return to the investigation of the second cumulant. The compact form (5-39) could be written by leaving unperformed one summation over $\sigma = s-s'$ and the integration over τ. To investigate the effect of these operations, consider a representative contribution to Eq. (5-39), say the term corresponding to the nth power of the correlation operator (5-38). Letting aside all the factors not relevant to the point, we find the following part

$$\sum_{\sigma} \int_{0}^{\beta} d\tau \; e^{i(\underset{\sim}{q}_1 + .. \underset{\sim}{q}_n)\underset{\sim}{R}_\sigma + 2i\pi(\nu_1 + .. \nu_n)\frac{\tau}{\beta}}$$

$$= \Delta(\underset{\sim}{q}_1 + .. \underset{\sim}{q}_n) \;\; \beta\, \delta_{\nu_1 + \nu_2 + .. \nu_n,\, 0} \tag{5-44}$$

This means that in addition to the law of wave vector conservation, one obtains a kind of energy conservation law which was trivially satisfied in the classical limit, since there all ν_i were zero. The most interesting consequence of this law will be uncovered by taking up the next problem of the perturbation calculus, namely the quantum analogue of the ring diagram summation performed in section (3-1) as a preparation for the renormalisation program.

To properly transfer this method from the classical to the quantum case, it is important to rewrite $\ell n Z_h$ of Eq. (5-9) in a way illustrating again the correspondence principle. Considering

$$\ell n\, Z_h = \sum_q \ell n\, z_q = - \sum_q \ell n\; 2 \,\text{Sinh}\, \frac{1}{2} \beta_q$$

as a function of the variables β_q, one forms the total derivative

$$d\,\ell n Z_h = \sum_q \frac{\partial\, \ell n z_q}{\partial \beta_q} \; d\beta_q$$

$$= - \frac{1}{2} \sum_q \text{Cotgh}\,(\frac{1}{2}\beta_q) \;\; d\beta_q$$

substitutes

$$\text{Cotgh}\left(\frac{1}{2}\beta_q\right) = 2\frac{\omega_q}{\hbar} L_q(0)$$

$$= 2\frac{\omega_q}{\hbar}\sum_{\nu}\frac{KT}{\omega_q^2 + \left(\frac{2\pi\nu}{\hbar\beta}\right)^2}$$

$$= \sum_{\nu} 2\frac{\beta_q}{(2\pi\nu)^2 + \beta_q^2}$$

by means of Eqs (5-40), (5-42a) and one gets

$$d\ell n Z_h = -\frac{1}{2}\sum_{q\nu}\frac{2\beta_q}{(2\pi\nu)^2 + \beta_q^2}\, d\beta_q$$

$$= -\frac{1}{2}\sum_{q\nu}\frac{\partial}{\partial\beta_q}\ell n\left((2\pi\nu)^2 + \beta_q^2\right)\cdot d\beta_q$$

again a total derivative. Therefore

$$\ell n Z_h = -\frac{1}{2}\sum_{q\nu}\ell n\left((2\pi\nu)^2 + \beta_q^2\right)$$

$$= -\frac{1}{2}\sum_{q\nu}\ell n\, \beta\hbar^2 L_{q\nu}^{-1}$$

$$= -\frac{1}{2}\sum_{\underset{\sim}{q}\nu}\text{Tr}\ \ell n\, \beta\hbar^2 L_{\underset{\sim}{q}\nu}^{-1} \qquad (5\text{-}45)$$

and one notes indeed that the term $\nu = 0$ yields $\ell n\, Z_h$ in the classical limit (Eq. (1-72)). It is therefore anticipated that the single propagator function L_{qo} of the classical theory will be replaced everywhere in the quantum case by the set of Fourier components $L_{q\nu}$. Let us deal next with the first order ring diagram summation as in section (3-1). We start from $\bar{\kappa}_k$ (ring) now expressed in terms of the correlation operators $\underline{w}_{ij}$ of Eq. (5-38). To do that we use of course the pairing theorem. Since the operators $\underline{w}_{ij}(|\beta^{(i)} - \beta^{(j)}|)$ take into account the ordering effect of the $\beta^{(j)}$ explicitly we can permute the vertices at will and thus apply exactly the same combinatorial analysis here as in the classical case. We then go over to the normal mode representation and find instead of Eq. (3-3)

$$\bar{\kappa}_k(\text{ring}) = \frac{1}{2}(k-1)! \sum_{\underset{\sim}{q} j_1 \cdots j_k} \int_0^\beta d\beta^{(1)} \cdots \int_0^\beta d\beta^{(k)}$$

$$\times \; \gamma_{\underset{\sim}{q} j_k j_1} L_{\underset{\sim}{q} j_1}(|\beta^{(1)} - \beta^{(2)}|)\, \gamma_{\underset{\sim}{q} j_1 j_2} L_{\underset{\sim}{q} j_2}(|\beta^{(2)} - \beta^{(3)}|)$$

$$\times \; \cdots \gamma_{\underset{\sim}{q} j_{k-1} j_k} L_{\underset{\sim}{q} j_k}(|\beta^{(k)} - \beta^{(1)}|) \qquad (5\text{-}46)$$

The diagrammatic representation of Eq. (5-46) can be taken over from Fig. 1a (p. 77) with minor changes. Here, each vertex (i) is in addition assigned a variable $\beta^{(i)}$. The vertex symbol of the Fig. (5-1b) is, however, unchanged. Yet, and evidently, in the vertex function $\gamma_{\underset{\sim}{q} jj'}$ given by Eq. (3-2), the smeared potential function Φ_ρ is now expressed in terms of λ_ρ given by Eqs (5-34) and (5-34a). Lastly the algebraic value of a linking line is here $L_{\underset{\sim}{q} j}(|\beta' - \beta''|)$. Going over to their Fourier transform, we can perform the $\beta^{(i)}$

integration. Letting aside all irrelevant factors we find

$$\sum_{\nu_1 \ldots \nu_k} L_{\underset{\sim}{q}j_1\nu_1} \cdots L_{\underset{\sim}{q}j_k\nu_k} \int_0^\beta d\beta^{(1)} \cdots \int_0^\beta d\beta^{(k)}$$

$$\times \; e^{2i\pi\nu_1 \frac{(\beta^{(1)}-\beta^{(2)})}{\tau} + 2i\pi\nu_2 \frac{(\beta^{(2)}-\beta^{(3)})}{\tau} + 2i\pi\nu_k \frac{(\beta^{(k)}-\beta^{(1)})}{\tau}}$$

$$= \sum_{\nu_1 \ldots \nu_k} L_{\underset{\sim}{q}j_1\nu_1} \cdots L_{qj_k\nu_k} \beta^k \delta_{\nu_1, \nu_2} \delta_{\nu_2, \nu_3} \cdots \delta_{\nu_k, \nu_1}$$

Here appears the interesting consequence of the "energy" conservation law. Together with the wave vector conservation, these laws say that one and the same quadri-vector $(\underset{\sim}{q}, \frac{2\pi\nu}{\hbar\beta})$ runs through the loop represented by the ring diagram. Note, however, that the $\frac{\nu}{\beta}$ conservation has nothing to do with the conservation of phonon energy, which does not occur in equilibrium properties as the polarization mixing manifested at each vertex clearly indicates. Then, converting as in section (3-1) $\gamma_{\underset{\sim}{q}jj'} L_{\underset{\sim}{q}j'\nu}$ into the matrix form $C_{\underset{\sim}{q}} L_{\underset{\sim}{q}\nu}$ with $C_{\underset{\sim}{q}}$ given by Eq. (3-2a) we find

$$\bar{\kappa}_k(\text{ring}) = \frac{1}{2}(k-1)! \sum_{\underset{\sim}{q}\nu} \operatorname{Tr}(\beta C_{\underset{\sim}{q}} L_{\underset{\sim}{q}\nu})^k$$

Multiplying $\bar{\kappa}_k$ by $(-1)^k \frac{1}{k!}$ and summing over k from 2 to ∞ yields

$$\frac{1}{2} \sum_{k=2}^{\infty} \sum_{\underset{\sim}{q}\nu} \operatorname{Tr} \frac{(-1)^k}{k} (\beta C_{\underset{\sim}{q}} L_{\underset{\sim}{q}\nu})^k$$

$$= \frac{1}{2}\beta \sum_{\underset{\sim}{q}\nu} \operatorname{Tr} C_{\underset{\sim}{q}} L_{\underset{\sim}{q}\nu} - \frac{1}{2} \sum_{\underset{\sim}{q}\nu} \operatorname{Tr} \ln (1 + \beta C_{\underset{\sim}{q}} L_{\underset{\sim}{q}\nu}) \quad (5\text{-}47)$$

The logarithmic part of this equation can be combined with $\ln Z_h$ of Eq. (5-45) and one finds

$$- \frac{1}{2} \sum_{\underset{\sim}{q}\nu} \operatorname{Tr} \ln \beta\hbar^2 (L^{-1}_{\underset{\sim}{q}\nu} + \beta C_{\underset{\sim}{q}})$$

with

$$\frac{1}{\beta} L^{-1}_{\underset{\sim}{q}\nu} + C_{\underset{\sim}{q}}$$

$$= (\frac{2\pi\nu}{\hbar\beta})^2 + D_{\underset{\sim}{q}h} + \frac{1}{M} \sum_{\rho} (1 - \cos \underset{\sim}{q}\underset{\sim}{R}_{\rho}) \underset{\sim}{p}^2 (\Phi^{(h)}_{\rho} - \varphi_{\rho})$$

Noting the cancellation of D_{qh} with the last term of the above expression, a perturbed propagator matrix can be defined as

$$L^{(1)}_{\underset{\sim}{q}\nu} = KT\left((\frac{2\pi\nu}{\hbar\beta})^2 + D^{(1)}_{\underset{\sim}{q}} \right)^{-1}$$

with

$$D^{(1)}_{\underset{\sim}{q}} = \frac{1}{M} \sum_{\rho} (1 - \cos \underset{\sim}{q}\underset{\sim}{R}_{\rho}) \underset{\sim}{p}^2 \, \Phi^{(h)}_{\rho}$$

where the smeared potential $\Phi^{(h)}_{\rho}$ is evaluated in terms of the unperturbed self-linked correlation functions. Next, collecting the first term of Eq. (5-47) with the first cumulant left out by the ring diagram summation we note the cancellation of the contributions containing the bare potential functions φ_ρ and find

$$\varkappa_1^{(1)} = \beta N \frac{1}{2} \sum_\rho (1 - \frac{1}{2} \lambda_\rho \underset{\sim}{p}^2) \Phi_\rho^{(h)}$$

in such a way that

$$\ln Z^{(1)}(\text{ring}) = -\beta N \frac{1}{2} \sum_\rho (1 - \frac{1}{2} \lambda_\rho \underset{\sim}{p}^2) \Phi_\rho^{(h)}$$
$$- \frac{1}{2} \sum_{\underset{\sim}{q}\nu} \text{Tr} \ln \beta \hbar^2 L_{\underset{\sim}{q}\nu}^{(1)-1}$$

Let us proceed with the inclusion of second order components, as depicted in Fig. 3 (p. 91), into the first run of ring diagram summation. By closely following the classical analysis and expressing the quadri-vector $(\underset{\sim}{q}, \frac{2\pi\nu}{\hbar\beta})$ conservation law, we find rather easily the perturbed propagator matrix

$$L_{\underset{\sim}{q}\nu}^{(1,2)} = KT \left\{ (\frac{2\pi\nu}{\hbar\beta})^2 + D_{\underset{\sim}{q}}^{(1)} + C_{\underset{\sim}{q}}^{(2a)} + C_{\underset{\sim}{q}\nu}^{(2b)} \right\}^{-1} \tag{5-48}$$

with

$$D_{\underset{\sim}{q}}^{(1)} + C_{\underset{\sim}{q}}^{(2a)} = \frac{1}{M} \sum_\rho (1 - \cos \underset{\sim}{q}\underset{\sim}{R}_\rho)$$
$$\times \left\{ 1 - \frac{1}{2} \sum_{\rho'\sigma} \int_0^\beta d\tau \left[e^{\lambda^\sigma_{\rho\rho'}(|\tau|)\underset{\sim}{p}\underset{\sim}{p}'} - 1 - \frac{1}{2}(\lambda^\sigma_{\rho\rho'}(|\tau|)\underset{\sim}{p}\underset{\sim}{p}')^2 \right] \Phi_{\rho'}^{(h)} \right\}$$
$$\times \underset{\sim}{p}^2 \Phi_\rho^{(h)} \tag{5-49}$$

and

$$C^{(2b)}_{\underset{\sim}{q}\nu} = \frac{-1}{MN}\left(\frac{1}{2}\right)^2 \sum_{\rho\rho'\sigma} \eta_\rho(\underset{\sim}{q})\,\eta_{\rho'}(-\underset{\sim}{q})\, e^{i\underset{\sim}{q}\underset{\sim}{R}_\sigma}$$

$$\times \int_0^\beta d\tau\, e^{2i\pi\nu\frac{\tau}{\beta}} \left(e^{\lambda^\sigma_{\rho\rho'}(|\tau|)\underset{\sim\sim}{pp'}} - 1 - \lambda^\sigma_{\rho\rho'}(|\tau|)\underset{\sim\sim}{pp'} \right)$$

$$\times\ \underset{\sim}{p}\,\Phi^{(h)}_\rho\,\underset{\sim}{p}'\,\Phi^{(h)}_{\rho'} \tag{5-50}$$

The new feature revealed by this example is that the perturbed dynamical matrix has become ν dependent. This fact suggests that by virtue of the correspondence principle the mean value

$$\frac{1}{2}\sum_{\underset{\sim}{q}} \mathrm{Tr}\, D_q L_q = \frac{1}{2}\sum_{\underset{\sim}{q}} \mathrm{Tr}\, D_{qo} L_{qo} = 3N'$$

of the classical self-consistent theory will become

$$\frac{1}{2}\sum_{\underset{\sim}{q}\nu} \mathrm{Tr}\, D_{\underset{\sim}{q}\nu} L_{\underset{\sim}{q}\nu}$$

with

$$L_{\underset{\sim}{q}\nu} = KT\left(\left(\frac{2\pi\nu}{\hbar\beta}\right)^2 + D_{\underset{\sim}{q}\nu}\right)^{-1}$$

in the quantum case. The sum rule $3N'$ will however no longer apply†. In other words, the self-consistent field method which could

† Remember that this is due to β times the mean kinetic energy now being temperature dependent.

be formulated in terms of a single trial dynamical matrix $\mathbb{D}_{\underset{\sim}{q}}$ in section (3-2) will now be formulated in terms of the set of trial $\mathbb{D}_{\underset{\sim}{q}\nu}$, determined in complete analogy with D_{qo} by taking the derivative with respect to $L_{\underset{\sim}{q}\nu}$ of the irreducible cumulant expansion constructed from Eq. (5-33) with the same rules which lead to the function $\mathcal{K}$ of Eq. (3-25a). Inspection of Eq. (5-50) indicates that the component $C^{2b}_{\underset{\sim}{q}\nu}$ may be precisely obtained in this way from $\bar{\kappa}_{2,ir}$, yet unrenormalized. The component $C^{2a}_{\underset{\sim}{q}\nu}$ is also correctly obtained by this operation since it derives from the cut of a self-linked correlation function which is only a function of $L_{\underset{\sim}{q}}(0) = \sum_{\nu} L_{\underset{\sim}{q}\nu}$. Therefore C^{2a}_{q} is independent of ν.

To establish the set of self-consistent equations in the quantum case we can thus follow a path based on replacing the arguments of ℓnZ_h of Eq. (5-45) by a set of trial propagator matrices

$$\frac{1}{\beta}\left(\left(\frac{2\pi\nu}{\hbar\beta}\right)^2 + \mathbb{D}_{\underset{\sim}{q}\nu} \right)^{-1}$$

and requiring the annihilation of the generalized perturbed part

$$\sum_{k-1}^{\infty} \mathbb{C}^{(k)}_{\underset{\sim}{q}\nu}$$

yielding

$$\mathbb{D}^{(1)}_{q\nu} = \mathbb{D}_{q\nu} + \sum_{k=1}^{\infty} \mathbb{C}^{(k)}_{k\nu}$$

as a result of one run of ring diagram summation. While this mixed variational perturbation method suits our purposes very well, its physical interpretation is not easily seen. For this reason we shall first develop in the next section a qualitative picture of the renormalized theory, thereby introducing some concepts of physical interest.

We still wish to make here a few remarks about the Lagrangian structure of the correlation functions (5-27) and (5-40) of the unperturbed system by expressing them in the density matrix formalism. Dropping for this purpose the index q and considering, for a moment, only the domain

$$0 \leqslant \tau \leqslant \beta$$

where the two expressions match one another, we have derived above, in the usual formalism where H_h is diagonal that

$$L(\tau) = M\langle x(\tau)x\rangle = \frac{\hbar}{2\omega}\,\frac{\operatorname{Cosh}(\frac{1}{2}\beta - \tau)\hbar\omega}{\operatorname{Sinh}\frac{1}{2}\beta\hbar\omega}$$

Let us now consider the solution $\xi(\vartheta, x, t \,|\, x', 0)$ given in the first section in terms of the Lagrangian boundary conditions, rewrite it by replacing ϑ by $-i\hbar\tau$ and t by $-i\hbar\beta$, that is

$$\xi(\tau, x, \beta \,|\, x', 0) = x'\operatorname{Cosh}\tau\hbar\omega + \frac{x - x'\operatorname{Cosh}\beta\hbar\omega}{\operatorname{Sinh}\beta\hbar\omega}\operatorname{Sinh}\tau\hbar\omega$$

and let us take its "diagonal" part obtained by putting $x' = x$. Then

$$\xi(\tau, x, \beta \,|\, x, 0) = x(\operatorname{Cosh}\tau\hbar\omega + \frac{1 - \operatorname{Cosh}\beta\hbar\omega}{\operatorname{Sinh}\beta\hbar\omega}\operatorname{Sinh}\tau t\omega)$$

$$= x\,\frac{\operatorname{Cosh}(\frac{1}{2}\beta - \tau)\hbar\omega}{\operatorname{Cosh}\frac{1}{2}\beta\hbar\omega}$$

corresponds to that motion of the particle where the initial and final position are identical and we note that

$$L(\tau) = M \frac{1}{z} \int_{-\infty}^{+\infty} dx\ \xi(\tau, x, \beta \mid x, 0)\, xK_h(x, \beta \mid x, 0)$$

$$= M \langle \xi(\tau) x \rangle_h = \frac{\hbar}{2\omega} \frac{\mathrm{Cosh}\,(\frac{1}{2}\beta - \tau)\hbar\omega}{\mathrm{Sin}\,\frac{1}{2}\beta\hbar\omega}$$

While this exercise illustrates the conceptual differences between the Hamiltonian and Lagrangian formalisms it should help to render the latter more familiar, which it certainly deserves. Note that from the above equation one recovers the symmetric Green's function (5-40) in the domain $-\beta \leqslant \tau \leqslant +\beta$ in terms of

$$L(|\tau|) = M \langle \xi(|\tau|) x \rangle_h$$

With

$$\frac{d}{d\tau} = \frac{\tau}{|\tau|} \frac{d}{d|\tau|}$$

$$\frac{d^2}{d\tau^2} = 2\delta(\tau) \frac{d}{d|\tau|} + \frac{d^2}{d|\tau|^2}$$

and setting $\tau = \beta' - \beta''$, $L(|\beta' - \beta''|)$ is further noted to satisfy the inhomogeneous equation

$$\frac{d^2}{d(\hbar\beta')^2} L(|\beta' - \beta''|) - \omega^2 L(|\beta' - \beta''|) = -\delta(\beta' - \beta'') \quad (5\text{-}52)$$

and to assume the boundary conditions

$$L(|\pm\beta|) = L(0) = \frac{\hbar}{2\omega}\ \mathrm{Cotgh}\ \frac{1}{2}\beta\hbar\omega$$

Similarly, the Fourier transform $L_{\underset{\sim}{q}}(|\beta' - \beta''|)$ of Eq. (5-39b) satisfies the equation, written here in matrix form

$$\frac{d^2}{d(\hbar\beta')^2} L_{\underset{\sim}{q}}(|\beta'-\beta''|) - D_{\underset{\sim}{q}h} L_{\underset{\sim}{q}}(|\beta'-\beta''|) = -\delta(\beta'-\beta'') \qquad (5\text{-}52a)$$

While speaking of Green's functions it should lastly be mentioned that if a perturbation series for the exact density matrix $K(..Q_{\underset{\sim}{q}}\beta|Q_q^{(1)}0)$ is written as

$$K(..Q_q\beta|..Q_q^{(1)},..0) = K_h(..Q_q..,\beta|..Q_q^{(1)},..0)$$

$$-\int d\Omega' \int_0^\beta d\beta'\, K_h(..Q_q..\beta|..Q_q'..\beta')$$

$$\times\ V'(..Q_q'..)K_h(..Q_q'\beta'|..Q_q^{(1)}..0)$$

$$+\int d\Omega' \int d\Omega'' \int_0^\beta d\beta' \int_0^{\beta'} d\beta''\, K_h(..Q_q..\beta|..Q_q'..\beta')\, V'(..Q_q'..)$$

$$\times\ K_h(..Q_q'..\beta'|..Q_q''..\beta'')$$

$$\times\ V'(..Q_q''..)K_h(..Q_q''..\beta''|..Q_q^{(1)}..,0) - \ldots \qquad (5\text{-}53)$$

then, here, one eliminates the telescopic integral by defining the Green's functions

$$G_h(..Q'_q..\beta'|..Q''_q..\beta'') = K_h(..Q'_q..\beta'|..Q''_q..\beta'') \quad \beta' > \beta''$$
$$= 0 \qquad\qquad \beta' < \beta''$$

which satisfy the inhomogeneous equation

$$\frac{\partial G_h}{\partial \beta'} + H_h G_h = \delta(\beta' - \beta'') \prod_q{}' \delta(Q'_q - Q''_q) \tag{5-54}$$

In the time-dependent formalism the Green's functions $G_h(Q'_{\underset{\sim}{q}}, t' \; Q''_{\underset{\sim}{q}}, t'')$ have been used by R. P. Feynman in his famous "Space-Time Approach to Quantum Electrodynamics"†. In Quantum Statistics the corresponding "space imaginary time approach" has been fruitfully developed since the early fifties and we wish to refer to the very instructive monograph by G. Baym and L. Kadanoff ([10]) for further information about this method. The above remarks should suffice to point out the variety of means available to treat the anharmonic lattice problem.

5-3 SELF-CONSISTENT EQUATIONS

We wish to begin this section with a qualitative presentation of the "molecular field" idea in the quantum theory of anharmonicity: It will help to go back to section (3-4) of the classical theory, where we have noted two kinds of contributions to the renormalized $D_{\underset{\sim}{q}}$: the ones

† Phys. Rev. 76, 769, 1949

derived from the cut of self-linked lines, the others derived from the cut of linking lines in any diagram representing a term of the irreducible series $\mathcal{K}$ of Eq. (3-25a). As of now it will be convenient to distinguish by $D^{(s)}_{\underset{\sim}{q}}$ and $D^{(\ell)}_{\underset{\sim}{q}}$ respectively these two parts. Substituting $\lambda_{ij}\underset{\sim}{p}_i\underset{\sim}{p}_j$ for $\underline{w}_{ij}$ in $\mathcal{K}$, a re-decomposition of Eq. (3-26a) yields

$$\frac{1}{2} D_{\underset{\sim}{q}\alpha\alpha'} = \frac{d}{dL_{\underset{\sim}{q}\alpha\alpha'}} \mathcal{K}(\ldots \lambda_\rho \underset{\sim}{p}^2 \ldots, \ldots \lambda^\sigma_{\rho\rho'} \underset{\sim}{p}\underset{\sim}{p}' \ldots, \beta\varphi)$$

$$= \frac{1}{MN} \sum_\rho \eta_\rho(\underset{\sim}{q})\eta_\rho(-\underset{\sim}{q}) \left(\frac{\partial\mathcal{K}}{\partial\lambda_{\rho\alpha\alpha'}}\right)_{\lambda^\sigma_{\rho\rho'}}$$

$$+ \frac{1}{MN}\frac{1}{2} \sum_{\rho\rho'\sigma} e^{i\underset{\sim}{q}\underset{\sim}{R}_\sigma} \eta_\rho(\underset{\sim}{q})\eta_{\rho'}(-\underset{\sim}{q}) \left(\frac{\partial\mathcal{K}}{\partial\lambda^\sigma_{\rho\rho'\alpha\alpha'}}\right)_{\lambda_\rho}$$

$$\equiv \frac{1}{2} D^{(s)}_{\underset{\sim}{q}\alpha\alpha'} + \frac{1}{2} D^{(\ell)}_{\underset{\sim}{q}\alpha\alpha'} \tag{5-55}$$

We then define two kinds of renormalized force constants, namely

$$\frac{1}{4} A_{\rho\alpha\alpha'} = \frac{1}{N}\left(\frac{\partial\mathcal{K}}{\partial\lambda_{\rho\alpha\alpha'}}\right)_{\lambda^\sigma_{\rho\rho'}} \tag{5-56}$$

and

$$\frac{1}{2} A^\sigma_{\rho\rho'\alpha\alpha'} \equiv \frac{1}{N}\left(\frac{\partial\mathcal{K}}{\partial\lambda^\sigma_{\rho\rho'\alpha\alpha'}}\right)_{\lambda_\rho} \tag{5-57}$$

While both Eqs (5-56) and (5-57) convey the "molecular field" concept, they differ in that the latter displays an additional non-local character owing to its dependence upon $\sigma = s - s'$. In so doing, we have in matrix form

$$D^{(s)}_{\underset{\sim}{q}} = \frac{1}{M}\frac{1}{2}\sum_{\rho} \eta_\rho(\underset{\sim}{q})\,\eta_\rho(-\underset{\sim}{q})\,A_\rho$$

$$= \frac{1}{M}\sum_{\rho}(1-\cos \underset{\sim}{q}\underset{\sim}{R}_\rho)\,A_\rho \tag{5-58}$$

an expression which clearly recalls the familiar ones in the harmonic approximation where $A_{\rho\,\alpha\alpha'} = \varphi_{\alpha\alpha'}(R_\rho)$ or in the R. H. A. where $A_{\rho\,\alpha\alpha'} = \Phi_{\alpha\alpha'}(R_\rho, \lambda_\rho)$ and

$$D^{(\ell)}_{\underset{\sim}{q}} = \frac{1}{M}\frac{1}{2}\sum_{\rho\rho'\sigma} e^{i\underset{\sim}{q}\underset{\sim}{R}_\sigma}\,\eta_\rho(\underset{\sim}{q})\,\eta_{\rho'}(-\underset{\sim}{q})\,A^{\sigma}_{\rho\rho'} \tag{5-59}$$

an expression without, at least explicit, equivalence in the usual theories. We have furthermore that the sum rule of the classical self-consistent field theory, namely

$$3N' = \beta\langle W\rangle_W = \beta\,\frac{1}{2}\sum_{\underset{\sim}{q}} \mathrm{Tr}\,D_{\underset{\sim}{q}}L_{\underset{\sim}{q}}$$

$$\equiv \beta\,\frac{1}{2}\sum_{\underset{\sim}{q}} \mathrm{Tr}\,(D^{(s)}_{\underset{\sim}{q}} + D^{(\ell)}_{\underset{\sim}{q}})\,L_{\underset{\sim}{q}}$$

now assumes the dual form

$$3N' = \frac{N}{4}\,\beta\sum_{\rho}\mathrm{Tr}\,\lambda_\rho A_\rho + \frac{N}{4}\,\beta\sum_{\rho\rho'\sigma}\mathrm{Tr}\,\lambda^{\sigma}_{\rho\rho'}A^{\sigma}_{\rho\rho'} \tag{5-60}$$

The above equation clearly expresses the objective of classical lattice dynamics that is the determination of the renormalized force constants $A_{\rho\alpha\alpha'}$ and $A^{\sigma}_{\rho\rho'\alpha\alpha'}$.

From here it is proper to branch out to the quantum theory and ask about the corresponding structure of Eq. (5-60) as well as about the nature of W itself. Let us begin with the first equation. An immediate observation is that while $A^{\sigma}_{\rho\rho'}$ of Eq. (5-57) is a non-local quantity in the space variables it is still a local one in the temperature variable. This suggests that in the quantum case "temperature relaxed" force constants $A^{\sigma}_{\rho\rho'}(\tau)$ will come into play. Considering the conjugated character of the force constants and correlation functions, this feature will reflect the fact that a one parameter family of functions $\lambda^{\sigma}_{\rho\rho'}(\tau)$ has had to be defined in the preceding section (see Eqs (5-35) and (5-43a)). Summing over the non-local effects in the space and temperature variables will amount to replacing $\beta\sum_{\sigma}\cdot$ in Eq. (5-60) by $\int_0^{\beta} d\tau \sum_{\sigma}\cdot$ in its quantum counterpart. On the other hand the force constants $A_{\rho\alpha\alpha'}$, conjugated to $\lambda_{\rho\alpha\alpha'}$, will remain local quantities. It is therefore expected that the r.h.s. of Eq. (5-60) will be replaced by

$$\beta \frac{N}{4} \sum_{\rho} \mathrm{Tr}\, \lambda_{\rho} A_{\rho} \;+\; \frac{N}{4} \sum_{\rho\rho'\sigma} \mathrm{Tr} \int_0^{\beta} d\tau\; \lambda^{\sigma}_{\rho\rho'}(\tau) A^{\sigma}_{\rho\rho'}(\tau)$$

That the factor β can no longer be separated from the above expression means that a temperature dependent self-consistent field method will have to be used in order to permit the derivation of such mean values. The l.h.s. of Eq. (5-60) will thus be replaced by

$$\beta \langle W(\beta)\rangle_W$$

and the quantum analogue of Eq. (5-60) will read

$$\beta \langle W(\beta)\rangle_W = \beta \frac{N}{4} \sum_{\rho} \mathrm{Tr}\, \lambda_\rho A_\rho$$

$$+ \frac{N}{4} \sum_{\rho\rho'\sigma} \mathrm{Tr} \int_0^\beta d\tau \quad \lambda^\sigma_{\rho\rho'}(\tau)\, A^\sigma_{\rho\rho'}(\tau) \tag{5-61}$$

The above equation shows us the objective of lattice dynamics in the quantum case, that is the determination of the local and non-local renormalized force constants $A_{\rho\alpha\alpha'}$ and $A^\sigma_{\rho\rho'\alpha\alpha'}(\tau)$. If so a dual form of this equation can be expressed in terms of local and temperature relaxed dynamical matrices $D^{(s)}_{\underset{\sim}{q}}$ and $D^{(\ell)}_{\underset{\sim}{q}}(\tau)$, these quantities being taken over from Eqs (5-58) and (5-59) whereby $A^\sigma_{\rho\rho'}(\tau)$ now occurs in the r.h.s. of Eq. (5-59). The τ dependence of $D^{(\ell)}_{\underset{\sim}{q}}(\tau)$ clearly parallels the ν dependence of its Fourier transform, a property exemplified by the second order component $C^{(2b)}_{\underset{\sim}{q}\nu}$ calculated in the preceding section. We can thus write the dual form of Eq. (5-61) as

$$\beta \langle W(\beta)\rangle_W = \beta \frac{1}{2} \sum_{\underset{\sim}{q}} \mathrm{Tr}\, D^{(s)}_{\underset{\sim}{q}} L_{\underset{\sim}{q}}(0)$$

$$+ \frac{1}{2} \sum_{\underset{\sim}{q}} \mathrm{Tr} \int_0^\beta d\tau\, D^{(\ell)}_{\underset{\sim}{q}}(\tau)\, L_{\underset{\sim}{q}}(\tau) \tag{5-62}$$

Goingover to the Fourier transforms

$$D^{(\ell)}_{\underset{\sim}{q}}(\tau) = \sum_{\nu} D^{(\ell)}_{\underset{\sim}{q}\nu} \, e^{-2i\pi\nu\frac{\tau}{\beta}} \tag{5-63}$$

with

$$D^{(\ell)}_{\underset{\sim}{q}\nu} = \frac{1}{\beta}\int_{o}^{\beta} d\tau \; e^{2i\pi\nu\frac{\tau}{\beta}} \, D^{(\ell)}_{\underset{\sim}{q}}(\tau) \tag{5-63a}$$

and

$$L_{\underset{\sim}{q}}(\tau) = \sum_{\nu} L_{\underset{\sim}{q}\nu} \, e^{2i\pi\nu\frac{\tau}{\beta}} \tag{5-64}$$

with

$$L_{\underset{\sim}{q}\nu} = \frac{1}{\beta}\int_{o}^{\beta} d\tau \; e^{-2i\pi\nu\frac{\tau}{\beta}} \, L_{\underset{\sim}{q}}(\tau) \tag{5-64a}$$

we finally expect the above mean value to read

$$\beta \langle W(\beta)\rangle_{W} = \beta\,\frac{1}{2}\sum_{\underset{\sim}{q}\nu} \mathrm{Tr}\, D_{\underset{\sim}{q}\nu} L_{\underset{\sim}{q}\nu} \tag{5-65}$$

with

$$D_{\underset{\sim}{q}\nu} = D^{(s)}_{\underset{\sim}{q}} + D^{(\ell)}_{\underset{\sim}{q}\nu}$$

which is exactly the form conjectured in section (5-2) on the basis of the correspondence-principle. The path followed to arrive at

Eq. (5-65) is, however, rather different and therefore provides an independent support for this equation.

We can now take up the next question, that of the structure of the effective potential energy $W(\beta)$ itself. Together with the kinetic energy this potential energy will constitute an effective Hamiltonian of the form

$$H_W = \frac{1}{2M} \sum_{\underset{\sim}{q}} p_{\underset{\sim}{q}} p_{-\underset{\sim}{q}} + W(\beta) \tag{5-66}$$

Then, with

$$\underset{\sim}{u}_{\underset{\sim}{q}}(\tau) = e^{\tau H_W} \underset{\sim}{u}_{\underset{\sim}{q}} e^{-\tau H_W} \tag{5-67}$$

and with

$$L_{\underset{\sim}{q}}(|\tau|) = M \langle T \underset{\sim}{u}_{\underset{\sim}{q}}(\tau) \underset{\sim}{u}_{-\underset{\sim}{q}}(0) \rangle_W \tag{5-68}$$

we find that the Ansatz

$$W(\beta) = \frac{M}{2} \sum_{\underset{\sim}{q}} D^{(s)}_{\underset{\sim}{q}} \underset{\sim}{u}_{\underset{\sim}{q}} \underset{\sim}{u}_{-\underset{\sim}{q}} + \frac{M}{2} \frac{1}{\beta} \int_0^\beta d\tau \, D^{(\ell)}_{\underset{\sim}{q}}(\tau) \underset{\sim}{u}_{\underset{\sim}{q}}(\tau) \underset{\sim}{u}_{-\underset{\sim}{q}}(0) \tag{5-69}$$

simulates all the features required by the above analysis.

We are left with the task of determining the yet unspecified $D_{\underset{\sim}{q}\nu}$ by means of self-consistent equations analogous to Eqs (3-26c). Here, as before, this problem is connected with a self-consistent reduction of ℓnZ. One way of doing this is to employ the variational perturbative method indicated in the preceding section. For, we rewrite the above equations in the trial form

$$\mathbb{D}_{\underset{\sim}{q}\nu} = \mathbb{D}^{(s)}_{\underset{\sim}{q}} + \mathbb{D}^{(\ell)}_{\underset{\sim}{q}\nu} \tag{5-70}$$

$$L_{q\nu} = \frac{1}{\beta}\left(\left(\frac{2\pi\nu}{\hbar\beta}\right)^2 + \mathbb{D}_{\underset{\sim}{q}\nu}\right)^{-1} \tag{5-71}$$

$$W(\beta) = \frac{1}{2}\sum_{\underset{\sim}{q}} \mathbb{D}^{(s)}_{\underset{\sim}{q}} \underset{\sim}{u}_{\underset{\sim}{q}} \underset{\sim}{u}_{-\underset{\sim}{q}}$$

$$+ \frac{1}{2}\sum_{\underset{\sim}{q}} \frac{1}{\beta}\int d\tau\, \mathbb{D}^{(\ell)}_{\underset{\sim}{q}}(\tau)\underset{\sim}{u}_{\underset{\sim}{q}}(\tau)\underset{\sim}{u}_{-\underset{\sim}{q}} \tag{5-72}$$

we set

$$H = H_W + V - W(\beta) \tag{5-73}$$

and rewrite the cumulant expansion (5-33) in the form

$$\ell n Z = \ell n Z_W + \langle T(\mathbb{S}(\beta) - 1)\rangle_{W,L} \tag{5-74}$$

with

$$\ell n Z_W = -\frac{1}{2}\sum_{\underset{\sim}{q}\nu} \mathrm{Tr}\, \ell n\left((2\pi\nu)^2 + \hbar^2\beta^2\mathbb{D}_{\underset{\sim}{q}\nu}\right) \tag{5-75}$$

In its yet unreduced form the second term of Eq. (5-74) has the same formal structure as the corresponding term in Eq. (5-33), the propagator matrices of the harmonic approximation being replaced by the $L_{\underset{\sim}{q}\nu}$ of Eq. (5-71) and $V' = V - V_h$ by $V' = V - W(\beta)$. Thus and for instance the first cumulant of Eq. (5-33)

$$\beta \langle V' \rangle_h = \beta \langle V \rangle_h - \beta \langle V_h \rangle_h$$

now reads

$$\beta \langle V' \rangle_W = \beta \langle V \rangle_W - \beta \langle W(\beta) \rangle_W$$

that is

$$\langle V_h \rangle_h = \frac{1}{2} \sum_{\underset{\sim}{q}\nu} \mathrm{Tr}\, D_{\underset{\sim}{q}h} \frac{KT}{\left(\frac{2\pi\nu}{\hbar\beta}\right)^2 + D_{\underset{\sim}{q}h}}$$

becomes

$$\langle W(\beta) \rangle_W = \frac{1}{2} \sum_{\underset{\sim}{q}\nu} \mathrm{Tr}\, \mathbb{D}_{\underset{\sim}{q}\nu} \frac{KT}{\left(\frac{2\pi\nu}{\hbar\beta}\right)^2 + \mathbb{D}_{\underset{\sim}{q}\nu}} \tag{5-76}$$

while $\langle V \rangle_h$ and $\langle V \rangle_W$ differ by the definition of λ_ρ given in terms of either the harmonic or trial propagator matrices.

Note at this point that the same substitution characterizing the change from $\langle V_h \rangle_h$ to $\langle W(\beta) \rangle_W$ applies to the mean kinetic energy which, in the harmonic approximation was

$$\langle T \rangle_h = \frac{1}{2M} \sum_{\underset{\sim}{q}} \langle \not{p}_{\underset{\sim}{q}} \not{p}_{-\underset{\sim}{q}} \rangle_h = \langle V_h \rangle_h$$

and now reads

$$\langle T\rangle_W = \langle W(\beta)\rangle_W = \frac{1}{2}\sum_{\underset{\sim}{q}\nu} \mathrm{Tr}\, \mathbb{D}_{\underset{\sim}{q}\nu} L_{\underset{\sim}{q}\nu} \tag{5-77}$$

Observe also that in the classical limit $(\nu = 0)\ \beta\langle T\rangle_W = 3N'$. The reduction of Eq. (5-74) is now carried out in a few straightforward steps. Just as in the classical theory the reducible part of the cumulants $\bar{\kappa}_k$ is absorbed by the ring diagram summation performed here for any quadrivector $(\underset{\sim}{q}, \frac{2\pi\nu}{\hbar\beta})$ as shown in section (5-2). The irreducible part of the $\bar{\kappa}_k$ is represented by all the diagrams where three or more linking lines $L_{\underset{\sim}{q}}(|\beta^i - \beta^j|)$ emerge from each vertex, no subcomponent of a diagram being separable from the rest by cutting two lines. Thus $W(\beta)$ drops out of $\bar{\kappa}_{k,ir}$ which reads

$$\bar{\kappa}_{k,ir} = \int_0^\beta d\beta_1 \cdot\cdot \int_0^\beta d\beta_k \langle T\, V(\beta_1) \ldots V(\beta_k)\rangle_{W,irL} \tag{5-78}$$

with

$$V(\beta_1) = e^{\beta_1 H_W}\, V\, e^{-\beta_1 H_W} \tag{5-79}$$

From $\bar{\kappa}_{k,ir}$ are derived all the components $C^{(k)}_{\underset{\sim}{q}\nu}$ which are inserted as "boxes" into the basic ring diagram by the simple operation established in sections (5-2) and (3-4), that is, for $k > 1$

$$-\frac{1}{2}\beta \mathbb{C}^{(k)}_{\underset{\sim}{q}\nu\alpha\alpha'} = \frac{(-1)^k}{k!} \frac{d}{dL_{\underset{\sim}{q}\nu\alpha\alpha'}} \bar{\kappa}_{k,ir}(\cdot\cdot L_{\underset{\sim}{q}'\nu}\cdot\cdot) \tag{5-80}$$

and for $k = 1$

$$\frac{1}{2}\,\mathbb{C}^{(1)}_{\underset{\sim}{q}\nu\,\alpha\alpha'} = \frac{d}{dL_{\underset{\sim}{q}\nu\,\alpha\alpha'}}\langle V\rangle_W - \frac{1}{2}\,\mathbb{D}_{\underset{\sim}{q}\nu} \tag{5-81}$$

Carrying out the ring diagram summation yields the perturbed trial dynamical matrix

$$\mathbb{D}^{(1)}_{\underset{\sim}{q}\nu} = \mathbb{D}_{\underset{\sim}{q}\nu} + \sum_{k=1}^{\infty}\mathbb{C}^{(k)}_{\underset{\sim}{q}\nu} \tag{5-82}$$

Defining then the quantum analogue of Eq. (3-15a) by

$$\mathcal{K} = \langle V\rangle_W - \frac{1}{\beta}\sum_{k=2}^{\infty}\frac{(-1)^k}{k!}\,\bar{\varkappa}_{k,\,ir}$$

$$= \langle V\rangle_W - \frac{1}{\beta}\langle T(\mathbb{S}(\beta) - 1 - \beta V)\rangle_{W,\,irL}$$

$$= \langle V\rangle_W + \frac{1}{\beta}\int_0^1 ds\,\langle T\int_0^\beta d\beta'\,V(\beta')$$

$$\times\,(\exp\left[-s\int_0^\beta d\beta''\,V(\beta'')\right] - 1\,)\rangle_{W,\,irL} \tag{5-83}$$

and requiring the annihilation of the perturbed part of $\mathbb{D}^{(1)}_{\underset{\sim}{q}\nu}$ we finally obtain the set of self-consistent equations

$$\frac{1}{2}\,D_{\underset{\sim}{q}\nu\,\alpha\alpha'} = \frac{d}{dL_{\underset{\sim}{q}\nu\,\alpha\alpha'}}\mathcal{K}(\cdot\cdot\lambda_\rho(L_{\underset{\sim}{q}'\nu'}),\ \lambda^{\sigma}_{\rho\rho'}(L_{\underset{\sim}{q}'\nu'}),\beta\,,\varphi) \tag{5-84a}$$

$$\lambda^{\sigma}_{\rho\rho'}(\tau) = \frac{1}{MN} \sum_{\underset{\sim}{q}\nu} e^{i\underset{\sim}{q}\underset{\sim}{R}_{\sigma} + i2\pi\nu\frac{\tau}{\beta}} \eta_{\rho}(\underset{\sim}{q})\,\eta_{\rho'}(-\underset{\sim}{q}) L_{\underset{\sim}{q}\nu} \tag{5-84b}$$

$$L_{\underset{\sim}{q}\nu} = KT\left(\left(\frac{2\pi\nu}{\hbar\beta}\right)^2 + D_{\underset{\sim}{q}\nu}\right)^{-1} \tag{5-84c}$$

$$\ell n Z = \beta\frac{1}{2} \sum_{\underset{\sim}{q}\nu} \mathrm{Tr}\, D_{\underset{\sim}{q}\nu} L_{\underset{\sim}{q}\nu} - \beta\mathcal{K}(\beta, \upsilon, \ldots L_{\underset{\sim}{q}\nu}\ldots)$$

$$+ \frac{1}{2} \sum_{\underset{\sim}{q}\nu} \mathrm{Tr}\, \ell n \frac{KT}{\hbar^2} L_{\underset{\sim}{q}\nu} \tag{5-84}$$

From the above equations it follows that $\ell n Z$ remains stationary with respect to a variation $\delta D_{\underset{\sim}{q}\nu}$, of $D_{\underset{\sim}{q}\nu}$ at υ, T fixed. We have indeed

$$\delta\, \ell n Z = \beta\frac{1}{2} \sum_{\underset{\sim}{q}\nu} \mathrm{Tr}\, \delta D_{\underset{\sim}{q}\nu} L_{\underset{\sim}{q}\nu} - \frac{1}{2}\beta^2 \sum_{\underset{\sim}{q}\nu} \mathrm{Tr}\, D_{\underset{\sim}{q}\nu} L_{\underset{\sim}{q}\nu}^{\;2} \delta D_{\underset{\sim}{q}\nu}$$

$$+ \beta^2 \frac{1}{2} \sum_{\underset{\sim}{q}\nu} \mathrm{Tr}\, D_{\underset{\sim}{q}\nu} L_{\underset{\sim}{q}\nu}^{\;2}\, \delta D_{\underset{\sim}{q}\nu} - \frac{1}{2}\beta \sum_{\underset{\sim}{q}\nu} \mathrm{Tr}\, L_{\underset{\sim}{q}\nu}\, \delta D_{\underset{\sim}{q}\nu}$$

$$= 0$$

Furthermore, by inverting Eq. (5-84c) and resolving $D_{\underset{\sim}{q}\nu}$ into $D^{(s)}_{\underset{\sim}{q}}$ and $D^{(\ell)}_{\underset{\sim}{q}\nu}$, the Green's functions $L_{\underset{\sim}{q}\,\alpha\alpha'}(|\beta' - \beta'''|)$ are seen to obey the following equations, written in matrix form

$$\frac{d^2}{d(\hbar\beta')^2} L_{\underset{\sim}{q}}(|\beta' - \beta'''|) - D_{\underset{\sim}{q}}^{(s)} L_{\underset{\sim}{q}}(|\beta' - \beta'''|)$$

$$= -\delta(\beta' - \beta''') + \frac{1}{\beta} \int_0^\beta d\beta'' \, D_{\underset{\sim}{q}}^{(\ell)}(|\beta' - \beta''|) L_{\underset{\sim}{q}}(|\beta'' - \beta'''|) \quad (5\text{-}85)$$

It is thus clearly desirable to split the complete renormalized $D_{\underset{\sim}{q}}$ into the two parts $D_{\underset{\sim}{q}}^{(s)}$, $D_{\underset{\sim}{q}}^{(\ell)}$ and not into a harmonic and anharmonic part. This will be exemplified at the end of this section. It is also useful to express $\mathcal{K}$ of Eq. (5-83) in terms of a parametric integration similar to the one established in section (4-1). Switching on the set of propagator matrices from zero to their value $L_{\underset{\sim}{q}\nu}$, we find

$$\mathcal{K}(1) = \mathcal{K}(0) + \int_0^1 d\xi \, \frac{d\mathcal{K}(\ldots \xi L_{\underset{\sim}{q}\nu} \ldots)}{d\xi}$$

$$= V_{st} + \frac{1}{2} \sum_{\underset{\sim}{q}\nu} \operatorname{Tr} L_{\underset{\sim}{q}\nu} \int_0^1 d\xi \, D_{\underset{\sim}{q}\nu}(\ldots \xi L_{\underset{\sim}{q}'\nu'} \ldots) \qquad (5\text{-}87)$$

Alternatively, Eq. (5-77) can also be written as

$$\mathcal{K}(1) = V_{st} + \frac{1}{2} \sum_{\underset{\sim}{q}} \operatorname{Tr} \int_0^1 d\xi$$

$$\times \left(L_{\underset{\sim}{q}}(0) D_{\underset{\sim}{q}}^{(s)}(\xi) + \frac{1}{\beta} \int_0^\beta d\tau \, L_{\underset{\sim}{q}}(\tau) D_{\underset{\sim}{q}}^{(\ell)}(\tau, \xi) \right) \qquad (5\text{-}87a)$$

or in the dual form

$$\mathcal{H}(1) = V_{st} + \frac{N}{4} \sum_{\rho} \mathrm{Tr} \int_{0}^{1} d\xi$$

$$\times \left(\lambda_{\rho} A_{\rho}(\xi) + \sum_{\rho'\sigma} \frac{1}{\beta} \int_{0}^{\beta} d\tau \; \lambda^{\sigma}_{\rho\rho'}(\tau) A^{\sigma}_{\rho\rho'}(\tau, \xi) \right) \qquad (5\text{-}87b)$$

It is worth terminating this section with a few applications of the equations established above. We shall do this in the first and second order approximation. In the following figures are drawn the corresponding Dyson's equations for the renormalized $D_{\underset{\sim}{q}\nu}$; these diagrams clearly exemplify what is meant by the components $D^{(s)}_{\underset{\sim}{q}}$ and $D^{(\ell)}_{\underset{\sim}{q}\nu}$

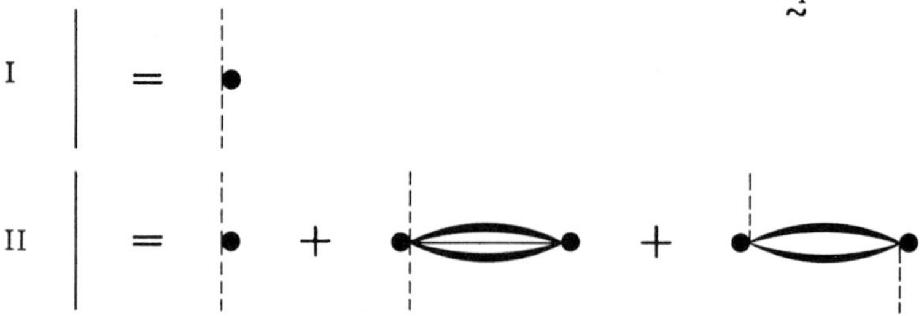

Fig. 11 Dyson's equations in I° and II° order

Fig. I. Dyson's equation in first order or in the renormalized harmonic approximation. The heavy dot represents the sum from 0 to ∞ of the effects of self-linked lines†.

Fig. II. Dyson's equation in second order showing how the first two components contribute to $D^{(s)}_{\underset{\sim}{q}}$, the third one to $D^{(\ell)}_{\underset{\sim}{q}\nu}$. The bows represent the sum from 1 to ∞ of the effects of simple linking lines†.

† Note that each self-linked or linking line is the sum of a reduced phonon "internal" and "external" line in Van Hove's nomenclature. ([7]; Fig. 11-12, p. 93)

Setting

$$\Phi_\rho = \Phi_\rho(\xi) \qquad \text{for} \qquad \xi = 1$$

with

$$\Phi_\rho(\xi) = e^{\frac{1}{2}\xi\lambda_\rho \underset{\sim}{p}^2} \varphi_\rho$$

the various forms assumed by $\mathcal{K}$ in the R. H. A. are

$$\mathcal{K}^{(I)} = N\frac{1}{2}\sum_\rho \Phi_\rho$$

$$= N\frac{1}{2}\sum_\rho \varphi_\rho + N\frac{1}{4}\sum_\rho \mathrm{Tr}\,\lambda_\rho \int_0^1 d\xi\, \underset{\sim}{p}^2\, \Phi_\rho(\xi)$$

$$= V_{st} + N\frac{1}{4}\sum_\rho \mathrm{Tr}\,\lambda_\rho \int_0^1 d\xi\, A_\rho(\xi)$$

$$= V_{st} + \frac{1}{2}\sum_{\underset{\sim}{q}\nu} \mathrm{Tr}\, L_{\underset{\sim}{q}\nu} \int_0^1 d\xi\, D_{\underset{\sim}{q}}(\ldots\xi L_{\underset{\sim}{q}'\nu'}\ldots)$$

$$= V_{st} + \frac{1}{2}\sum_{\underset{\sim}{q}} \mathrm{Tr}\, L_{\underset{\sim}{q}}(0) \int_0^1 d\xi\, D_{\underset{\sim}{q}}(\ldots\xi\lambda_\rho\ldots)$$

that is

$$A_{\rho} = \underset{\sim}{p}^2 \Phi_{\rho}$$

$$A^{\sigma}_{\rho\rho'}(\tau) = 0$$

$$D^{(\ell)}_{\underset{\sim}{q}}(\tau) = 0$$

$$D^{(s)}_{\underset{\sim}{q}} = D_{\underset{\sim}{q}} = \frac{1}{M} \sum_{\rho} (1 - \cos \underset{\sim}{q}\underset{\sim}{R}_{\rho}) A_{\rho}$$

The summation over ν can be carried out in all the relevant quantities such as

$$\lambda_{\rho} = \frac{2}{MN} \sum_{\underset{\sim}{q}} (1 - \cos \underset{\sim}{q}\underset{\sim}{R}_{\rho}) \, L_{\underset{\sim}{q}}(0)$$

with

$$L_{\underset{\sim}{q}}(0) = \frac{\hbar}{2\sqrt{D_{\underset{\sim}{q}}}} \operatorname{Cotgh} \frac{1}{2} \beta\hbar \sqrt{D_{\underset{\sim}{q}}}$$

and

$$\ell n \, Z^{(I)} = \beta \frac{1}{2} \sum_{\underset{\sim}{q}} \operatorname{Tr} L_{\underset{\sim}{q}}(0) \left\{ D_{\underset{\sim}{q}} - \int_{0}^{1} d\xi \, D_{\underset{\sim}{q}}(\xi \lambda_{\rho}) \right\}$$

$$- \beta V_{st} - \sum_{\underset{\sim}{q}} \operatorname{Tr} \ell n \, 2 \operatorname{Sinh} \frac{1}{2} \beta\hbar \sqrt{D_{\underset{\sim}{q}}} \qquad (5\text{-}88)$$

This latter expression shows to what extent $\ell n \, Z$ of the R. H. A. differs from its corresponding harmonic approximation, namely by the

λ_ρ dependence of $D_{\underset{\sim}{q}}$. It is also noted that the same equation for $\ln Z$ holds for the full $D_{\underset{\sim}{q}}^{(s)}$ part of the general $D_{\underset{\sim}{q}}$. However, going beyond the R.H.A. with $D_{\underset{\sim}{q}}^{(s)}$ only implies neglecting other effects of the same order of magnitude. These effects come into play in the next order of approximation, now treated.

In the second order we have

$$\mathcal{K}^{(II)} = N\frac{1}{2}\sum_{\rho}\Phi_\rho - N\frac{1}{2}\left(\frac{1}{2}\right)^2 \sum_{\rho\rho'\sigma} \mathrm{Tr}\int_0^\beta d\tau$$

$$\times \left(e^{\lambda^\sigma_{\rho\rho'}(\tau)\underset{\sim}{p}\underset{\sim}{p}'} - 1 - \frac{1}{2}(\lambda^\sigma_{\rho\rho'}\underset{\sim}{p}\underset{\sim}{p}')^2\right)\Phi_\rho\Phi_{\rho'}$$

Substituting λ_ρ, $\lambda^\sigma_{\rho\rho'}(\tau)$ by $\xi\lambda_\rho$, $\xi\lambda^\sigma_{\rho\rho'}(\tau)$ and differentiating $\mathcal{K}^{(II)}(\xi)$ so obtained with respect to ξ leads to writing

$$\mathcal{K}^{(II)} = V_{st} + \frac{1}{4}N\sum_{\rho}\mathrm{Tr}\int_0^1 d\xi$$

$$\times \left(\lambda_\rho A_\rho(\xi) + \sum_{\rho'\sigma}\frac{1}{\beta}\int_0^\beta d\tau\, \lambda^\sigma_{\rho\rho'}(\tau) A^\sigma_{\rho\rho'}(\tau,\xi)\right)$$

with

$$A_\rho(\xi) = \left(1 - \frac{1}{2}\sum_{\rho'\sigma}\mathrm{Tr}\int_0^1 d\tau\left[e^{\xi\lambda^\sigma_{\rho\rho'}(\tau)\underset{\sim}{p}\underset{\sim}{p}'}\right.\right.$$

$$\left.\left. - 1 - \frac{1}{2}(\xi\lambda^\sigma_{\rho\rho'}(\tau)\underset{\sim}{p}\underset{\sim}{p}')^2\right]\Phi_{\rho'}(\xi)\right)\Phi_\rho(\xi)$$

and

$$A^{\sigma}_{\rho\rho'}(\tau,\xi) = -\frac{1}{2}\beta\left(e^{\xi\lambda^{\sigma}_{\rho\rho'}(\tau)\underset{\sim}{p}\underset{\sim}{p}'} - 1 - (\xi\lambda^{\sigma}_{\rho\rho'}(\tau)\underset{\sim}{p}\underset{\sim}{p}')\right)\underset{\sim}{p}\Phi_{\rho}(\xi)\underset{\sim}{p}'\Phi_{\rho'}(\xi)$$

Thus

$$D^{(s)}_{\underset{\sim}{q}}(\xi) = \frac{1}{2M}\sum_{\rho} \eta_{\rho}(\underset{\sim}{q})\,\eta_{\rho}(-\underset{\sim}{q})A_{\rho}(\xi)$$

$$D^{(\ell)}_{\underset{\sim}{q}}(\tau,\xi) = \frac{1}{2M}\sum_{\rho\rho'\sigma} \eta_{\rho}(\underset{\sim}{q})\,\eta_{\rho'}(-\underset{\sim}{q})\,e^{i\underset{\sim}{q}\underset{\sim}{R}_{\sigma}}\, A^{\sigma}_{\rho\rho'}(\tau,\xi)$$

$$D_{\underset{\sim}{q}\nu}(\xi) = D^{(s)}_{\underset{\sim}{q}}(\xi) + \frac{1}{\beta}\int_{0}^{\beta} d\tau\, e^{2i\pi\nu\frac{\tau}{\beta}}\, D^{(\ell)}_{\underset{\sim}{q}}(\tau,\xi)$$

and the dual form of $\mathcal{H}^{(II)}$ can be written as well as $\ell n\, Z^{(II)}$. Here the summation over ν of the terms

$$\frac{1}{2}\,\ell n\, \frac{KT}{\hbar^2}\, L_{\underset{\sim}{q}\nu}$$

in Eq. (5-84) can no longer be performed without having recourse to certain schemes of approximation. At low temperature where a large number of ν values come into play, an expansion of this term in a power series of $D^{(\ell)}_{\underset{\sim}{q}\nu} = D_{\underset{\sim}{q}\nu} - D^{(s)}_{\underset{\sim}{q}}$ is advisable. The corrections to $\ell n\, Z^{(s)}$ appear then as certain convolution products which will not be written here. For temperatures larger or equal to the Debye temperature another scheme of approximation based on retaining a few values of ν , such as $\nu = 0$ and ± 1 for example, can be considered. In any case the quantum counterpart of the program carried out in chapter 4 is what we need next.

5-4 THERMAL PROPERTIES

The quantum theoretical generalization of the classical theory given in chapter 4 is most conveniently obtained by introducing the correspondence principle into the thermodynamical procedure of calculation. The intermediate "state variables" $L_{\underset{\sim}{q}}$ will now be the propagator matrices

$$L_{\underset{\sim}{q}\nu} = KT\,[(\frac{2\pi\nu}{\hbar\beta})^2 + D_{\underset{\sim}{q}\nu}]^{-1}$$

A given set of these matrices will characterize a state of motional fluctuations of the system and here again this state will be denoted by

$$\lambda = \left\{ \frac{1}{M} L_{\underset{\sim}{q}\nu} \right\}$$

The matrices $D_{\underset{\sim}{q}\nu}$ are thus characterized as functions of υ , T and λ . The shorthand notation for the subscripts

$$\underset{\sim}{q}, \nu \equiv p \qquad (5\text{-}89)$$

is furthermore introduced here.

Let us consider then the thermal equation of state. From Eq. (5-84, a, b, c) one finds

$$P = \frac{1}{\beta}\left(\frac{\partial \ell nZ}{\partial \upsilon}\right)_T = \frac{1}{\beta}\left(\frac{\partial \ell nZ}{\partial \upsilon}\right)_{T,\{D_p\}} + 0$$

$$= \frac{1}{\beta}\left(\frac{\partial \ell nZ}{\partial \upsilon}\right)_{T,\{L_p\}} = -\left(\frac{\partial \mathcal{K}(\upsilon, T, \lambda)}{\partial \upsilon}\right)_{T,\lambda} \qquad (5\text{-}90)^{\dagger}$$

$$= P_{st} + \frac{1}{\upsilon}\sum_p \mathrm{Tr}\, L_p \int_0^1 d\xi\, (-\tfrac{1}{2})\left(\frac{\partial D_p(\upsilon, T, \lambda')}{\partial \ell n\upsilon}\right)_{T,\lambda'} \qquad (5\text{-}90a)$$

where, as usual, $\lambda' = \xi\lambda = \left\{\frac{1}{M}\xi L_p\right\}$. If, at this point, one wishes to generalize the definition of the matrices $\Gamma_{\underset{\sim}{q}T\lambda}$ of Eq. (4-5) then it is appropriate to recall that $D_{\underset{\sim}{q}\nu} = D^{(s)}_{\underset{\sim}{q}} + D^{(\ell)}_{\underset{\sim}{q}\nu}$ and accordingly to introduce

$$\Gamma^{(s)}_{\underset{\sim}{q}T\lambda} = -\frac{1}{2}\frac{1}{D^{(s)}_{\underset{\sim}{q}}}\left(\frac{\partial D^{(s)}_{\underset{\sim}{q}}}{\partial \ell n\,\upsilon}\right)_{T,\lambda}$$

and

$$\Gamma^{(\ell)}_{\underset{\sim}{q}\nu T\lambda} = -\frac{1}{2}\frac{1}{D^{(\ell)}_{\underset{\sim}{q}\nu}}\left(\frac{\partial D^{(\ell)}_{\underset{\sim}{q}\nu}}{\partial \ell n\,\upsilon}\right)_{T,\lambda}$$

Writing next $\Gamma^{(\ell)}_{\underset{\sim}{q}\nu T\lambda}$ as the Fourier transform of the matrix $\Gamma^{(\ell)}_{\underset{\sim}{q}T\lambda}(\tau)$, namely

---

† Note that, by analogy with Eq. (4-2), we have also
$$P = -\left(\frac{\partial \mathcal{K}}{\partial \upsilon}\right)_{T,w} + \frac{1}{3\upsilon}\sum_p \mathrm{Tr}\, D_p\, L_p$$

$$\Gamma^{(\ell)}_{\underset{\sim}{q}\nu T\lambda} = \frac{1}{\beta}\int_0^\beta d\tau\; e^{2i\pi\nu\frac{\tau}{\beta}}\; \Gamma^{(\ell)}_{\underset{\sim}{q}\nu T\lambda}(\tau)$$

and making use of Eq. (5-63) we obtain the convolution relation

$$-\frac{1}{2}\left(\frac{\partial D^{(\ell)}_{\underset{\sim}{q}}(\tau)}{\partial\,\ell n\,\upsilon}\right)_{T,\lambda} = \frac{1}{\beta}\int_0^\beta d\tau'\; D^{(\ell)}_{\underset{\sim}{q}}(\tau-\tau')\;\Gamma^{(\ell)}_{\underset{\sim}{q}T\lambda}(\tau')$$

while

$$-\frac{1}{2}\left(\frac{\partial D^{(s)}_{\underset{\sim}{q}}}{\partial\,\ell n\,\upsilon}\right)_{T,\lambda} = D^{(s)}_{\underset{\sim}{q}}\;\Gamma^{(s)}_{\underset{\sim}{q}T\lambda}$$

It follows that a straightforward generalization of the classical matrices $\Gamma_{\underset{\sim}{q}T\lambda}$ can be made with the self-linked part $D^{(s)}_{\underset{\sim}{q}}$ of $D_{\underset{\sim}{q}\nu}$ only. The complete s. c. generalization of the Mie-Grüneisen equation of state is therefore

$$P = P_{st}(\upsilon) + \frac{1}{\upsilon}\sum_{\underset{\sim}{q}} \mathrm{Tr}\left\{L_{\underset{\sim}{q}}(0)\int_0^1 d\xi\; D^{(s)}_{\underset{\sim}{q}}(0,\lambda')\Gamma^{(s)}_{\underset{\sim}{q}T\lambda'}\right.$$

$$\left. + \frac{1}{\beta^2}\int_0^\beta d\tau\, L_{\underset{\sim}{q}}(\tau)\int_0^\beta d\tau'\int_0^1 d\xi\; D^{(\ell)}_{\underset{\sim}{q}}(|\tau-\tau'|,\lambda')\Gamma^{(\ell)}_{\underset{\sim}{q}T\lambda'}(\tau')\right\} \tag{5-91}$$

In this form both the local and non-local quantum dynamical effects brought about by the renormalized theory are clearly expressed. Alternatively, if we set

$$D^{(s)}_{\underset{\sim}{q}} \Gamma^{(s)}_{\underset{\sim}{q}T\lambda} + D^{(\ell)}_{\underset{\sim}{q}\nu} \Gamma^{(\ell)}_{\underset{\sim}{q}\nu T\lambda} \equiv D_{\underset{\sim}{q}\nu} \Gamma_{\underset{\sim}{q}\nu T\lambda} = D_p \Gamma_{pT\lambda} \tag{5-92}$$

and introduce the mean value

$$\overline{X}_{p\lambda} \equiv \frac{1}{D_p(\lambda)} \int_0^1 d\xi \, D_p(\lambda') \, X_{p\lambda'} \tag{5-93}$$

then Eq. (5-91) becomes

$$P = P_{st}(\upsilon) + \frac{1}{\upsilon} \sum_p L_p \int_0^1 d\xi \, D_p(\upsilon, T, \lambda') \Gamma_{pT\lambda'} \tag{5-91a}$$

$$= P_{st}(\upsilon) + \frac{1}{\upsilon} \sum_p \operatorname{Tr} L_p D_p \overline{\Gamma}_{pT\lambda} \tag{5-91b}$$

In this form one observes that the dynamical contribution to P is weighted by the factors $L_p D_p$ which were equal to KT in the classical theory. A suitable generalization of the classical parameter γ_1 (Eq. 4-9a) may then be proposed by setting

$$\gamma_1 \sum_p \operatorname{Tr} L_p D_p \equiv \sum_p L_p D_p \overline{\Gamma}_{pT\lambda} \tag{5-94}$$

The normalization factor in Eq. (5-94) is seen to be twice the mean kinetic energy. Designating this quantity by

$$E \equiv \sum_p \operatorname{Tr} L_p D_p \tag{5-95}$$

results in writing the pressure equation in the final form

$$P = P_{st}(\upsilon) + \frac{E}{\upsilon}\gamma_1 \tag{5-91c}$$

which goes over to the familiar Mie-Grüneisen equation of state in the harmonic approximation.

Let us proceed with the internal energy. Applying the correspondence principle to Eq. (4-18) results in replacing the classical mean kinetic energy

$$\frac{3}{2}NKT = \frac{1}{2}\sum_{\underset{\sim}{q}} \mathrm{Tr}\, D_{\underset{\sim}{q}} L_{\underset{\sim}{q}}$$

by

$$\frac{1}{2}\sum_{p} \mathrm{Tr}\, D_p L_p$$

thus obtaining

$$U = \frac{1}{2}\sum_{p} \mathrm{Tr}\, D_p L_p + \mathcal{K} - T\left(\frac{\partial \mathcal{K}}{\partial T}\right)_{\upsilon,\lambda} \tag{5-96}$$

That this equation is correct is most simply shown by replacing the variables D_p and L_p by

$$B_p = \hbar^2\beta^2 D_p \tag{5-97}$$

and

$$G_p = \frac{1}{\hbar^2\beta} L_p = [(2\pi\nu)^2 + B_p]^{-1} \tag{5-97a}$$

Indeed, with the new variables $\ell n Z$ of Eq. (4-84) reads

$$\ell n Z = \frac{1}{2}\sum_p \mathrm{Tr}\, B_p G_p - \beta\mathcal{H}(\beta, v, \hbar^2\beta G_p)$$

$$+ \frac{1}{2}\sum_p \mathrm{Tr}\, \ell n G_p \tag{5-98}$$

It is stationary with respect to variations δB_p of the B_p's at v, T, fixed and one has

$$\frac{1}{2} B_p = \left(\frac{\partial}{\partial G_p}\beta\mathcal{H}\right)_{T,v} \tag{5-98a}$$

then

$$U = -\left(\frac{\partial}{\partial\beta}\ell n Z\right)_v = -\left(\frac{\partial}{\partial\beta}\ell n Z\right)_{v,\{B_p\}} + 0$$

$$= -\left(\frac{\partial}{\partial\beta}\ell n Z\right)_{v,\{G_p\}} = \left(\frac{\partial}{\partial\beta}\beta\mathcal{H}\right)_{v,\{G_p\}} \tag{5-99}$$

$$= \left(\frac{\partial}{\partial\beta}\beta\mathcal{H}\right)_{v,\{L_p\}} + \sum_p \mathrm{Tr}\left(\frac{\partial\beta\mathcal{H}}{\partial L_p}\right)_{v,\beta}\left(\frac{\partial L_p}{\partial\beta}\right)_{v,\{G_p\}}$$

$$= \mathcal{H} - T\left(\frac{\partial\mathcal{H}}{\partial T}\right)_{v,\lambda} + \frac{1}{2}\sum_p \mathrm{Tr}\, D_p L_p \tag{5-99a}$$

which is Eq. (5-96). In passing, note the formal symmetry between the internal energy and pressure equation (5-90) when the variables B_p and G_p are used instead of the variables D_p and L_p. Another way of writing the internal energy equation may be found by introducing the isochoric-isofluctuational matrices

$$\Gamma_{p\upsilon\lambda} \equiv -\frac{1}{2}\frac{1}{D_p}\left(\frac{\partial D_p}{\partial \ell n T}\right)_{\upsilon,\lambda} \tag{5-100}$$

Noting from Eq. (5-93) that $\bar{1}$ differs from unity, except in the harmonic approximation, we have

$$U = V_{st} + \frac{1}{2}\sum_p \mathrm{Tr}\, L_p D_p + \frac{1}{2}\sum_p L_p \int_0^1 d\xi\, D_p(\lambda')(1+2\Gamma_{p\upsilon\lambda}) \tag{5-96a}$$

$$= V_{st} + \frac{1}{2}\sum_p L_p D_p \left\{1 + (\bar{1} + 2\,\bar{\Gamma}_{p\upsilon\lambda})\right\} \tag{5-96b}$$

$$= V_{st} + \frac{1}{2} E(1 + \gamma_2) \tag{5-96c}$$

We now must take up the rather elaborate analysis of the second order partial derivatives of $\ell n Z$ with respect to υ and T. Before embarking upon these developments, however, it is worth while establishing some useful preliminaries. For this purpose consider the first variation of $\ell n Z$, namely

$$\delta\, \ell n Z = \frac{1}{2}\beta \sum_p \mathrm{Tr}\, \delta L_p \left(D_p - 2\left(\frac{\partial \mathcal{H}}{\partial L_p}\right)_{\upsilon, T}\right)$$

which is known to vanish for D_p satisfying Eq. (5-84a). Here δL_p is the variation of L_p induced by a variation δD_p of D_p at υ, T fixed. This amounts to

$$\delta L_p = -\beta L_p \, \delta D_p L_p \tag{5-101}$$

Construct next the second order variation of $\ell n Z$ at υ, T fixed, that is

$$\delta^2 \ell n Z = 0 + \frac{1}{2}\beta \sum_p \mathrm{Tr}\, \delta L_p \, \delta D_p$$

$$- \beta \sum_{pp'} \mathrm{Tr}\, \delta L_p \left(\frac{\partial^2 \mathcal{H}}{\partial L_p \partial L_{p'}} \right)_{\upsilon, T} \delta L_{p'} \tag{5-102}$$

By introducing Eq. (5-101) into Eq. (5-102) three equivalent forms of $\delta^2 \ell n Z$ can be obtained, namely

$$\delta^2 \ell n Z = \frac{1}{2}\beta \sum_{pp'} \delta L_p^+ : (1_{p;p'} + \overline{G}_{p;p'}) : \delta D_{p'} \tag{5-103}$$

or

$$\delta^2 \ell n Z = \frac{1}{2}\beta \sum_{pp'} \delta D_p^+ : (1_{p;p'} + \tilde{G}_{p;p'}) : \delta L_{p'} \tag{5-103a}$$

or

$$\delta^2 \ell n Z = -\frac{1}{2}\beta^2 \sum_{pp'} \delta D_p^+ L_p^+ : (1_{p;p'} + G_{p;p'}) : L_{p'} \delta D_{p'} \tag{5-103b}$$

where $1_{p;p'}$ is a unit tensor when $p = p'$ and is zero otherwise. In component form, the three tensors read

$$\overline{G}_{p\alpha_1\alpha_2;p'\alpha_5\alpha_6} = 2\beta \sum_{\alpha_3\alpha_4} \left(\frac{\partial^2 \mathcal{H}}{\partial L_{p\alpha_1\alpha_2} \partial L_{p'\alpha_3\alpha_4}} \right)_{\upsilon, T}$$

$$\times \; L_{p'\alpha_3\alpha_5} L^{+}_{p'\alpha_4\alpha_6} \tag{5-104}$$

$$\tilde{G}_{p\alpha_1\alpha_2;p'\alpha_5\alpha_6} = 2\beta \sum_{\alpha_3\alpha_4} L_{p\alpha_1\alpha_3} L^{+}_{p\alpha_2\alpha_4}$$

$$\times \left(\frac{\partial^2 \mathcal{H}}{\partial L_{p\alpha_3\alpha_4} \partial L_{p'\alpha_5\alpha_6}} \right)_{\upsilon, T} \tag{5-104a}$$

and

$$G_{p\alpha_1\alpha_2;p'\alpha_5\alpha_6} = 2\beta \sum_{\alpha_3\alpha_4} L_{p\alpha_1\alpha_3} \left(\frac{\partial^2 \mathcal{H}}{\partial L_{p\alpha_3\alpha_2} \partial L_{p'\alpha_5\alpha_4}} \right)_{\upsilon, T}$$

$$\times \; L^{+}_{p'\alpha_4\alpha_6} \tag{5-104b}$$

It is apparent from the above that a knowledge of these tensors will bear information on the thermodynamical stability of anharmonic solids. Also, they constitute the basic ingredients of the vertex corrections found in calculating the thermal properties by the method of correlation functions. Their occurence is neatly exemplified in considering the isothermal derivatives

$$\left(\frac{\partial D_p}{\partial \ln \upsilon} \right)_T, \; \left(\frac{\partial L_p}{\partial \ln \upsilon} \right)_T, \; L_p \left(\frac{\partial D_p}{\partial \ln \upsilon} \right)_T, \; \left(\frac{\partial L_p}{\partial \ln \upsilon} \right)_T \frac{1}{L_p}$$

One has indeed

$$\left(\frac{\partial D_p}{\partial \ln \upsilon}\right)_T = \left(\frac{\partial D_p}{\partial \ln \upsilon}\right)_{T,\lambda} + \sum_{p'} \frac{\partial D_p}{\partial L_{p'}} : \left(\frac{\partial L_{p'}}{\partial \ln \upsilon}\right)_T \tag{5-105}$$

but

$$\left(\frac{\partial L_{p'}}{\partial \ln \upsilon}\right)_T = -\beta L_{p'} \left(\frac{\partial D_{p'}}{\partial \ln \upsilon}\right)_T L_{p'} \tag{5-105a}$$

thus

$$\left(\frac{\partial D_p}{\partial \ln \upsilon}\right)_T = \left(\frac{\partial D_p}{\partial \ln \upsilon}\right)_{T,\lambda}$$

$$- 2\beta \sum_{p'} \left(\frac{\partial^2 \mathcal{K}}{\partial L_p \partial L_{p'}}\right)_{\upsilon, T} : L_{p'} \left(\frac{\partial D_{p'}}{\partial \ln \upsilon}\right)_T L_{p'}$$

$$= \left(\frac{\partial D_p}{\partial \ln \upsilon}\right)_{T, \lambda} - \sum_{p'} \bar{G}_{p;p'} : \left(\frac{\partial D_{p'}}{\partial \ln \upsilon}\right)_T$$

or

$$\left(\frac{\partial D_p}{\partial \ln \upsilon}\right)_T = \sum_{p'} \left(\frac{1}{1+\bar{G}}\right)_{p;p'} : \left(\frac{\partial D_{p'}}{\partial \ln \upsilon}\right)_{T, \lambda} \tag{5-106}$$

For the other three derivatives one finds similarly

$$\left(\frac{\partial L_p}{\partial \ln \upsilon}\right)_T = \sum_{p'} \left(\frac{1}{1+\tilde{G}}\right)_{p;p'} : \left(\frac{\partial L_{p'}}{\partial \ln \upsilon}\right)_{T, \lambda} \tag{5-106a}$$

$$L_p\left(\frac{\partial D_p}{\partial \ell n\, \upsilon}\right)_T = \sum_{p'}\left(\frac{1}{1+G}\right)_{p;p'} : L_{p'}\left(\frac{\partial D_{p'}}{\partial \ell n\, \upsilon}\right)_{T,\lambda} \tag{5-106b}$$

and

$$\left(\frac{\partial L_p}{\partial \ell n\, \upsilon}\right)_T \frac{1}{L_p} = \sum_{p'}\left(\frac{1}{1+G}\right)_{p;p'} : \left(\frac{\partial L_p}{\partial \ell n\, \upsilon}\right)_{T,\lambda} \frac{1}{L_p} \tag{5-106c}$$

We know from the classical theory that, in one form or another, the above derivatives will occur in the isothermal compressibility equation. To complete the picture let us establish the dual expressions for the isochoric derivatives

$$\left(\frac{\partial D_p}{\partial \ell n T}\right)_\upsilon, \quad \left(\frac{\partial L_p}{\partial \ell n T}\right)_\upsilon, \quad L_p\left(\frac{\partial D_p}{\partial \ell n T}\right)_\upsilon, \quad \left(\frac{\partial L_p}{\partial \ell n T}\right)_\upsilon \frac{1}{L_p}$$

One has

$$\left(\frac{\partial D_p}{\partial \ell n T}\right)_\upsilon = \left(\frac{\partial D_p}{\partial \ell n T}\right)_{\upsilon,\lambda} + \sum_{p'}\left(\frac{\partial D_p}{\partial L_{p'}}\right)_{\upsilon,T} : \left(\frac{\partial L_{p'}}{\partial \ell n T}\right)_\upsilon \tag{5-107}$$

but

$$\left(\frac{\partial L_{p'}}{\partial \ell n T}\right)_\upsilon = - L_{p'}\left(\frac{\partial L_{p'}^{-1}}{\partial \ell n T}\right)_\upsilon L_{p'}$$

$$= \beta L_{p'}\left(D_{p'} - \left(\frac{2\pi \nu'}{\hbar\beta}\right)^2 - \left(\frac{\partial D_{p'}}{\partial \ell n T}\right)_\upsilon\right) L_{p'} \tag{5-107a}$$

Here one observes that the first two terms are obtained by

differentiating $L_{p'}$ with respect to $\ell n\ T$ at fixed υ and fixed $D_{p'}$. It is then convenient to designate this part by

$$\left(\frac{\partial L_{p'}}{\partial \ell nT}\right)_{\upsilon, D} \equiv \beta L_{p'} \left(D_{p'} - \left(\frac{2\pi \nu'}{\hbar \beta}\right)^2\right) L_{p'} \tag{5-108}$$

For comparison we note that

$$\left(\frac{\partial L_{p'}}{\partial \ell nT}\right)_{\upsilon, \lambda} = \beta L_{p'} \left(D_{p'} - \left(\frac{2\pi \nu'}{\hbar \beta}\right)^2 - \left(\frac{\partial D_{p'}}{\partial \ell nT}\right)_{\upsilon, \lambda}\right) L_{p'}$$

$$= \left(\frac{\partial L_{p'}}{\partial \ell nT}\right)_{\upsilon, D} - \beta L_{p'} \left(\frac{\partial D_{p'}}{\partial \ell nT}\right)_{\upsilon, \lambda} L_{p'} \tag{5-109}$$

Thus

$$\left(\frac{\partial D_p}{\partial \ell nT}\right)_{\upsilon} = \left(\frac{\partial D_p}{\partial \ell nT}\right)_{\upsilon, \lambda} + \sum_{p'} \left(\frac{\partial D_p}{\partial L_{p'}}\right)_{\upsilon, T} : \left(\frac{\partial L_{p'}}{\partial \ell nT}\right)_{\upsilon, D}$$

$$- \sum_{p'} \overline{G}_{p;p'} : \left(\frac{\partial D_{p'}}{\partial \ell nT}\right)_{\upsilon}$$

or with

$$\overline{C}_{p;p'} = \left(\frac{1}{1 + \overline{G}}\right)_{p;p'} \tag{5-110}$$

$$\left(\frac{\partial D_p}{\partial \ell nT}\right)_{\upsilon} = \sum_{p'} \overline{C}_{p;p'} :$$

$$: \left(\left(\frac{\partial D_{p'}}{\partial \ell n T} \right)_{\upsilon, \lambda} + \sum_{p''} \left(\frac{\partial D_{p'}}{\partial L_{p''}} \right)_{\upsilon, T} : \left(\frac{\partial L_{p''}}{\partial \ell n T} \right)_{\upsilon, D} \right) \tag{5-111}$$

For the next quantity one finds

$$\left(\frac{\partial L_p}{\partial \ell n T} \right)_{\upsilon} = \left(\frac{\partial L_p}{\partial \ell n T} \right)_{\upsilon, D} - L_p \left(\frac{\partial D_p}{\partial \ell n T} \right)_{\upsilon, \lambda} L_p$$

$$\sum_{p'} \beta L_p \left(\frac{\partial D_p}{\partial L_{p'}} \right)_{\upsilon, T} L_p : \left(\frac{\partial L_{p'}}{\partial \ell n T} \right)_{\upsilon}$$

$$= \left(\frac{\partial L_p}{\partial \ell n T} \right)_{\upsilon, \lambda} - \sum_{p'} \tilde{G}_{p;p'} : \left(\frac{\partial L_{p'}}{\partial \ell n T} \right)_{\upsilon}$$

or with

$$\tilde{C}_{p;p'} = \left(\frac{1}{1 + \tilde{G}} \right)_{p;p'} \tag{5-110a}$$

$$\left(\frac{\partial L_p}{\partial \ell n T} \right)_{\upsilon} = \sum_{p'} \tilde{C}_{p;p'} : \left(\frac{\partial L_{p'}}{\partial \ell n T} \right)_{\upsilon, \lambda} \tag{5-111a}$$

The remaining two derivatives are easily shown to assume the form

$$L_p \left(\frac{\partial D_p}{\partial \ell n T} \right) = \sum_{p'} C_{p;p'} :$$

$$: \left(L_{p'} \left(\frac{\partial D_{p'}}{\partial \ell n T} \right)_{\upsilon,\lambda} + \sum_{p''} L_{p'} \left(\frac{\partial D_{p'}}{\partial L_{p''}} \right)_{\upsilon, T} : \left(\frac{\partial L_{p''}}{\partial \ell n T} \right)_{\upsilon, D} \right)$$

(5-111b)

and

$$\left(\frac{\partial L_p}{\partial \ell n T} \right)_{\upsilon} \frac{1}{L_p} = \sum_{p'} C_{p;p'} : \left(\frac{\partial L_{p'}}{\partial \ell n T} \right)_{\upsilon,\lambda} \frac{1}{L_{p'}} \tag{5-111c}$$

where

$$C_{p;p'} = \left(\frac{1}{1+G} \right)_{p;p'} \tag{5-110b}$$

is in Eq. (4-47) of the classical theory. One sees that the isochoric derivatives are more complicated than the isothermal ones. This is evidently due to L_p displaying an explicit temperature dependence. However, both derivatives contain the same information relevant to the question of the system's stability.

We can proceed to study the compressibility χ_T, the latent heat of expansion L_υ and the specific heat C_υ. We have first

$$\frac{1}{\chi_T} = - \upsilon \left(\frac{\partial P}{\partial \upsilon} \right)_T = \upsilon \left(\frac{\partial^2 \mathcal{K}}{\partial \upsilon^2} \right)_{T,\lambda}$$

$$+ \frac{1}{2\upsilon} \sum_p \mathrm{Tr} \left(\frac{\partial D_p}{\partial \ell n \upsilon} \right)_{T,\lambda} \left(\frac{\partial L_p}{\partial \ell n \upsilon} \right)_T \tag{5-112}$$

$$= \frac{1}{\chi_{st}} + \frac{1}{\upsilon} \sum_p \mathrm{Tr}\, L_p \int_0^1 d\xi \, \frac{-1}{2} \upsilon^2 \left(\frac{\partial^2 D_p(\upsilon, T, \lambda')}{\partial \upsilon^2} \right)_{T,\lambda'}$$

$$- \frac{1}{\upsilon} \sum_p \operatorname{Tr} L_p D_p \Gamma_{pT\lambda} \left(\frac{\partial L_p}{\partial \ell n \upsilon}\right)_T \frac{1}{L_p} \tag{5-112a}$$

$$= \frac{1}{\chi_{st}} + \frac{1}{\upsilon} \sum_p \operatorname{Tr} L_p D_p \overline{\left(\frac{-\upsilon^2}{2D_p} \frac{\partial^2 D_p}{\partial \upsilon^2}\right)}_{T,\lambda}$$

$$- \frac{2}{\upsilon} \sum_{p;p'} (L_p D_p \Gamma_{pT\lambda})^+ : C_{p;p'} : (\beta L_{p'} D_{p'} \Gamma_{p'T\lambda}) \tag{5-112b}$$

It will also be useful to write the second term of the above equation as

$$\frac{1}{\upsilon} \sum_p \operatorname{Tr} L_p D_p \left(\overline{\Gamma}_{pT\lambda} + 2\,\overline{\Gamma^2_{pT\lambda}} - \overline{\Gamma'}_{pT\lambda}\right) \tag{5-112c}$$

Introducing

$$\Delta_{p\upsilon} \equiv \left(\frac{\partial L_p}{\partial \ell n T}\right)_\upsilon \frac{1}{L_p} \tag{5-113}$$

$$\Delta_{p\upsilon\lambda} \equiv \left(\frac{\partial L_p}{\partial \ell n T}\right)_{\upsilon,\lambda} \frac{1}{L_p} \tag{5-113a}$$

$$\Delta_{p\upsilon D} \equiv \left(\frac{\partial L_p}{\partial \ell n T}\right)_{\upsilon,D} \frac{1}{L_p} \tag{5-113b}$$

and noting that

$$\Delta_{p\upsilon\lambda} = \beta L_p \left(D_p - \left(\frac{2\pi\nu}{\hbar\beta}\right)^2 - \left(\frac{\partial D_p}{\partial \ell n T}\right)_{\upsilon,\lambda} \right) \tag{5-113c}$$

$$= \Delta_{p\upsilon D} + 2\beta L_p D_p \Gamma_{p\upsilon\lambda} \tag{5-113d}$$

we have next

$$L_\upsilon = T\left(\frac{\partial P}{\partial T}\right)_\upsilon = -T\left(\frac{\partial^2 \mathcal{H}}{\partial \upsilon\, \partial T}\right)_\lambda$$

$$- \frac{1}{2\upsilon} \sum_p \mathrm{Tr}\left(\frac{\partial D_p}{\partial \ell n \upsilon}\right)_{T,\lambda} \left(\frac{\partial L_p}{\partial \ell n T}\right)_\upsilon \tag{5-114}$$

$$= -\frac{1}{2\upsilon} \sum_p \mathrm{Tr}\, L_p \int_0^1 d\xi \left(\frac{\partial^2 D_p(\upsilon, T, \lambda')}{\partial \ell n \upsilon\ \partial \ell n T}\right)_{\lambda'}$$

$$+ \frac{1}{\upsilon} \sum_p \mathrm{Tr}\, L_p D_p \Gamma_{pT\lambda} \left(\frac{\partial L_p}{\partial \ell n T}\right)_\upsilon \frac{1}{L_p} \tag{5-114a}$$

$$= \frac{1}{\upsilon} \sum_p \mathrm{Tr}\, L_p D_p \left(\overline{\frac{-1}{2D_p} \frac{\partial^2 D_p}{\partial \ell n \upsilon\, \partial \ell n T}}\right)_\lambda$$

$$+ \frac{1}{\upsilon} \sum_{p;p'} (L_p D_p \Gamma_{pT\lambda})^+ : C_{p;p'} : (\Delta_{p'\upsilon D} + 2\beta L_{p'} D_{p'} \Gamma_{p'\upsilon\lambda}) \tag{5-114b}$$

We begin to recognize the structure of the various thermal coefficients. In the classical limit Eq. (5-112b) goes over to Eqs (4-49 & 36), and Eq. (5-114b) to Eqs (4-51 & 40) if we recall the definition (5-113c) of $\Delta_{p\upsilon\lambda}$. We are left with the specific heat C_υ which is the more complicated of the three quantities under investigation. Using Eq. (5-107) for $(\partial D_p/\partial \ell n T)_\upsilon$ we have

$$\frac{1}{K} C_\upsilon = \frac{1}{K}\left(\frac{\partial U}{\partial T}\right)_\upsilon = -\frac{T}{K}\left(\frac{\partial^2 \mathcal{K}}{\partial T^2}\right)_{\upsilon,\lambda} + \frac{1}{2}\sum_p \mathrm{Tr}\,\beta L_p \left(\frac{\partial D_p}{\partial \ell n T}\right)_{\upsilon,\lambda}$$

$$\frac{1}{2}\sum_p \mathrm{Tr}\,\beta\left(D_p - \left(\frac{\partial D_p}{\partial \ell n T}\right)_{\upsilon,\lambda}\right)\left(\frac{\partial L_p}{\partial \ell n T}\right)_\upsilon$$

$$+ \frac{1}{2}\sum_{p;p'} \beta\, L_p \frac{\partial D_p}{\partial L_{p'}} : \left(\frac{\partial L_{p'}}{\partial \ell n T}\right)_\upsilon$$

$$+ \frac{1}{2}\sum_p \mathrm{Tr}\;\beta D_p \left(\frac{\partial L_p}{\partial \ell n T}\right)_\upsilon \tag{5-115}$$

$$= -\frac{T}{K}\left(\frac{\partial^2 \mathcal{K}}{\partial T^2}\right)_{\upsilon,\lambda} + \frac{1}{2}\sum_p \mathrm{Tr}\,\beta\, L_p\left(\frac{\partial D_p}{\partial \ell n T}\right)_{\upsilon,\lambda}$$

$$+ \frac{1}{2}\sum_p \mathrm{Tr}\,\beta\, L_p\left(D_p - \left(\frac{\partial D_p}{\partial \ell n T}\right)_{\upsilon,T}\right) : \Delta_{p\upsilon}$$

$$+ \frac{1}{2}\sum_{p;p'} G_{p;p'} : \Delta_{p'\upsilon} + \frac{1}{2}\sum_p \mathrm{Tr}\,\beta L_p D_p \Delta_{p\upsilon} \tag{5-115a}$$

Here we branch out to consider two further manipulations of Eq. (5-115a). The first one is devised to obtain an expression for C_υ which is comparable to the classical equations (4-50 & 37). For this purpose one makes use of the identity

$$\beta L_p \left(D_p + \left(\frac{2\pi\nu}{\hbar\beta}\right)^2\right) \equiv 1$$

to convert the last term of Eq. (5-115a) into

$$\frac{1}{2}\sum_{p}\left(1-\beta L_p\left(\frac{2\pi\nu}{\hbar\beta}\right)^2\right)\Delta_{p\upsilon}$$

Adding this to the second term of Eq. (5-115a) yields, according to Eq. (5-113c),

$$\frac{1}{2}\sum_{p}\mathrm{Tr}\,\Delta_{p\upsilon}+\frac{1}{2}\sum_{p}\mathrm{Tr}\,\Delta_{p\upsilon\lambda}\Delta_{p\upsilon}$$

Next, adding the third term of Eq. (5-115a) to the first term of the above equation results in

$$\frac{1}{2}\sum_{p}\mathrm{Tr}\,\Delta_{p\upsilon}+\frac{1}{2}\sum_{p;p'}G_{p;p'}\Delta_{p'\upsilon}=\frac{1}{2}\sum_{p}\mathrm{Tr}\,\Delta_{p\upsilon\lambda}$$

according to Eqs (5-113), (5-111c) and (5-113a). Lastly by adding this result to the second term of Eq. (5-115a) one obtains

$$\frac{1}{2}\sum_{p}\mathrm{Tr}\,\Delta_{p\upsilon\lambda}+\frac{1}{2}\sum_{p}\mathrm{Tr}\,\beta L_p\left(\frac{\partial D_p}{\partial \ell n T}\right)_{\upsilon,\lambda}=\frac{1}{2}\sum_{p}\mathrm{Tr}\,\Delta_{p\upsilon D}$$

Therefore

$$\frac{1}{K}C_\upsilon=-\frac{T}{K}\left(\frac{\partial^2\mathcal{K}}{\partial T^2}\right)_{\upsilon,\lambda}+\frac{1}{2}\sum_{p}\mathrm{Tr}\,\Delta_{p\upsilon D}$$

$$+\frac{1}{2}\sum_{p;p'}\Delta^{+}_{p\upsilon\lambda}:C_{p;p'}:\Delta_{p\upsilon\lambda} \qquad (5\text{-}115b)$$

If we now retain only the contributions with $p = \underset{\sim}{q}, 0$ and note that $\Delta_{qo\upsilon D} = 1$ we recover exactly Eqs (4-50 & 37). As it stands Eq. (5-115b) can be used to obtain quantum corrections to C_υ at high temperature, where a few values of ν need be taken into account. However it cannot be used for low temperature since, ultimately, the second term diverges. This divergence is of course compensated by opposite contributions arising from the last term of Eq. (5-115b). One observes indeed that

$$\frac{1}{2} \sum_p \mathrm{Tr}\left(\Delta_{p\upsilon D} + \Delta_{p\upsilon D} \Delta_{p\upsilon D} \right)$$

$$= \frac{1}{2} \sum_p \mathrm{Tr} \left(1 + \beta L_p D_p \left(D_p - \left(\frac{2\pi\nu}{\hbar\beta}\right)^2 \right) \right) \Delta_{p\upsilon D}$$

$$= \sum_p \mathrm{Tr}\, \beta L_p \Delta_{p\upsilon D}$$

converges. Thus, returning to Eq. (5-115a) we have in an alternative form comparable to Eqs (5-112b) and (5-114b)

$$\frac{1}{K} C_\upsilon = \sum_p \beta L_p D_p \left(\overline{\left(\frac{-T^2}{2D_p} \frac{\partial^2 D_p}{\partial T^2} \right)_{\upsilon,\lambda}} - \Gamma_{p\upsilon\lambda} \right)$$

$$+ \sum_{p\,p'p''} \beta \Bigg((L_p D_p)^+ 1_{p;p'} + (L_p D_p \Gamma_{p\upsilon\lambda})^+ 1_{p;p'}$$

$$+ \frac{1}{2} L_p D_p \left(\frac{1}{D_p} \frac{\partial D_p}{\partial L_{p'}} \right)_{\upsilon,T} L^+_{p'} \Bigg) :$$

$$: \; C_{p';p''} \; : \; (\Delta_{p''\upsilon D} + 2\beta L_{p''} D_{p''} \Gamma_{p''\upsilon\lambda}) \qquad (5\text{-}115c)$$

In practice, however, it is more convenient to write the first term of this equation in its original form

$$\sum_p L_p D_p \left(\frac{-T^2}{2D_p} \overline{\frac{\partial^2 D_p}{\partial T^2}} \right)_{\upsilon,\lambda} = -\frac{T}{K} \left(\frac{\partial^2 \mathcal{K}}{\partial T^2} \right)_{\upsilon,\lambda}$$

$$= -\beta^2 \left(\frac{\partial^2}{\partial \beta^2} \beta \mathcal{K}(\upsilon, T, \lambda) \right)_{\upsilon,\lambda}$$

which expresses the isofluctuational contribution of the potential function $\mathcal{K}(\upsilon, T, \lambda)$ to C_υ . Also, for future reference it will be useful to introduce the tensor

$$M_{p;p'} \equiv (L_p D_p)^+ 1_{p;p'} + (L_p D_p \Gamma_{p\upsilon\lambda})^+ 1_{p;p'}$$

$$+ \frac{1}{2} L_p \left(\frac{\partial D_p}{\partial L_{p'}} \right)_{\upsilon, T} L^+_{p'} \qquad (5\text{-}115d)$$

With Eqs (5-112b), (5-114b) and (5-115c) we dispose of a set of general relations which permits us to check any approximation calculated by other means. From a practical standpoint, however, the above equations are not yet very useful since they relate macroscopic quantities to a very large number of microscopic objects. Our next task is therefore to set up an intermediate theory aimed at facilitating the evaluation and interpretation of actual thermal data.

For this purpose let us focus our attention on the latent heat of expansion which is a mixed derivative of $\ell n Z$ with respect to υ and

T. Inspection of Eq. (5-114b) indicates that the different contributions to L_υ are weighted by the three factors

a) $L_p D_p$

b) $L_p D_p \Delta_{p\upsilon D}$

c) $L_p D_p \beta L_p D_p$

These factors are obtained in formally setting $C_{p;p'} = 1_{p;p'}$, $\Gamma_{pT\lambda} = \Gamma_{p\upsilon\lambda} = 1$ in Eq. (5-114b). In the classical limit all three factors were equal to KT times the unit matrix and this fact permitted us to introduce the parameter γ_{12} of Eq. (4-54). In the quantum case this simple procedure is no longer applicable and we must resolve L_υ into its three constituents. A suitable normalization of the latter will be given by the norm of the weighting factors. In dealing with the pressure equation we have already encountered the norm of the factors a), which amounts to twice the mean kinetic energy, and was designated by

$$E \equiv \sum_p \operatorname{Tr} L_p D_p \tag{5-95}$$

The norm of the factors b) is

$$\sum_p \operatorname{Tr} L_p D_p \Delta_{p\upsilon D} = \sum_p L_p D_p \beta L_p \left(D_p - \left(\frac{2\pi\nu}{\hbar\beta}\right)^2 \right)$$

$$= T \sum_p D_p \left(\frac{\partial L_p}{\partial T}\right)_{D_p} = T\left(\frac{\partial E}{\partial T}\right)_D \equiv T C_{\upsilon D} \tag{5-116}$$

Let us remark here that the specific heat $C_{\upsilon D}$ just defined is not the harmonic approximation to C_{υ}, in spite of the fact that it yields 3 NK in the classical limit by virtue of the generalized Dulong-Petit law established in section (4-2), Eq. (4-61). To find the norm of the factors c) one observes that, multiplying the factors a) by $\beta L_p(D_p + (\frac{2\pi\nu}{\hbar\beta})^2)$, which is a unit matrix by definition, and then adding the result to the factors b) yields

$$E + TC_{\upsilon D} = 2 \sum_{p} \mathrm{Tr}\, L_p D_p \beta L_p D_p \tag{5-116a}$$

This norm is seen to be dependent upon the former two. Now if we wish to set up the framework of an intermediate theory we are led to introduce parameters $\gamma_{12}^{a,b,c}$ as

$$E\gamma_{12}^{a} \equiv \sum_{p} \mathrm{Tr}\, L_p D_p \left(\frac{-1}{2D_p} \overline{\frac{\partial^2 D_p}{\partial \ell n\upsilon\, \partial \ell nT}} \right)_{\lambda} \tag{5-117a}$$

$$TC_{\upsilon D}\gamma_{12}^{b} \equiv \sum_{p;p'} (L_p D_p \Gamma_{pT\lambda})^{+} : C_{p;p'} : \Delta_{p'\upsilon D} \tag{5-117b}$$

and

$$(E + TC_{\upsilon D})\gamma_{12}^{c} \equiv 2 \sum_{p;p'} (L_p D_p \Gamma_{pT\lambda})^{+} : C_{p;p'} : \beta L_{p'} D_{p'} \Gamma_{p'\upsilon\lambda} \tag{5-117c}$$

The latent heat of expansion is then written as

$$L_{\upsilon} = \frac{1}{\upsilon} C_{\upsilon D} T(\gamma_{12}^{b} + \gamma_{12}^{c}) + \frac{1}{\upsilon} E(\gamma_{12}^{a} + \gamma_{12}^{c}) \tag{5-117}$$

Before commenting on the meaning of this equation let us consider the compressibility and specific heat. In the case of χ_T we have weighting factors of type a) and c) only and we set accordingly

$$E\gamma_{11}^{a} \equiv \sum_{p} \mathrm{Tr}\, L_p D_p \left(\overline{\Gamma}_{pT\lambda} + 2\overline{\Gamma^{2}}_{pT\lambda} - \overline{\Gamma'}_{pT\lambda}\right) \tag{5-118a}$$

and

$$(E + C_{\upsilon D} T)\gamma_{11}^{c} \equiv 2 \sum_{p;p'} (L_p D_p \Gamma_{pT\lambda})^{+} : C_{p;p'} : \beta L_{p'} D_{p'} \Gamma_{p'T\lambda} \tag{5-118b}$$

so as to write

$$\frac{1}{\chi_T} = \frac{1}{\chi_{st}} + \frac{1}{\upsilon} E(\gamma_{11}^{a} - \gamma_{11}^{c}) - \frac{1}{\upsilon} C_{\upsilon D} T \gamma_{11}^{c} \tag{5-118}$$

For the specific heat C_υ we have lastly

$$\beta E\gamma_{22}^{a} = -\beta^{2} \frac{\partial^{2}}{\partial \beta^{2}} (\beta \mathcal{H})_{\upsilon,\lambda} - \beta \sum_{p} L_p D_p \Gamma_{p\upsilon\lambda}$$

$$\frac{1}{K} C_{\upsilon D} \gamma_{22}^{b} = \sum_{p;p'p''} \beta M_{p;p'} : C_{p';p''} : \Delta_{p''\upsilon D}$$

$$(\beta E + \frac{1}{K} C_{\upsilon D})\gamma_{22}^{c} = \sum_{p;p'p''} \beta M_{p;p'} : C_{p';p''} : 2\beta L_{p''} D_{p''} \Gamma_{p''\upsilon\lambda}$$

so that

$$\frac{1}{K} C_\upsilon = \frac{1}{K} C_{\upsilon D}(\gamma_{22}^b + \gamma_{22}^c) + \beta E(\gamma_{22}^a + \gamma_{22}^c) \qquad (5\text{-}119)$$

It is now important to understand the meaning of the intermediate formalism presented above. For this purpose let us consider first the familiar harmonic approximation. Here, $\gamma_2 = 1$, $\gamma_{22}^a = 0$, $\gamma_{22}^b = 1$, $\gamma_{22}^c = 0$ and, evidently

$$E = E_h$$

$$C_\upsilon = C_{\upsilon D} = C_{\upsilon h}$$

Next, one has $\gamma_{12}^a = 0$, $\gamma_{12}^c = 0$, $\gamma_{12}^b = \gamma$, the usual Grüneisen parameter, and consequently

$$L_{\upsilon h} = \frac{T}{\upsilon} C_{\upsilon h} \gamma \qquad (5\text{-}117d)$$

It is in this approximation only that the latent heat of expansion is directly related to the specific heat. This fact explains why L_υ does not explicitly occur in the standard treatment of the thermal properties of crystal lattices. Lastly, one has $\gamma_1 = \gamma$, $\gamma_{11}^a = \gamma + 2\gamma^2$ and $\gamma_{11}^c = \gamma^2$. Furthermore with

$$\frac{1}{\chi_{st}(\upsilon)} = \frac{1}{\chi_o} + \mu P_{st} + 0\left(\frac{\upsilon - \upsilon_o}{\upsilon}\right)^2 \qquad (4\text{-}35a)$$

$$P = P_{st} + \frac{E}{\upsilon} \gamma_1 \qquad (5\text{-}91c)$$

that is

$$\frac{1}{\chi_{st}(\upsilon)} = \frac{1}{\chi_o} + \mu\left(P - \frac{E}{\upsilon} \gamma_1\right) + 0(\delta^2)$$

whereby, according to Eqs (4.33a to 4.34)

$$-\mu = \left(\frac{d\ell n\chi}{d\ell n\rho}\right)_{\rho=\rho_o} = 1 + \upsilon_o\left(\frac{d^3V_{st}}{d\upsilon^3} / \frac{d^2V_{st}}{d\upsilon^2}\right)_{\upsilon=\upsilon_o}$$

and setting $P = 0$ one obtains

$$\frac{1}{\chi_{Th}} = \frac{1}{\chi_o} + \left(2 + \upsilon_o\left(\frac{d^3V_{st}}{d\upsilon^3} / \frac{d^2V_{st}}{d\upsilon^2}\right)_{\upsilon=\upsilon_o}\right)\frac{E_h}{\upsilon}\gamma$$

$$- \frac{\gamma^2}{\upsilon}(C_{\upsilon h}T - E_h) \qquad (5\text{-}120)$$

which is Born & Huang's Eq. (4-55) (I, p. 51). In this framework, given V_{st}, E_h and $C_{\upsilon h}$ one interprets the thermal properties with the help of one single parameter which reflects the fact that $D_{qh}(\upsilon)$ is a function of υ only. This dependence is mediated by the static force constants $\varphi_{\alpha\beta}(R_\rho)$. The next step to be taken for improving this scheme is then to consider the dynamical matrices related to the effective force constants $\Phi_{\alpha\beta}(R_\rho, \lambda_\rho)$ which depend upon υ and λ but not upon T explicitly. This is the R.H.A. now treated.

In the R.H.A. the isochoric-isofluctuational derivatives $\Gamma_{\upsilon\lambda p}$ are zero. Therefore $\gamma^a_{22} = \gamma^c_{22} = 0$ and also $\gamma^a_{12} = \gamma^c_{12} = 0$. Next, the isothermal-isofluctuational derivative $\Gamma_{T\lambda \tilde{q}}$ will be assumed to be independent of $\tilde{q}$, which is true in the long wave limit where $D^{(I)}_{\tilde{q}}$ is a quadratic function of $\tilde{q}$. A further simplification will be made to replace the remaining quantity by a scalar function designated by $\Gamma_{T\lambda}$ as in the classical case (Eq. (4-45a)). Now, the new functions coming into play in the R.H.A. are the isothermal-isochoric derivatives $(\partial D_p / \partial L_p)_{\upsilon, T}$. Since $D^{(I)}_{\tilde{q}}(\upsilon, \lambda)$ is independent of ν we need only to consider $D^{(I)}_{\underset{\sim}{q}}$ as a function of the set of $L_{\underset{\sim}{q}'}(0) = \sum_{\nu} L_{\underset{\sim}{q}'\nu}$.

Deleting the roman index I for simplicity we start from

$$D_{\underset{\sim}{q}\alpha\beta} = \frac{1}{M} \sum_{\rho}{}' (1 - \cos(\underset{\sim}{q}\underset{\sim}{R}_\rho)) \Phi_{\alpha\beta}(R_\rho, \lambda_\rho)$$

and find

$$\left(\frac{\partial D_{\underset{\sim}{q}\alpha\beta}}{\partial L_{\underset{\sim}{q}'\gamma\delta}}\right)_{\upsilon, T} = \frac{1}{NM^2} \sum_{\rho} (1 - \cos \underset{\sim}{q}\underset{\sim}{R}_\rho)(1 - \cos \underset{\sim}{q}'\underset{\sim}{R}_\rho)$$

$$\times \Phi_{\alpha\beta\gamma\delta}(R_\rho, \lambda_\rho) \qquad (5\text{-}121)$$

Inspecting this vertex tensor, we see that in the long wave limit it factorizes into a product of quadratic forms in $\underset{\sim}{q}$ and $\underset{\sim}{q}'$. This important feature is known to greatly simplify the calculations. It is then natural to synthesize the effect of the vertex corrections by setting

$$\frac{\partial D_{\underset{\sim}{q}\alpha\beta}}{\partial L_{q'\gamma\delta}(0)} \equiv D_{\underset{\sim}{q}\alpha\beta} \frac{1}{N} Y(\upsilon, \lambda) D_{\underset{\sim}{q}'\gamma\delta} \qquad (5\text{-}121a)$$

the quantity $Y(\upsilon, \lambda)$ being again taken as a scalar function of υ and λ for simplicity. This is done so as to reduce the number of microscopic parameters to a minimum and to then learn how the intermediate coefficients $\gamma_{ij}^{a,b,c}$ are related to these microscopic parameters and to one another. We note that since

$$Y(\upsilon, \lambda) \sim \Phi_{(IV)}/(\Phi^2_{(II)})$$

its inverse has the dimension of energy. Lastly we suppose that $D_{\underset{\sim}{q}}$ has been diagonalized so as to yield

$$\sum_{\beta} D_{\underset{\sim}{q}\alpha\beta}\, e^{j}_{\beta}(\underset{\sim}{q}) = e^{j}_{\alpha}(\underset{\sim}{q})\, \Omega^{2}_{\underset{\sim}{q}j} \tag{5-122}$$

Then, invoking again the convention that $\underset{\sim}{q}, j \equiv q$ we have

$$E^{(I)} = \sum_{\underset{\sim}{q}\nu} \operatorname{Tr} D_{\underset{\sim}{q}} L_{\underset{\sim}{q}\nu} = \sum_{\underset{\sim}{q}} \operatorname{Tr} D_{\underset{\sim}{q}} L_{\underset{\sim}{q}}(0)$$

$$= \sum_{q} \frac{1}{2}\hbar\Omega_q \operatorname{Cotgh} \frac{1}{2}\beta\hbar\Omega_q$$

and

$$C^{(I)}_{\upsilon D} \equiv C_{\Omega} = \left(\frac{\partial E^{(I)}}{\partial T}\right)_{\Omega}$$

$$= K \sum_{q} \left(\frac{1}{2}\beta\hbar\Omega_q \,/\, \operatorname{Sh}\frac{1}{2}\beta\hbar\Omega_q\right)^{2}$$

Gathering all the elements prepared up to now we have next

$$\sum_{\underset{\sim}{q}\nu} \operatorname{Tr}\beta D_{\underset{\sim}{q}} \left(\frac{\partial L_{\underset{\sim}{q}\nu}}{\partial \ell n T}\right)_{\upsilon} \equiv \frac{1}{K} C_{\Omega}$$

$$- \sum_{\underset{\sim}{q}\nu,\, \underset{\sim}{q}'\nu'} \operatorname{Tr}\beta\, D_{\underset{\sim}{q}} L_{\underset{\sim}{q}\nu}\, D_{\underset{\sim}{q}} \frac{Y}{N} L_{\underset{\sim}{q}\nu}\, \beta D_{\underset{\sim}{q}'} \left(\frac{\partial L_{q'\nu'}}{\partial \ell n T}\right)_{\upsilon}$$

$$= \frac{1}{K} C_\Omega - (E^{(I)} + C_\Omega T) \frac{Y}{2N} \sum_{\underset{\sim}{q}'\nu'} \mathrm{Tr}\beta D_{\underset{\sim}{q}'} \left(\frac{\partial L_{\underset{\sim}{q}'\nu'}}{\partial \ln T} \right)_\upsilon$$

or, setting

$$\frac{1}{N} E^{(I)} \equiv \varepsilon \tag{5-123}$$

and

$$\frac{1}{N} C_\Omega T \equiv \varepsilon' \tag{5-123a}$$

$$\sum_{\underset{\sim}{q}} \mathrm{Tr} \;\beta D_{\underset{\sim}{q}} \left(\frac{\partial L_{\underset{\sim}{q}}(0)}{\partial \ln T} \right)_{\upsilon, I} = \frac{1}{K} C_\Omega \frac{1}{1 + \frac{1}{2}(\varepsilon + \varepsilon')Y}$$

Furthermore

$$\frac{1}{2} \sum_{\underset{\sim}{q}\nu, \underset{\sim}{q}'\nu'} \beta L_{\underset{\sim}{q}'\nu'} \frac{\partial D_{\underset{\sim}{q}}}{\partial L_{\underset{\sim}{q}'\nu'}} : \left(\frac{\partial L_{\underset{\sim}{q}'\nu'}}{\partial \ln T} \right)_\upsilon$$

$$= \frac{1}{2} \sum_{\underset{\sim}{q}, \underset{\sim}{q}'} \mathrm{Tr}\, \beta L_{\underset{\sim}{q}}(0)\, D_{\underset{\sim}{q}} \frac{Y}{N} D_{\underset{\sim}{q}'} \left(\frac{\partial L_{\underset{\sim}{q}'}(0)}{\partial \ln T} \right)_\upsilon$$

$$= \frac{1}{2K} \varepsilon Y C_\Omega \frac{1}{1 + \frac{1}{2}(\varepsilon + \varepsilon')Y}$$

and, therefore

$$C_{\upsilon}^{(I)} = C_{\Omega}\left(1 + \frac{1}{2}\,\varepsilon\, Y\right) \frac{1}{1 + \frac{1}{2}(\varepsilon + \varepsilon')Y} \tag{5-124}$$

We see that under the assumption of a polarisation and wave vector independent vertex function $Y(\upsilon, \lambda)$, the specific heat in the R. H. A. can be written in a simple form which permits us to draw some interesting conclusions. In the next chapter we shall investigate this question rather closely. From (5-124) it follows that

$$\gamma_{22}^{b(I)} = \left(1 + \frac{1}{2}\,\varepsilon\, Y\right) \frac{1}{1 + \frac{1}{2}(\varepsilon + \varepsilon')\, Y} \tag{5-124a}$$

This is an equation which relates the intermediate coefficient $\gamma_{22}^{b(I)}$ to the microscopic parameters of the system. We note that, in the classical limit $\gamma_{22}^{b(I)}$ becomes

$$\frac{1}{2} + \frac{1}{2}\,\frac{1}{1 + 3\,KTY}$$

of Eq. (4-64). Considering the inverse of Eq. (5-124a) we find that its zero temperature limit and its classical limit are given by

$$\frac{1}{\gamma_{22}^{b(I)}} = 1 + \frac{\frac{1}{2}\,\varepsilon' Y}{1 + \frac{1}{2}\,\varepsilon Y} = \begin{cases} 1 & T = 0 \\ 1 + \dfrac{\frac{3}{2} KTY}{1 + \frac{3}{2} KTY} & T \gg 0 \end{cases}$$

These limits provide a preliminary idea about the variation of $\gamma_{22}^{b(I)}$ as a function of T. Performing similar manipulations upon the compressibility we find, with $\rho = N/\upsilon$

$$\frac{1}{\chi_T^{(I)}} = \upsilon\left(\frac{\partial^2 \mathcal{K}^{(I)}}{\partial \upsilon^2}\right)_\lambda + \frac{1}{2\upsilon}\sum_{\underset{\sim}{q}\nu} \mathrm{Tr}\left(\frac{\partial D_{\underset{\sim}{q}}}{\partial \ln \upsilon}\right)_\lambda \left(\frac{\partial L_{\underset{\sim}{q}\nu}}{\partial \ln \upsilon}\right)_T$$

$$= \frac{1}{\chi_{st}} + \rho\,\varepsilon\,(\bar{\Gamma}_{T\lambda} + 2\bar{\Gamma}^2_{T\lambda} - \bar{\Gamma}'_{T\lambda})$$

$$- \rho\,(\varepsilon + \varepsilon')\,\Gamma_{T\lambda}\frac{1}{1 + \frac{1}{2}(\varepsilon + \varepsilon')\,Y}\,\Gamma_{T\lambda} \tag{5-125}$$

and consequently

$$\gamma_{22}^{a(I)} = \bar{\Gamma}_{T\lambda} + 2\,\bar{\Gamma}^2_{T\lambda} - \bar{\Gamma}'_{T\lambda} \tag{5-125a}$$

$$\gamma_{22}^{c(I)} = \Gamma_{T\lambda}\,\frac{1}{1 + \frac{1}{2}(\varepsilon + \varepsilon')\,Y}\,\Gamma_{T\lambda} \tag{5-125b}$$

We notice here the occurrence of the isothermal Grüneisen parameter

$$\Gamma_T = \Gamma_{T\lambda}\,\frac{1}{1 + \frac{1}{2}(\varepsilon + \varepsilon')\,Y} \tag{5-126}$$

which we have encountered in the classical theory. From the high temperature limit of this equation, it follows in particular that the factor g of Eq. (4-45d) is given by

$$g = 3\,KT\,Y \tag{5-127}$$

Proceeding with the latent heat of expansion we have lastly

$$L_{\upsilon}^{(I)} = \frac{-1}{2\upsilon} \sum_{\underset{\sim}{q}\nu} \mathrm{Tr} \left(\frac{\partial D_{\underset{\sim}{q}}}{\partial \ell n \upsilon} \right)_{T\lambda} \left(\frac{\partial L_{\underset{\sim}{q}\nu}}{\partial \ell n\ T} \right)_{\upsilon}$$

$$= \frac{T}{\upsilon}\ \Gamma_{T\lambda}\ \frac{1}{1 + \frac{1}{2}(\varepsilon + \varepsilon')\ Y}\ C_{\Omega} \qquad (5\text{-}128)$$

$$= \frac{T}{\upsilon}\ C_{\Omega}\ \Gamma_{T} = \rho\ \varepsilon'\ \Gamma_{T} \qquad (5\text{-}128a)$$

and consequently

$$\gamma_{12}^{b(I)} = \Gamma_{T} \qquad (5\text{-}128b)$$

It is thus apparent that, both from a theoretical and experimental point of view, the latent heat of expansion deserves more attention than has been given in the past. From Eqs (5-124) and (5-128) it follows that the important ratio $\upsilon L_{\upsilon}/TC_{\upsilon}$ now reads

$$\frac{\upsilon L_{\upsilon}^{(I)}}{T\ C_{\upsilon}^{(I)}} = \frac{\gamma_{12}^{b(I)}}{\gamma_{22}^{b(I)}} = \Gamma_{T\lambda}\ \frac{1}{1 + \frac{1}{2}\varepsilon Y} \qquad (5\text{-}129)$$

In the present approximation we observe that the usual designation of this ratio as Grüneisen parameter no longer applics. We find instead partial cancellations of vertex corrections between $L_{\upsilon}^{(I)}$ and $C_{\upsilon}^{(I)}$ which result in a ratio differing both from $\Gamma_{T\lambda}$ and Γ_{T}.

In short, the simplified R. H. A. just treated suggests that, given representative expressions for V_{st}, ε and ε' one trics to analyze $L_{\upsilon}, C_{\upsilon}, \chi_{T}$ and C_{p} data in terms of the intermediate coefficients $\gamma_{ij}^{a,b,c}$ and then correlate the latter with the two microscopic parameters $\Gamma_{T\lambda}$ and Y. At this stage already, we see how modifications of this framework can be made so that more general situations are gradually covered. For example, deleting the isotropy assumption results in distinguishing polarization dependent parameters $\Gamma_{T\lambda j}$ and $Y_{jj'}$. Next, permitting some explicit temperature dependence of the dynamical matrices leads to introducing isochoric-isofluctuational parameters $\Gamma_{\upsilon\lambda}$ and consequently to relating the ten coefficients γ_i and $\gamma_{ij}^{a,b,c}$ to the three fundamental tensors $\Gamma_{T\lambda}$, $\Gamma_{\upsilon\lambda}$ and Y. However, proceeding with such generalizations assumes a deeper understanding of the new features brought about by the R. H. A., to interpret and predict the temperature dependence of the thermal coefficients. Actually this remark also applies to the questions raised by the hard core problem as dealt with in section (4-4). It will be more profitable to postpone the quantum theoretical generalization of this treatment until the consequences entailed by the integrability assumption of the interatomic potential functions have been fully clarified. Qualitative and, for some specific models, quantitative answers to these questions will be given in the forthcoming sections.

We now wish to terminate this chapter with the zero temperature limit of some of the equations established above, thus completing the presentation which started with the classical theory valid at high temperature. As $\beta \to \infty$ we introduce the continuous variable

$$\frac{2\pi\nu}{\hbar\beta} \to \omega \quad , \quad \frac{2\pi}{\hbar\beta} \to d\omega \tag{5-130}$$

thus, $D_{q\nu}^{(\ell)}$, actually a function of $\frac{2\pi\nu}{\hbar\beta}$, becomes $D_{\underset{\sim}{q}}^{(\ell)}(\omega)$, furthermore

$$\beta L_{\underset{\sim}{q}\nu} \to \frac{1}{\omega^2 + D_{\underset{\sim}{q}}^{(s)} + D_{\underset{\sim}{q}}^{(\ell)}(\omega)} = \mathcal{L}_{\underset{\sim}{q}}(\omega) = \mathcal{L}_{\underset{\sim}{q}}(-\omega) \tag{5-131}$$

$$\sum_{\nu=-\infty}^{+\infty} \to \frac{\hbar\beta}{2\pi} \int_{-\infty}^{+\infty} d\omega$$

In this limit the mean kinetic energy

$$\frac{1}{2} E = \frac{1}{2} \sum_{\underset{\sim}{q}\nu} \text{Tr } L_{\underset{\sim}{q}\nu} D_{\underset{\sim}{q}\nu}$$

becomes, if we set

$$D_{\underset{\sim}{q}}(\omega) = D_{\underset{\sim}{q}}^{(s)} + D_{\underset{\sim}{q}}^{(\ell)}(\omega) \tag{5-132}$$

$$\frac{1}{2} E_o = \sum_{\underset{\sim}{q}} \text{Tr } \frac{\hbar}{4\pi} \int d\omega \, \mathcal{L}_{\underset{\sim}{q}}(\omega) \, D_{\underset{\sim}{q}}(\omega) \tag{5-133}$$

Let us consider next a typical contribution with n linking lines in the potential function $\mathcal{K}^{(II)}$ for example. Letting aside all the factors not relevant to the point we have an expression of the type

$$\sum_{\nu_1 .. \nu_n} \int_o^\beta d\tau \; e^{\frac{2i\pi\tau}{\beta}(\nu_1 + \nu_2 + .. \nu_n)} L_{\underset{\sim}{q}_1 \nu_1} .. L_{\underset{\sim}{q}_n \nu_n}$$

$$= \sum_{\nu_1 .. \nu_n} \beta \, \delta_{\nu_1 + \nu_2 + .. \nu_n, 0} \; L_{\underset{\sim}{q}_1 \nu_1} .. L_{\underset{\sim}{q}_n \nu_n}$$

which, with

$$\beta \delta_{\nu_1+\nu_2+\,..\,\nu_n, o} = \beta \delta_{\frac{\hbar\beta}{2\pi}(\omega_1+\,...\,\omega_n)} \to \frac{2\pi}{\hbar}\,\delta(\omega_1+\,...\,\omega_n)$$

becomes, at $T = 0$

$$\left(\frac{\hbar}{2\pi}\right)^{(n-1)} \int_{-\infty}^{+\infty} d\omega_1\, d\omega_2 \,...\, d\omega_n\, \delta(\omega_1+\,..\,\omega_n)\, \mathcal{L}_{\underset{\sim}{q}_1}(\omega_1) ... \mathcal{L}_{\underset{\sim}{q}_n}(\omega_n)$$

If $\mathcal{K}_o$ designates the zero temperature limit of the irreducible cumulant expansion $\mathcal{K}$, the s.c. Eq. (5-89a)

$$\frac{1}{2} D_{\underset{\sim}{q}\nu} = \left(\frac{\partial \mathcal{K}}{\partial L_{\underset{\sim}{q}\nu}}\right)_{\upsilon,\tau} = \frac{2\pi}{\hbar}\left(\frac{\partial \mathcal{K}}{(\frac{2\pi}{\hbar\beta}\,\beta L_{\underset{\sim}{q}\nu})}\right)_{\upsilon,\tau}$$

goes over to the functional derivative

$$\frac{1}{2} D_{\underset{\sim}{q}}(\omega) = \frac{2\pi}{\hbar}\left(\frac{\partial \mathcal{K}_o}{\partial(d\omega\, \mathcal{L}_q(\omega))}\right)_{\upsilon,o} = \frac{2\pi}{\hbar}\left(\frac{\delta \mathcal{K}_o}{\delta \mathcal{L}_q(\omega)}\right)_{\upsilon,o} \tag{5-134}$$

Thus, at $T = 0$, the energy U_o and pressure P read

$$U_o(\upsilon, o, \lambda) = \frac{1}{2} E_o + \mathcal{K}_o \tag{5-135}$$

$$= V_{st} + \sum_{\underset{\sim}{q}} \mathrm{Tr}\, \frac{\hbar}{4\pi} \int_{-\infty}^{+\infty} d\omega\, \mathcal{L}_{\underset{\sim}{q}}(\omega)\left((D_{\underset{\sim}{q}}(\omega,\lambda) + \int_0^1 d\xi\, D_q(\omega, \xi\lambda)\right) \tag{5-135a}$$

and

$$P(\upsilon, o, \lambda) = -\left(\frac{\partial \mathcal{H}_o}{\partial \upsilon}\right)_\lambda = \frac{1}{3\upsilon} E_o - \left(\frac{\partial \mathcal{H}_o}{\partial \upsilon}\right)_w$$

$$= P_{st} - \sum_{\underset{\sim}{q}} \mathrm{Tr} \frac{\hbar}{4\pi} \int_{-\infty}^{+\infty} d\omega\, \mathcal{L}_{\underset{\sim}{q}}(\omega) \int_0^1 d\xi \left(\frac{\partial D_{\underset{\sim}{q}}(\upsilon, \omega, \xi\lambda)}{\partial \upsilon}\right)_\lambda \quad (5\text{-}136)$$

Finally, for the compressibility we find, with β times the vertex tensor $G_{\underset{\sim}{q}\nu;\underset{\sim}{q}'\nu'}$ of Eq. (5-104b) becoming

$$\mathcal{G}_{\underset{\sim}{q};\underset{\sim}{q}'}(\omega, \omega') = 2\left(\frac{2\pi}{\hbar}\right)^2 \mathcal{L}_{\underset{\sim}{q}}(\omega) \frac{\delta^2 \mathcal{H}_o}{\delta \mathcal{L}_{\underset{\sim}{q}}(\omega)\, \delta \mathcal{L}_{\underset{\sim}{q}'}(\omega')} \mathcal{L}^+_{\underset{\sim}{q}'}(\omega') \quad (5\text{-}137)$$

with β times the tensor $C_{q\nu;q'\nu'}$ of Eq. (5-110b) satisfying the integral equation

$$\mathcal{C}_{q;q'}(\omega, \omega') = \frac{2\pi}{\hbar} \delta_{\underset{\sim}{q};\underset{\sim}{q}'}(\omega - \omega') - \sum_{\underset{\sim}{q}'} \frac{\hbar}{2\pi} \int_{-\infty}^{+\infty} d\omega''\, \mathcal{G}_{\underset{\sim}{q}';\underset{\sim}{q}''}(\omega, \omega'') : \mathcal{C}_{\underset{\sim}{q}'';\underset{\sim}{q}'}(\omega'', \omega') \quad (5\text{-}138)$$

$$\frac{1}{\chi_o} = \frac{1}{\chi_{st}} + \frac{1}{\upsilon} \sum_{\underset{\sim}{q}} \mathrm{Tr} \frac{\hbar}{2\pi} \int_{-\infty}^{+\infty} d\omega \int_0^1 d\xi\, \mathcal{L}_{\underset{\sim}{q}}(\omega) \left(\frac{-\upsilon^2}{2} \frac{\partial^2 D_{\underset{\sim}{q}}(\upsilon, \omega, \xi\lambda)}{\partial \upsilon^2}\right)_\lambda$$

$$- \frac{2}{\upsilon} \sum_{\underset{\sim}{q};\underset{\sim}{q}'} \left(\frac{\hbar}{2\pi}\right)^2 \int_{-\infty}^{+\infty} d\omega\, d\omega' \left(\mathcal{L}_{\underset{\sim}{q}}(\omega)\, D_{\underset{\sim}{q}}(\omega)\, \Gamma_{\underset{\sim}{q}o\lambda}(\omega)\right)^+ : \mathcal{C}_{\underset{\sim}{q};\underset{\sim}{q}'}(\omega, \omega') :$$

$$\times \left(\mathcal{L}_{\underset{\sim}{q}'}(\omega')\, D_{\underset{\sim}{q}'}(\omega')\, \Gamma_{\underset{\sim}{q}'o\lambda}(\omega')\right) \quad (5\text{-}139)$$

We see again that Eqs (5-137) and (5-138) yield informations about the stability of the anharmonic crystal. A preliminary analysis of this important question is reported in the next, and last, chapter.

Chapter 6

DYNAMICAL STABILITY

It has thus far been tacitly assumed that the s. c. Eqs (5-84) possess stable solutions in a certain domain of temperatures and densities. Here, these implications are inspected more closely, through model analysis of the s. c. equations. Then a few applications to problems of current interest in crystal physics are discussed. Lastly some investigations regarding the problem of a molecular field theory of crystallization are outlined.

6-1 ISOTROPIC MODELS IN THE R. H. A.

In the R. H. A. we have a set of implicit matrix equations relating, on the one hand, the dynamical matrices $D_{\underset{\sim}{q}}$ to the correlation functions λ_ρ and to the lattice constant a via the effective force constants $A_\rho(a, \lambda_\rho)$ and, on the other hand, the λ_ρ's to the $D_{\underset{\sim}{q}}$'s and to the temperature via the expectation values $\langle Q_{\underset{\sim}{qj}} Q^*_{\underset{\sim}{qj}} \rangle$. In order to learn how this situation can be dealt with, it is worth while treating examples amenable to practical analysis.

To begin with we consider the pedagogical case of the linear chain with nearest neighbors interactions. Deleting the index 1 of λ_1 for simplicity we have, here

$$\omega_q^2 = (1-\cos qa)\,\frac{2\,A(a,\lambda)}{M} \tag{6-1}$$

$$\lambda = \frac{2}{MN}\sum_q (1-\cos qa)\,\langle Q_q Q_{-q}\rangle$$

$$= \frac{1}{N}\sum_q (1-\cos qa)\,\frac{\hbar}{M\omega_q}\,\mathrm{Cothh}\tfrac{1}{2}\beta\hbar\omega_q$$

$$= \frac{1}{N}\sum_q (1-\cos qa)^{\frac{1}{2}}\,\frac{\hbar}{\sqrt{2MA}}\,\mathrm{Cotgh}\tfrac{1}{2}\beta\hbar\omega_q \tag{6-1a}$$

$$A(a,\lambda) = \left(\frac{\partial^2\Phi(a,\lambda)}{\partial a^2}\right)_\lambda = 2\left(\frac{\partial\Phi(a,\lambda)}{\partial\lambda}\right)_a \tag{6-1b}$$

The next quantity of interest is ε defined by Eq. (5-123), that is, twice the mean kinetic energy

$$\varepsilon = \frac{1}{M}\langle p_s^2\rangle = \frac{1}{N}\sum_q \langle P_q P_{-q}\rangle = \frac{1}{N}\sum_q \omega_q^2\langle Q_q Q_{-q}\rangle \tag{6-2}$$

We have indeed the dual expressions, generally valid in any self-linked approximation, namely

$$\varepsilon = \frac{1}{2N} \sum_q \hbar\omega_q \, \mathrm{Cotgh} \frac{1}{2} \beta\hbar\omega_q \tag{6-2a}$$

and

$$\varepsilon = \frac{1}{2} \sum_\rho \lambda_\rho A_\rho = \lambda A(a, \lambda) = 2\lambda \frac{\partial\Phi(a, \lambda)}{\partial\lambda} \tag{6-2b}$$

It is recalled that the latter relation is obtained by introducing ω_q^2 in Eq. (6-2), by permuting the summations over q and ρ, and by using the definition of λ_ρ. For completeness we have also the pressure equation

$$P = -\left(\frac{\partial\Phi(a, \lambda)}{\partial a}\right)_\lambda \tag{6-3}$$

It is noted that, in the example now treated, there is one internal state variable λ. Thus, with Eqs (6-1, a, b; 6-2 a, b; 6-3) and given T, P as well as a bare potential function $\varphi(a)$, the problem is, in principle, completely determined. To see this more precisely, we introduce some convenient notations. Let

$$m = \left(\frac{\pi}{2\sqrt{2}}\right)^2 M$$

$$\omega = \frac{2\sqrt{2}}{\pi} \omega_{qa=\frac{\pi}{2}} = \frac{2\sqrt{2}}{\pi} \sqrt{\frac{2A}{M}} = \sqrt{\frac{2A}{m}}$$

that is

$$\omega_q = \frac{\pi}{2\sqrt{2}} \omega (1-\cos qa)^{\frac{1}{2}} = \frac{\pi}{2} \omega \left|\sin(q\frac{a}{2})\right|$$

and let

$$\vartheta = \beta\hbar\omega$$

then

$$\lambda = \frac{\hbar}{m\omega}\frac{\pi}{N}\sum_q{}' \sin(\tfrac{qa}{2})\ \mathrm{Cotgh}(\tfrac{\pi}{4}\vartheta\sin\tfrac{qa}{2}) \tag{6-4}$$

Setting

$$\varphi = \frac{qa}{2}$$

$$\frac{\pi}{N}\sum_q{}' \rightarrow \int_0^{\pi/2} d\varphi$$

and defining the function

$$I(\vartheta) = \int_0^{\pi/2} d\varphi\ \sin\varphi\ \ \mathrm{Cotgh}(\tfrac{\pi}{4}\vartheta\sin\varphi) \tag{6-4a}$$

which, at $T = 0$, is unity and in the classical limit is $\frac{2}{\vartheta} = \frac{2KT}{\hbar\omega}$,we can write

$$\lambda = \frac{\hbar}{m\omega} I(\vartheta) \tag{6-4b}$$

with the two limits of particular interest

$$\lambda = \frac{\hbar}{m\omega} = \frac{2}{\pi}\frac{\hbar}{\sqrt{MA}} \qquad T = 0$$

$$\lambda = \frac{2KT}{m\omega^2} = \frac{KT}{A} \qquad KT > \hbar\omega$$

For the energy ε we have next, from Eq (6-2a)

$$\varepsilon = \frac{\hbar\omega}{2}\ \frac{\pi}{N} \sum_q{}' \sin\left(\frac{qa}{2}\right) \ \mathrm{Cotgh}\left(\frac{\pi}{4}\ \vartheta \sin\frac{qa}{2}\right)$$

$$= \frac{\hbar\omega}{2}\ I(\vartheta) \tag{6-5}$$

On the other hand, from Eq. (6-2b) and $A = \frac{1}{2} m\omega^2$,we have also

$$\varepsilon = \frac{1}{2} m\omega^2 \lambda = 2\lambda \frac{\partial \Phi}{\partial \lambda} \tag{6-5a}$$

Designating the potential energy per atom by

$$\psi(a, \lambda) = 2\,\Phi(a, \lambda) \tag{6-5b}$$

the above relations are then usefully re-written in the sequence

$$\varepsilon = \lambda \left(\frac{\partial \psi}{\partial \lambda}\right)_a \tag{6-6}$$

$$\frac{\hbar^2}{2m}\ I^2(\vartheta) = \varepsilon\,\lambda \tag{6-7}$$

$$\frac{m}{2}\ \omega^2 = \varepsilon/\lambda \tag{6-8}$$

$$P = -\frac{1}{2}\left(\frac{\partial \psi}{\partial a}\right)_\lambda \tag{6-3}$$

Indeed, the procedure of analysis is as follows. Given a lattice constant a and an interatomic potential function φ (a) we construct $\Phi(a,\lambda)$ and $\frac{\partial\Phi}{\partial\lambda}$. To a given value of λ corresponds a certain $\varepsilon(a,\lambda)$. In the classical limit this yields directly $T(a,\lambda)$ owing to the kinetic energy sum rule. In general the quantity $\vartheta(a,\lambda)$ is first obtained with the help of the product $\varepsilon\lambda$. Next, with the ratio ε/λ we determine $\omega^2(a,\lambda)$ and then find $T = \frac{\hbar\omega}{K\vartheta} = T(a,\lambda)$, that is, also $\lambda(a,T)$. Finally the pressure equation is used to find $a(P,\lambda)$ and $a(P,T)$. Of course it is desirable to eliminate, wherever possible, first a as a function of P,λ and to proceed as indicated above. From this example already, we see that it is desirable to know more about Eq. (6-6). This is the object of the next section.

As a second example, we consider a mono atomic cubic crystal with nearest neighbor interactions in a λ_ρ isotropic and Debye spherical limit. This will again provide a model with one internal state variable.

Designating by λ_n one component of λ_ρ for the nth shell of neighbors, we start from the equation for the trace

$$3\lambda_n = \frac{1}{MN}\sum_{\underset{\sim}{q}j}(1-\cos\underset{\sim}{q}\underset{\sim}{R}_n)\,\frac{\hbar}{\omega_{\underset{\sim}{q}j}}\,\mathrm{Cotgh}\frac{1}{2}\beta\hbar\omega_{\underset{\sim}{q}j}$$

Setting next

$$\omega_{\underset{\sim}{q}j} = S\,q$$

$$\omega_D = S\,q_D = \frac{K\Theta_D}{\hbar}$$

$$q/q_D = u$$

$$\frac{1}{N}\sum_{\underset{\sim}{q}} = \frac{3}{4\pi q_D^3}\int_0^{q_D} d^3q = \frac{3}{4\pi}\int_0^1 d^3u$$

where $\frac{4\pi}{3}q_D^3$ is equal to the volume of the first Brillouin zone and defining for convenience

$$\omega = \frac{1}{2}\,\omega_D$$

$$m = \frac{4}{3}\,M$$

$$\vartheta = h\omega/KT$$

$$x_n = q\,R_n$$

results in

$$\lambda_n = \frac{1}{3}\,\frac{3\hbar}{M\omega}\,\frac{3}{4\pi}\int_0^1 d^3u\,(1-\cos \underset{\sim}{q}\,\underset{\sim}{R}_n)\,\frac{1}{u}\,\mathrm{Cotgh}\,\vartheta u$$

Integration over the angular variable yields

$$\lambda_n = \frac{3\hbar}{M\omega}\int_0^1 du\,u\,(1-\frac{\sin u\,x_n}{u\,x_n})\,\mathrm{Cotgh}\,\vartheta u$$

$$= \frac{\hbar}{m\omega}\,I\,(\vartheta, x_n) \qquad (6\text{-}9)$$

whereby

$$I(\vartheta, x_n) = 2\int_0^1 du\,u\,(1-\frac{\sin(u\,x_n)}{u\,x_n})\,\mathrm{Cotgh}(\vartheta u) \qquad (6\text{-}9a)$$

We see that λ_n possesses a term which oscillates as a function of x_n with decreasing amplitude and that, as $n \to \infty$, λ_n approaches an asymptotic value which appears in the exponent of the Debye-Waller factor as shown in Eq. (2-13). Identification of 1/2 time the motional fluctuation parameter $w = \lambda_\infty/a^2$ with the said exponent,usually designated by 2W , yields, with

$$k = \frac{1}{a}$$

$$\frac{1}{2} w = 2W = \frac{\hbar k^2}{2m\omega} I(\vartheta, \infty)$$

$$= 3 \frac{\hbar^2 k^2}{MK\Theta_D} \frac{1}{4} I(\vartheta, \infty) \qquad (6\text{-}10)$$

To conform with the usual notation, we rewrite $\frac{1}{4} I(\vartheta, \infty)$ by setting

$$u = \frac{T}{\Theta_D} x \quad , \quad \vartheta a = \frac{1}{2} x$$

$$\text{Cotgh}\, \vartheta u = 1 + \frac{2}{e^x - 1}$$

and thus obtain

$$\frac{1}{4} I(\vartheta, \infty) = \frac{1}{4} + \left(\frac{T}{\Theta_D}\right)^2 \int_0^{\Theta_D/T} dx \frac{x}{e^x - 1} \qquad (6\text{-}10a)$$

Going over to the expression for ε, we have next

$$\varepsilon = \frac{1}{2N} \sum_{\underset{\sim}{q}j} \hbar\omega_{\underset{\sim}{q}j} \text{Cotgh}(\tfrac{1}{2} \beta\hbar\omega_{\underset{\sim}{q}j})$$

$$= 3\hbar\omega \; 3 \int_0^1 u^2 \, du \, \text{Cotgh}\, \vartheta u \qquad (6\text{-}11)$$

$$= \frac{3}{2} \hbar\omega \; \hat{I}(\vartheta) \qquad (6\text{-}11a)$$

whereby

$$\hat{I}(\vartheta) = 3\,! \int_0^1 du\, u^3\, \mathrm{Cotgh}(\vartheta u) \tag{6-11b}$$

is $2/\vartheta$ in the classical limit and is $3/2$ at $T = 0$ which yields $\varepsilon_o = \frac{9}{8} K \Theta_D$ for the model. On the other hand we have also

$$\varepsilon = \sum_\rho \mathrm{Tr}\, \lambda_\rho \left(\frac{\partial \Phi}{\partial \lambda_\rho}\right)_a$$

Designating the nearest neighbors by $|\rho| = 1$ and deleting again the index 1 of λ_1, the above relation becomes, with

$$\psi = \sum_{|\rho| = 1} \Phi(R_\rho, \lambda)$$

$$\varepsilon = \lambda \left(\frac{\partial \psi}{\partial \lambda}\right)_a \tag{6-11c}$$ †

At this point we mention a useful though approximate relation between $\hat{I}(\vartheta)$ and $I(\vartheta, x_n)$ valid for $x_n < 1$. In this case we have indeed from Eq. (6-9a)

$$I(\vartheta, x_n) \cong \frac{2}{3!} \int_0^1 du\, x_n^2\, u^3\, \mathrm{Cotgh}(\vartheta u)$$

$$= \frac{1}{3.\,3!}\, x_n^2\, \hat{I}(\vartheta) \tag{6-12}$$

† Note that the apparently missing factor 3 on the r.h.s. of Eq. (6-11c) is automatically obtained from $\frac{\partial \psi}{\partial \lambda}$ owing to the degeneracy of the Kernel (2-10) of the diffusion equation (2-9) when $\lambda_{\rho\alpha\beta} = \delta_{\alpha\beta}\, \lambda$.

Conversely we note the exact relation that

$$\hat{I}(\vartheta) = 3\left(\frac{1}{x_n}\frac{d^2}{dx_n^2}x_n\ I(\vartheta, x_n)\right)_{x_n=0}$$

$$= 3\,\triangle\, I(\vartheta, x_n)\qquad x_n \to 0$$

where $\triangle$ is the Laplace operator. Let us pause here to generalize the above equation. For this purpose, consider the non local mean value

$$\varepsilon^{\sigma} = \frac{1}{M}\sum_{\alpha}\langle \not{p}_{s+\sigma,\alpha}\,\not{p}_{s,\alpha}\rangle$$

$$= \frac{1}{MN}\sum_{\underset{\sim}{q}\alpha}\cos(\underset{\sim}{q}\underset{\sim}{R}_{\sigma})\ \langle \not{p}_{\underset{\sim}{q}\alpha}\,\not{p}_{-\underset{\sim}{q}\alpha}\rangle$$

$$= \frac{1}{N}\sum_{\underset{\sim}{q}}\mathrm{Tr}\,\cos(\underset{\sim}{q}\underset{\sim}{R}_{\sigma})\ D_{\underset{\sim}{q}}L_{\underset{\sim}{q}}(0) \tag{6-14}$$

Insert above

$$D_{\underset{\sim}{q}} = \sum_{\rho}(1-\cos \underset{\sim}{q}\underset{\sim}{R}_{\rho})\ A_{\rho}$$

Recalling that $\underset{\sim}{R}_{\sigma} + \underset{\sim}{R}_{\rho} = \underset{\sim}{R}_{\sigma+\rho}$, using the identity

$$\cos(\underset{\sim}{q}\underset{\sim}{R}_{\sigma})\,(1-\cos \underset{\sim}{q}\underset{\sim}{R}_{\rho}) = -\,(1-\cos \underset{\sim}{q}\underset{\sim}{R}_{\rho}) + \frac{1}{2}(1-\cos \underset{\sim}{q}\underset{\sim}{R}_{\sigma+\rho})$$

$$+\ \frac{1}{2}(1-\cos \underset{\sim}{q}\underset{\sim}{R}_{\sigma-\rho})$$

or, in operator form †

$$(1-\cos \underset{\sim}{q}\underset{\sim}{R}_\rho) \cos \underset{\sim}{q}\,\underset{\sim}{R}_\sigma = (1-\mathrm{Ch}\, \underset{\sim}{R}_\rho \underset{\sim}{p}_\sigma) \cos \underset{\sim}{q}\underset{\sim}{R}_\sigma$$

$$= (\mathrm{Ch}\, \underset{\sim}{R}_\rho \underset{\sim}{p}_\sigma - 1)(1-\cos \underset{\sim}{q}\underset{\sim}{R}_\sigma)$$

permuting the summations over ρ and $\underset{\sim}{q}$ and recalling the definition of λ_ρ results in

$$\varepsilon^\sigma = \frac{1}{2} \sum_\rho \mathrm{Tr}\,(\lambda_{\sigma+\rho} + \lambda_{\sigma-\rho} - 2\lambda_\sigma) A_\rho(\lambda_\rho)$$

$$= \sum_\rho \mathrm{Tr}\,(\mathrm{Ch}\, \underset{\sim}{R}_\rho \underset{\sim}{p}_\sigma - 1)\, \lambda_\sigma A_\rho(\lambda_\rho) \tag{6-14a}$$

These difference equations convey the symmetry properties of the crystal in real space. In the classical limit we have $\varepsilon^\sigma = 3\,\mathrm{KT}\,\delta_{\sigma,o}$ and the set of Eqs (6-14a) constitutes generalized sum rules valid in any self-linked approximation. It is apparent that Eq. (6-13) follows from Eq. (6-14a), in the limit $\sigma \to 0$ if we expand $\mathrm{Ch}(\underset{\sim}{R}_\rho \underset{\sim}{p}_\sigma) - 1 \cong \frac{1}{2}(\underset{\sim}{R}_\rho \underset{\sim}{p}_\sigma)^2$ which corresponds to taking for $D_{\underset{\sim}{q}}$ a quadratic form in $\underset{\sim}{q}$. It is also clear that Eq. (6-12) is the first order approximation to the isotropic solution of the differential equation so obtained. Returning to the model and combining the relations obtained in a suitable way, we have

$$\psi(a,\lambda) = \sum_{|\rho|=1} \Phi(R_\rho, \lambda) \tag{6-15}$$

$$\varepsilon = \lambda \left(\frac{\partial \psi}{\partial \lambda}\right)_a \tag{6-16}$$

† This is permitted since $R_\rho \neq R_\sigma$.

$$\frac{\hbar^2}{2m} I(\vartheta)\hat{I}(\vartheta) = \frac{1}{3}\lambda\varepsilon \tag{6-17}$$

$$\frac{1}{2} m\omega^2 \frac{\hat{I}(\vartheta)}{I(\vartheta)} = \frac{1}{3}\frac{\varepsilon}{\lambda} \tag{6-18}$$

$$P = -\frac{N}{2}\frac{\partial\psi}{\partial\upsilon} \tag{6-3}$$

It is readily seen that the procedure of analysis follows closely the one discussed in the first example. From Eq. (6-16) we find $\varepsilon(a,\lambda)$, from Eq. (6-17) $\vartheta(a,\lambda)$ is determined, from Eq. (6-18), $\omega^2(a,\lambda)$, that is also the important Debye Temperature $\Theta_D(a,\lambda) = \frac{2\hbar\omega(a,\lambda)}{K}$ and then $KT = \hbar\omega/\vartheta$. In the approximation where Eq. (6-12) holds and if a_1 designates the nearest neighbor distance we find in particular the interesting relation

$$\frac{1}{3}\frac{\varepsilon}{\lambda} = \frac{1}{2} m\omega^2 \frac{\hat{I}(\vartheta)}{I(\upsilon)} \cong \frac{9m\omega^2}{x_1^2} = \frac{3M\omega_D^2}{(q_D a_1)^2} = \frac{3MS^2}{a_1^2}$$

or, with $w_1 = \lambda/a_1^2$

$$S \cong \frac{1}{3}\sqrt{\frac{\varepsilon}{Mw_1}} \tag{6-19}$$

that is, an approximate expression for the sound velocity. Again in this example, further inspection of Eq. (6-16) is needed.

As a third example we wish to treat the Einstein -Weiss limit of the R. H. A. In this limit interatomic motional correlations are neglected. This means that the fluctuating terms of λ_ρ are ignored or that the λ_ρ are taken in their asymtotic limit $\lambda_{\rho\to\infty} = \lambda_{as}$, whereby

$$\lambda_{as,\alpha\beta} = \langle u_{s+\rho,\alpha}\, u_{s+\rho,\beta}\rangle + \langle u_{s,\alpha}\, u_{s,\beta}\rangle = 2\langle u_{s,\alpha}\, u_{s,\beta}\rangle$$

Just as for the Weiss approximation in magnetism or in the lattice gas theory of condensation (see R.H. Brout [12] p. 8, 15, 48, 94), this limit is expected to be valid if a large number of neighbors contribute to the molecular field, that is, here, to the effective force constants acting on a given central atom. This occurs at best for closed packed structures and in the case of large motional fluctuations where the potential functions $\Phi(R_\rho, \lambda)$ become rather broadly smeared out, the range of the forces being thereby increased. Thus, this limit represents a first approximation for normal solids at elevated temperatures and for the quantum solids like He^3 and He^4 at T equal or near zero. Despite its restricted value this approximation is not without interest and, in fact, further connections with Weiss theory will be brought out in the next sections. It is clear that a direct derivation of this approximation can be made by replacing the diagonal part of the correlated density matrix (5-16) by a product of identical atomic gaussian functions of variable width[†]. At this point we must note that, in general, Hartree product for solids will not be built up of gaussian functions in order to avoid interpenetration of the atomic cores. However serious is this problem, dealt with at some length in section (4-4), it must also be said that its importance is overemphasized in this scheme, precisely since the latter does not take into account the effects of interatomic correlations. Another important aspect of this question will be discussed in the last section of this chapter. Now, for cubic crystals under hydrostatic pressure, λ_{as} is isotropic and we have again a model with one internal state variable. Thus, for each component of λ_{as} we have, with $m = M$, $\vartheta = \frac{\hbar\omega}{KT}$

[†] The single difference is that, in the preceding procedure, the mode $\underset{\sim}{q} = o$ remains excluded.

$$\lambda = 2\langle u^2\rangle = \frac{\hbar}{m\omega} \mathrm{Cotgh}\frac{1}{2}\vartheta$$

$$\equiv \frac{\hbar}{m\omega} I(\vartheta) \tag{6-20}$$

and

$$\varepsilon = \frac{3}{2} m\omega^2\lambda = \frac{3}{2}\hbar\omega\, I(\vartheta)$$

Next, the potential energy per atom is, at present, the sum over all neighbors interactions, that is

$$\psi(a,\lambda) = \sum_{\rho} \Phi(R_\rho, \lambda) \tag{6-21}$$

and

$$\varepsilon(a,\lambda) = \lambda\left(\frac{\partial\psi(a,\lambda)}{\partial\lambda}\right)_a \tag{6-22}$$

One can then write

$$\frac{\hbar^2}{2m} I^2(\vartheta) = \frac{\hbar^2}{2m}\mathrm{Cotgh}^2\frac{1}{2}\vartheta = \frac{1}{3}\lambda\varepsilon \tag{6-23}$$

and

$$\frac{1}{2}m\omega^2 = \frac{1}{3}\frac{\varepsilon}{\lambda} \tag{6-24}$$

In this case the inversion of $I(\vartheta)$ can be carried out by hand. One finds

$$\vartheta(a,\lambda) = \ell n \frac{1 + \sqrt{\dfrac{2m}{3\hbar^2}\lambda\varepsilon}}{1 - \sqrt{\dfrac{2m}{3\hbar^2}\lambda\varepsilon}} \tag{6-23a}$$

Next, if we assign an Einstein temperature Θ_E to $\frac{\hbar\omega}{K}$ we get, from Eq. (6-24)

$$\Theta_E(a,\lambda) = \frac{1}{K}\sqrt{\frac{2\hbar^2\varepsilon}{3m\lambda}} \tag{6-24a}$$

Lastly the temperature is obtained as

$$T(a.\lambda) = \frac{1}{K}\sqrt{\frac{2\hbar^2\varepsilon}{3m\lambda}} \left[\ell n \frac{1 + \sqrt{\dfrac{2m}{3\hbar^2}\lambda\varepsilon}}{1 - \sqrt{\dfrac{2m}{\hbar^2}\lambda\varepsilon}} \right]^{-1} \tag{6-25}$$

It is thus possible to make a rather accurate study of the Einstein-Weiss approximation. This suggests that we consider this limit as a starting point for analyzing the R. H. A. by an iterative procedure. Let us find out then, first in the classical case, the first order corrections to the Weiss approximation. For this purpose we recall the starting equations

$$D_{\underset{\sim}{q}} = \frac{1}{M}\sum_{\rho}(1-\cos \underset{\sim}{q}\underset{\sim}{R}_{\rho})\, A_{\rho}(\lambda_{\rho}) \qquad A_{\rho} = \underset{\sim}{p}^2\, \Phi_{\rho}$$

$$\lambda_{\rho} = \frac{2KT}{MN}\sum_{\underset{\sim}{q}}(1-\cos \underset{\sim}{q}\underset{\sim}{R}_{\rho})\frac{1}{D_{\underset{\sim}{q}}}$$

and we set

$$D_{\underset{\sim}{q}} = D - E_{\underset{\sim}{q}} \qquad \underset{\sim}{q} \neq 0 \tag{6-26}$$

$$\lambda_\rho = \lambda + \mu_\rho \qquad \rho \neq 0 \tag{6-26a}$$

where $D = \omega^2$ times the unit matrix and $\lambda = \lambda_{as}$. In first order we can write

$$\Phi_{\alpha\beta}(R_\rho, \lambda_\rho) = \Phi_{\alpha\beta}(R_\rho, \lambda + \mu_\rho) \cong \Phi_{\alpha\beta}(R_\rho, \lambda) +$$

$$+ \sum_{\gamma\delta} \mu_{\rho,\gamma\delta} \Phi_{\gamma\delta\alpha\beta}(R_\rho, \lambda)$$

$$\frac{1}{D_{\underset{\sim}{q}}} = \frac{1}{D} + \frac{1}{D} E_{\underset{\sim}{q}} \frac{1}{D_{\underset{\sim}{q}}} \cong \frac{1}{D} + \frac{1}{D} E_{\underset{\sim}{q}} \frac{1}{D}$$

Noticing that

$$\lambda = \frac{2KT}{M} \frac{1}{D} \equiv \frac{2KT}{MN} \sum_{\underset{\sim}{q}} (1 - \cos \underset{\sim}{q}\underset{\sim}{R}_\rho) \frac{1}{D}$$

we have thus

$$\mu_\rho = \frac{2KT}{MN} \sum_{\underset{\sim}{q}} (1 - \cos \underset{\sim}{q}\underset{\sim}{R}_\rho) \frac{1}{D} E_{\underset{\sim}{q}} \frac{1}{D}$$

Next, with

$$D = \frac{1}{M} \sum_\rho A_\rho(\lambda)$$

and in defining

$$E^{o}_{\underset{\sim}{q}} = \frac{1}{M} \sum_{\rho} \cos(\underset{\sim}{q}\underset{\sim}{R}_{\rho})\, A_{\rho}(\lambda)$$

we obtain

$$E_{\underset{\sim}{q}\alpha\beta} = E^{o}_{\underset{\sim}{q}\alpha\beta} - \frac{1}{M} \sum_{\rho\gamma\delta} (1-\cos \underset{\sim}{q}\underset{\sim}{R}_{\rho})\, \mu_{\rho\gamma\delta}\, \Phi_{\gamma\delta\alpha\beta}(R_{\rho},\lambda)$$

Inserting μ_{ρ} in the last equation and permuting the summations over ρ and q' we observe the occurrence, in a particular form, of the familiar vertex tensor

$$\bar{G}_{q'\gamma\delta;q\alpha\beta} = \frac{2KT}{M^{2}N} \sum_{\rho} (1-\cos \underset{\sim}{q}'\underset{\sim}{R}_{\rho})(1-\cos \underset{\sim}{q}\underset{\sim}{R}_{\rho}) \frac{1}{D^{2}}\, \Phi_{\gamma\delta\alpha\beta}(R_{\rho},\lambda)$$

which we have encountered in dealing with the thermal properties (Sections 4-2 and 5-4). Therefore

$$E_{\underset{\sim}{q}\alpha\beta} = E^{o}_{\underset{\sim}{q}\alpha\beta} - \sum_{\underset{\sim}{q}'\gamma\delta} E_{\underset{\sim}{q}'\gamma\delta}\, \bar{G}_{\underset{\sim}{q}'\gamma\delta;\underset{\sim}{q}\alpha\beta}$$

or

$$E_{\underset{\sim}{q}\alpha\beta} = \sum_{\underset{\sim}{q}'\gamma\delta} E^{o}_{\underset{\sim}{q}'\gamma\delta} \left(\frac{1}{1+\bar{G}}\right)_{\underset{\sim}{q}'\gamma\delta;\underset{\sim}{q}\alpha\beta} \tag{6-27}$$

and then, in this order

$$D_{\underset{\sim}{q}} = \frac{1}{M} \sum_{\rho} A_{\rho}(\lambda) \left[1 - \sum_{\underset{\sim}{q}'} \cos(\underset{\sim}{q}'\underset{\sim}{R}_{\rho}) \left(\frac{1}{1+\bar{G}}\right)_{\underset{\sim}{q}';q}\right] \tag{6-27a}$$

If we neglect the effects brought about by the vertex corrections to the Weiss limit, we have simply

$$D_{\underset{\sim}{q}} \cong D - E^{o}_{\underset{\sim}{q}} = \frac{1}{M} \sum_{\rho} (1 - \cos \underset{\sim\sim}{qR_{\rho}}) A_{\rho}(\lambda) \tag{6-28}$$

an approximation which may suffice in many applications. In this case we obtain

$$\mu_{\rho} \cong - \frac{\lambda}{MD} A_{\rho}(\lambda) \tag{6-29}$$

that is, in recalling that λ_{as} is λ times the unit matrix

$$\lambda_{\rho} \cong \lambda_{as} (1 - \frac{1}{MD} A_{\rho}(\lambda)) = \lambda_{as} \left(1 - \frac{A_{\rho}(\lambda)}{\sum_{\rho'} A_{\rho'}(\lambda)}\right) \tag{6-29a}$$

The last relation is interesting in that it shows how the λ_{as}-isotropy of the Weiss limit for cubic crystal is removed when interatomic correlations are taken into account and in that indeed the λ_{ρ} -anisotropy is inversely proportional for the number of nearest neighbors. It also tells us how rapidly this effect decreases with R_{ρ}, provided that the forces are not long range. The connection between the R. H. A. at high temperature and its wave vector independent limit is thereby established. The quantum case is correspondingly treated by using the propagator matrices $L_{\underset{\sim}{q}\nu} = KT\,((2\pi\nu/\hbar\beta)^{2} + D_{\underset{\sim}{q}})$. The calculations involved are again similar to those given in Section (5-4) and need not be reproduced here. It seems more important to point out the connection between the general s. c. equations (5-84) and their $\underset{\sim}{q}$ independent limit. For this purpose it suffices to observe that, if $D_{q\nu} = D_{\nu}$ $(q \neq 0)$, the linking correlation functions $\lambda^{\sigma}_{\rho\rho'}(|\tau|)$ contain the factor

$$\frac{1}{N} \sum_{\underset{\sim}{q}} e^{i\underset{\sim\sim}{qR_{\sigma}}} (e^{i\underset{\sim\sim}{qR_{\rho}}} - 1)(e^{-i\underset{\sim\sim}{qR_{\rho'}}} - 1)$$

which differs from zero only if certain relations between R_σ, R_ρ, and $R_{\rho'}$ are satisfied. We find indeed that

$$\lambda^{\sigma}_{\rho\rho'}(\{D_{q\nu} = D_\nu\}, |\tau|) = 1 \begin{cases} \lambda(|\tau|) & \underset{\sim}{R}_\sigma = 0 \quad \underset{\sim}{R}_{\rho'} = \underset{\sim}{R}_\rho \\ -\lambda(|\tau|) & 0 \neq \underset{\sim}{R}_\sigma = -\underset{\sim}{R}_\rho = \underset{\sim}{R}_{\rho'} \\ \frac{1}{2}\lambda(|\tau|) & \underset{\sim}{R}_\sigma = 0 \quad \underset{\sim}{R}_{\rho'} \neq \underset{\sim}{R}_\rho \\ \frac{1}{2}\lambda(|\tau|) & 0 \neq \underset{\sim}{R}_\sigma = \underset{\sim}{R}_{\rho'} - \underset{\sim}{R}_\rho \\ 0 & \text{otherwise} \end{cases} \tag{6-30}$$

whereby

$$\lambda(|\tau|) \,.\, 1 = \lambda_{as}(|\tau|) = \frac{2KT}{M} \sum_\nu \frac{e^{\frac{2i\pi\nu\tau}{\hbar\beta}}}{\left(\frac{2\pi\nu}{\hbar\beta}\right)^2 + D_\nu} \tag{6-31}$$

The above relations mean that the $\lambda^{\sigma}_{\rho\rho'}(|\tau|)$ are different from zero if the two pairs of indices $(s, s+\rho\,;\, s' = s-\sigma\,,\, s'+\rho')$ are either identical or articulated. We note that these are precisely the cases which were relevant in our analysis of the imperfect gas limit (there, of course, only the component $\nu = 0$ came into play). With the relations (6-30) the calculation of second and higher order terms of the irreducible cumulant expansion is greatly simplified. Some generalizations of the Einstein -Weiss approximation are therefore ame nable to practical analysis.

The cases treated up to now possess the common feature of relying upon models which contain one internal state variable. Although we shall concentrate on such models in the remainder of this chapter it is proper here to comment on the general situation where anisotropy effects are not treated on a perturbative basis. This raises the question of the number of independent internal state variables or parameters for a given crystal. An important point is that this number is considerably less than that which might be guessed at first sight from the variational method used to derive the s. c. equations or from the calculus employed in Sections (4-2) and (5-4) for dealing with the thermal coefficients. Considering the R. H. A. in the classical limit to illustrate this point, we write the equations for λ_ρ where now the D_q's are explicitly eliminated, that is

$$\lambda_\rho = \frac{1}{MN} \sum_{\underset{\sim}{q}} (1-\cos \underset{\sim}{q}\underset{\sim}{R}_\rho) \frac{KT}{\sum_{\rho'} (1-\cos \underset{\sim}{q}\underset{\sim}{R}_{\rho'}) \frac{\partial\Phi}{\partial\lambda_{\rho'}}} \tag{6-32}$$

We observe that, starting from a given λ_{ρ_o} belonging, say, to the first shell of neighbors, the $\lambda_{\rho\neq\rho_o}$ for R_ρ lying within the first, second and further shells, are determined i) from the symmetry properties of the perfect crystal, and ii) from the first few shells of neighbors for which the force constants are significantly different from zero. The λ_ρ's, being isomorphic to the effective force constants $A_\rho = 2 \frac{\partial\Phi}{\partial\lambda_\rho}$, can be analyzed by group theoretical methods similar to those employed in lattice dynamics for determining the structure of the matrix of coupling coefficients. In this respect we wish here to refer to Leibfried and Ludwig article ([4], p. 291). For the primitive cubic crystals, Eq. (6-32) suggests that we shall be left with no more than three parameters. As an example, consider the face-centered cubic lattice with nearest neighbors interactions. Here, symmetry considerations alone dictate that, ρ_o being taken as the (1, 1, 0) nearest neighbor

$$\lambda_{(110)} = \begin{pmatrix} \lambda & \mu & 0 \\ \mu & \lambda & 0 \\ 0 & 0 & \nu \end{pmatrix} \qquad (6\text{-}33)$$

With the conjugated variables

$$A_{(110)\alpha\beta} = 2\,\frac{\partial\Phi(R_{(110)},\lambda_{(110)})}{\partial\lambda_{(110),\alpha\beta}} = \Phi_{\alpha\beta}(\underset{\sim}{R},\lambda_{(110)})_{\underset{\sim}{R} = R_{(110)}} \qquad (6\text{-}33a)$$

one of the twelve equivalent matrix equations (6-32) accurately examplifies how a truly dynamical theory of crystal lattices reads, that is to say a theory which describes a crystalline phase as the result, at equilibrium, of the interplay between symmetry elements, interatomic forces,and dynamical elements. At low temperature, Einstein's zero point fluctuations constitute the dynamical part of the problem. Now, a s. c. theory with three parameters is not at all simple and, needless to say, more work needs to be done in this direction. However, there is fortunately considerable room for inspecting situations at a lower level of complexity. To begin with, λ_ρ isotropic limits can usefully be considered. The great simplification which applies here is that, at high temperature, the sum rule

$$\sum_\rho \operatorname{Tr} \lambda_\rho \frac{\partial\Phi}{\partial\lambda_\rho} = 3\,KT = \lambda\,\frac{\partial\psi}{\partial\lambda}$$

alone suffices to study the problem. The fact that, in these cases, the diffusion equation for $\Phi(R_\rho,\lambda)$ reads

$$\frac{\partial\Phi}{\partial\lambda} = \frac{1}{2}\,\Delta\,\Phi$$

means that we do obtain self-consistent information on one invariant only of the $D_{\tilde{q}}$'s, namely on their traces. Note, however, that isotropic λ_ρ's do not entail isotropic A_ρ's. Indeed the latter are calculated first for general λ_ρ's compatible with the symmetry requirements and then, but only then, approximated by $A_\rho(\lambda)$. This is an important prescription which guarantees that Eq. (6-33a) is always satisfied. Thus we do obtain conventional information on the other two invariants of $D_{\tilde{q}}$, that is, ultimately on the eigenvalues $\omega^2_{\tilde{q}}(\lambda, a)$.

With these limitations in mind, we return to the one parameter models elaborated in this section and, for facilitating comparative studies, the results obtained are summarized below. With the quantities $\varepsilon = \frac{1}{M}\langle \tilde{p}_s^2 \rangle$, $\vartheta = \frac{\hbar\omega}{KT}$, $w_1 = \lambda / a_1^2$, $x_1 = q_D a_1$ the equations applying to the three cases are

$$\varepsilon = \lambda \left(\frac{\partial \psi}{\partial \lambda} \right)_a \qquad (6\text{-}34)$$

$$\frac{\hbar^2}{2m} I(\vartheta)\, \hat{I}(\vartheta) = \frac{1}{n} \varepsilon\lambda \qquad (6\text{-}34a)$$

$$\frac{1}{2} m \omega^2 \frac{\hat{I}(\vartheta)}{I(\vartheta)} = \frac{1}{n} \frac{\varepsilon}{\lambda} \qquad (6\text{-}34b)$$

$$P = -\frac{1}{2} N \left(\frac{\partial \psi}{\partial v} \right)_\lambda \qquad (6\text{-}34c)$$

and the following table gives the corresponding definitions of the relevant functions.

	Linear chain n. n. int.	Debye spherical model	Hartree-Weiss limit
n (dim.)	1	3	3
m	$\left(\frac{\pi}{2\sqrt{2}}\right)^2 M$	$\frac{4}{3} M$	M
ω	$\frac{2\sqrt{2}}{\pi}\omega_{q=\frac{\pi}{2a}}$	$\frac{1}{2}\omega_D$	ω
$\psi(a,\lambda)$	$2\,\Phi(a,\lambda)$	$\sum_{\lvert\rho\rvert=1}\Phi(R_\rho,\lambda)$	$\sum_\rho \Phi(R_\rho,\lambda)$
λ	λ_1	$\lambda_{\lvert 1\rvert}$	λ_{as}
$\hat{I}(\vartheta)$	$I(\vartheta)$	$\frac{2}{3}\int_0^1 du\, u^3 \operatorname{Cotgh}\vartheta u$	$I(\vartheta)$
$I(\vartheta)$	$\int_0^{\pi/2} d\varphi \sin\varphi \operatorname{Cotgh}(\frac{\pi}{4}\vartheta\sin\varphi)$	$2\int_0^1 du\, u\,(1-\frac{\sin ux_1}{ux_1}) \operatorname{Cotgh}\vartheta u$ $\cong \frac{1}{3.\,3!}\, x_1^2\, \hat{I}(\vartheta)$	$\operatorname{Cotgh}\frac{1}{2}\vartheta$
S	$\sqrt{\varepsilon/Mw_1}$	$\sim\sqrt{\varepsilon/9Mw_1}$	

6-2 ANALYSIS OF THE S. C. EQUATIONS

The purpose of this section is to study, through a number of examples, the analytical properties of the functions $\Phi(R_\rho, \lambda)$ and of the solutions of Eq. (6-34). To begin with, we consider again the pedagogical case of the linear chain and assume that the atoms interact through a repulsive potential of exponential type, namely

$$\varphi(x) = \varphi_o\, e^{-\alpha|x|} \tag{6-35}$$

where φ_o is a disposable constant and $1/\alpha$ is the range of the potential. It is understood that, in this case, the linear chain is maintained in equilibrium with a lattice constant $|x| = a$ by means of a suitable external pressure. To obtain the effective potential $\Phi(a, \lambda)$, we start from

$$\Phi(a, \lambda) = \varphi_o \frac{1}{\sqrt{2\pi\lambda}} \int_{-\infty}^{+\infty} dx \; e^{-\frac{(x-a)^2}{2\lambda}} \; e^{-\alpha|x|} \tag{6-36}$$

$$= \varphi_o \frac{1}{\sqrt{2\pi\lambda}} \int_0^{\infty} dx \left[e^{-\frac{(x-a)^2}{2\lambda}} + e^{-\frac{(x+a)^2}{2\lambda}} \right] e^{-\alpha x}$$

Introducing the integration variables

$$t_{\mp} = \frac{1}{\sqrt{2\lambda}} (x + \alpha\lambda \mp a)$$

then yields

$$\Phi(a, \lambda) = \varphi_o \; e^{\frac{1}{2}\alpha^2\lambda - \alpha a} \; \frac{1}{2} \operatorname{erfc}\left(\frac{\alpha\lambda - a}{\sqrt{2\lambda}}\right)$$

$$+ \varphi_o \; e^{\frac{1}{2}\alpha^2\lambda + \alpha a} \; \frac{1}{2} \operatorname{erfc}\left(\frac{\alpha\lambda + a}{\sqrt{2\lambda}}\right) \tag{6-36a}$$

whereby

$$\operatorname{erfc}(\xi) = \frac{2}{\sqrt{\pi}} \int_{\xi}^{\infty} dt \; e^{-t^2}$$

In using the property

$$\text{erfc}(\xi) + \text{erfc}(-\xi) \equiv 2$$

we have also

$$\Phi(a,\lambda) = \varphi_o\, e^{\frac{1}{2}\alpha^2\lambda - \alpha a}$$

$$- \varphi_o\, e^{\frac{1}{2}\alpha^2\lambda - \alpha a}\, \frac{1}{2}\, \text{erfc}\left(\frac{a-\alpha\lambda}{\sqrt{2\lambda}}\right)$$

$$+ \varphi_o\, e^{\frac{1}{2}\alpha^2\lambda + \alpha a}\, \frac{1}{2}\, \text{erfc}\left(\frac{a+\alpha\lambda}{\sqrt{2\lambda}}\right) \tag{6-36b}$$

If, in particular, both arguments of the erfc's are $\gg 1$, we find approximately

$$\Phi(a,\lambda) \cong \varphi_o\, e^{\frac{1}{2}\alpha^2\lambda - \alpha a}$$

$$- \varphi_o\, \frac{1}{\sqrt{2}}\, e^{-\frac{a^2}{2\lambda}} \sqrt{\frac{\lambda}{a^2}}\, \frac{\alpha\lambda/a}{1-(\alpha\lambda/a)^2} \tag{6-36c}$$

From this asymptotic expansion, we see that its first term alone affords a power series expansion in λ . This means that the first order mean value of any polynomial expansion of the type (1-26), that is, here

$$\sum_{n=o}^{m} \frac{1}{n!} (u_{s+1} - u_s)^n \varphi^{(n)}(a)$$

derives from this term and, consequently, that, in the traditional context of anharmonicity theory, the non-analytic contributions to $\Phi(a, \lambda)$ are tacitly disregarded. One of their origins is that φ is a function of $|x|$. This is neatly illustrated in the present case if we notice that φ of Eq. (6-35) satisfies the equation

$$\frac{d^2\varphi}{dx^2} - \alpha^2 \varphi = - 2\alpha\varphi_o \, \delta(x)$$

and thus, from Eq. (6-36), that Φ is found to obey the inhomogeneous differential equation

$$\frac{\partial\Phi}{\partial\lambda} - \frac{1}{2}\alpha^2\Phi = - \varphi_o \frac{\alpha}{\sqrt{2\pi\lambda}} e^{-\frac{a^2}{2\lambda}} \qquad (6\text{-}37)$$

Now it is true that, as long as the fluctuation parameter $w = \lambda / a^2$ is much smaller than unity, the r. h. s. of Eq. (6-37) can be neglected. In this case a solution of the homogeneous equation remains, and this is precisely the first term of Eq.(6-36b). In practice there are indeed several situations, discussed below, where the non-analytic part of Φ can be disregarded, but there are some others where they cannot. One example of the latter is given now. In the following figure we have drawn Φ of Eq. (6-36a) as a function of $\alpha^2\lambda$ for a value of $\alpha a = 1$. This case represents a high density limit or a situation with rather long range forces. On the same figure the first term of Eq. (6-36b), designated by $\chi(\alpha a, \alpha^2\lambda)$, is drawn for comparison.

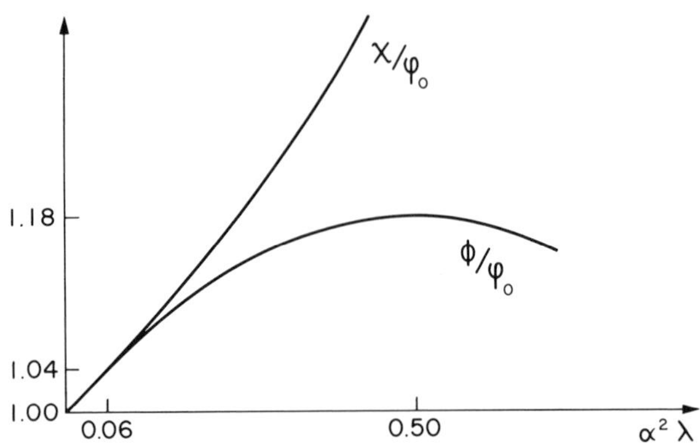

We observe that, while χ increases just exponentially, Φ increases first, then goes through an inflexion point at $\alpha^2\lambda = 0.06$, reaches a maximum, and finally decreases slowly toward zero as $\sim 1/\sqrt{\lambda}$. We can proceed to study the r.h.s. of Eq. (6-34) for any one of the models dealt with in the preceding section. For illustrative purposes, however, we shall confine ourselves to treating the **Einstein-Weiss** approximation in the classical limit. For this, we need the potential energy per atom $\psi(a,\lambda) = \sum_{n\neq o} \Phi(na,\lambda)$. Recalling that, for large λ, the superposition of these potential functions tends toward the imperfect gas limit, $\frac{N-1}{L}\int_{-\infty}^{+\infty} dx\, \varphi(|x|) = \frac{2}{a\alpha}\varphi_o$ in the present case, and noticing that the initial value is

$$\psi(a,o) = 2\,\varphi_o \sum_{n>o} e^{-na\alpha} = 2\,\varphi_o \frac{e^{-a\alpha}}{1-e^{-a\alpha}} < \frac{2}{\alpha a}\varphi_o$$

we find the behavior depicted in the following figure. For comparison, the sum of $\chi(na,\lambda)$, which diverges at large λ, has also been drawn.

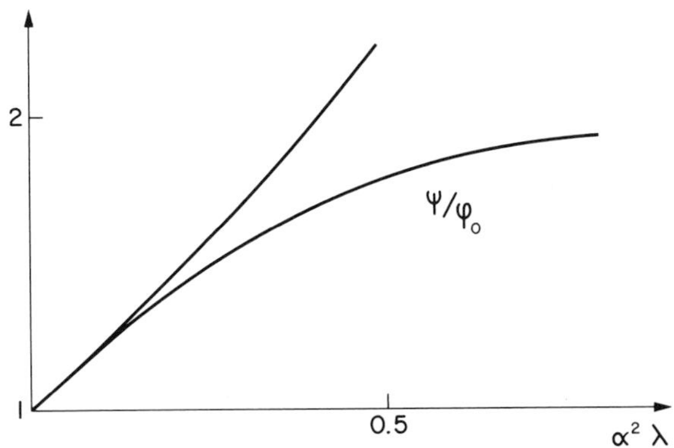

Notice that, at the inflexion point, the vertex function $Y(\lambda)$ vanishes since it is $\sim \frac{\partial^2 \psi}{\partial \lambda^2}$. This means that the specific heat takes, here, its harmonic value again. Below this point, $Y(\lambda)$ is > 0 and the vertex corrections tend to deplete C_υ below its harmonic value, whereas above the inflexion point $Y(\lambda)$ is < 0 and C_υ begins to increase more and more rapidly. From this figure we can immediately construct $\lambda \frac{\partial \psi}{\partial \lambda}$ and seek its intercepts with the horizontal $\varepsilon = KT$ in the classical limit. The result is plotted below

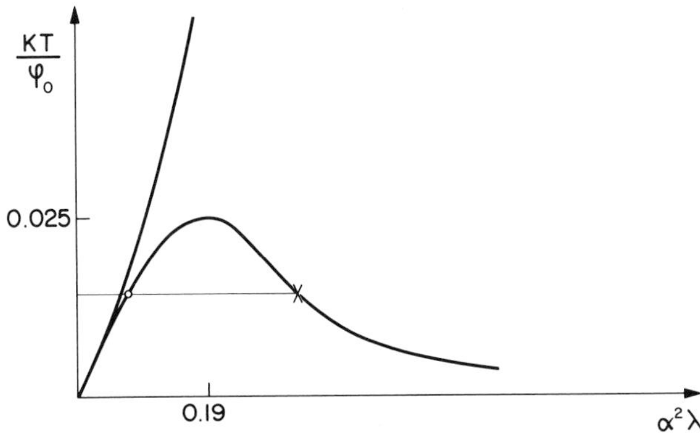

We uncover that, as long as $T < \bar{T}(\alpha a)$, there are two real roots which merge when T reaches $\bar{T}(\alpha a)$ and then become complex conjugate, that is, meaningless. To clarify the nature of these roots, we inspect the free energy $F(a, \lambda, T)$ as a function of λ for a fixed density $(1/a)$ and temperature. In the present case, we have simply

$$\frac{1}{N} F = -\frac{1}{2} KT \, \ell n \left(\frac{MKT}{2\hbar^2} \lambda \right) - \frac{1}{2} KT + \frac{1}{2} \psi(a, \lambda) \tag{6-38}$$

and we find the behavior schematically drawn in the following figure for four temperatures, $T = 0$, $T < \overline{T}$ (twice), $T = \overline{T}$, and for one given a

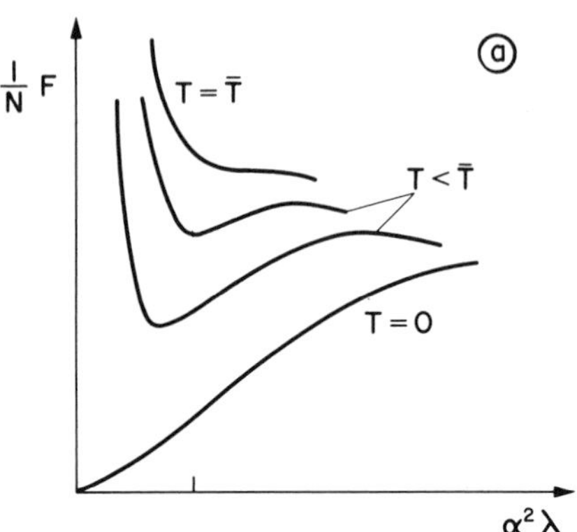

The extrema of $\frac{1}{N} F$, given by

$$\frac{1}{N} \left(\frac{\partial F}{\partial \lambda} \right)_{a, T} = 0 = -\frac{KT}{\lambda} + \left(\frac{\partial \psi}{\partial \lambda} \right)_a$$

clearly correspond to the two roots, and we conclude that the first one alone, at which the free energy has a minimum, is a stable root. As T reaches $\overline{T}$ the corresponding value $\overline{\lambda}$ represents an estimate of the largest motional fluctuation that atoms, forced to oscillate around mean positions in the chain, can sustain. This is, certainly, an artificial picture of the system, but it is consistent with the approximation used to describe its dynamics. It follows that, in a (T, a) diagram, the curve $\overline{T}(a)$ limits the domain of stability of Eq. (6-34) and that, on this curve, the function $g = KT\, Y(\lambda)$ reaches the critical value -1 as found in calculating

$$K \frac{\partial T}{\partial \lambda} = 0 = \frac{\partial \psi}{\partial \lambda} + \lambda \frac{\partial^2 \psi}{\partial \lambda^2} = \frac{\partial \psi}{\partial \lambda} \left(1 + KT\, Y(\lambda) \right)$$

We observe on the contrary that, in disregarding effects of non-analytic character in λ , no instability of the first order s. c. Eq. (6-34) is obtained, and this for all densities in the case of purely repulsive forces. This unsatisfactory feature holds at three dimensions and, in the normal case where attractive forces are added to the repulsive ones, for densities such that $\frac{\partial\psi}{\partial\lambda} > 0$.

As a counter example, we shall now treat a problem where the pressure instead of the density is fixed. For this, we assume that $\varphi(|x|)$ consists of a repulsive and attractive part which we write conveniently as a Morse-type potential function, that is

$$\varphi(x) = \epsilon\,(e^{\alpha a_o - \alpha|x|} - 2\,e^{\frac{1}{2}\alpha a_o - \frac{1}{2}\alpha|x|}) \tag{6-39}$$

Here, ϵ is the depth of the potential, a_o its minimum position, and we shall assume that the forces are short range, which means that αa_o is larger than one, say $\alpha a_o \cong 10$. In this case, no more than nearest neighbors interactions need be taken into account. We wish to inspect the stability of Eq. (6-34) for the particularly simple case where the pressure is zero. Anticipating that, under these conditions, the homogeneous part of the effective potential suffices to treat the problem, we write

$$\Phi(a, \lambda) = \epsilon\,(e^{\alpha(a_o - a) + \frac{1}{2}\lambda\alpha^2} - 2\,e^{\frac{\alpha}{2}(a_o - a) + \frac{1}{8}\lambda\alpha^2}) + 0\,(e^{-\frac{1}{w}})$$

Calculating the pressure

$$P = -\frac{1}{2}\left(\frac{\partial\psi}{\partial a}\right)_\lambda$$

$$= \epsilon\alpha\,(e^{\alpha(a_o - a) + \frac{1}{2}\lambda\alpha^2} - e^{\frac{1}{2}\alpha(a_o - a) + \frac{1}{8}\lambda\alpha^2}) + 0\,(e^{-\frac{1}{w}})$$

and setting $P = 0$ entails

$$\alpha(a_o - a) + \frac{1}{2}\lambda\alpha^2 = \frac{1}{2}\alpha(a_o - a) + \frac{1}{8}\lambda\alpha^2 + 0(e^{-\frac{1}{w}})$$

or

$$a(\lambda, P=0) = a_o + \frac{3}{4}\alpha\lambda + 0(e^{-\frac{1}{w}})$$

Introducing this relation for the lattice expansion into

$$KT(\lambda, a) = \lambda\left(\frac{\partial\psi}{\partial\lambda}\right)_a = 2\,\epsilon\,\lambda\,\alpha^2\left(\frac{1}{2}e^{\alpha(a_o - a) + \frac{1}{2}\lambda\alpha^2}\right.$$

$$\left. - \frac{1}{4}e^{\frac{\alpha}{2}(a_o - a) + \frac{1}{8}\lambda\alpha^2}\right) + 0(e^{-\frac{1}{w}}) \tag{6-40}$$

then yields

$$KT(\lambda, P=0) = \frac{1}{2}\epsilon\lambda\alpha^2\, e^{-\frac{1}{4}\alpha^2\lambda} + 0(e^{-\frac{1}{w}}) \tag{6-41}$$

We see that the first term on the r. h. s. has a maximum at $\alpha^2\lambda = 4$. The corresponding value of w is, at zero pressure,

$$w = \frac{\lambda}{a^2} = \frac{\lambda}{\left(a_o + \frac{3}{4}\lambda\alpha + 0(e^{-\frac{1}{w}})\right)^2} = \frac{4}{(\alpha a_o)^2\left(1 + \frac{3}{\alpha a_o} + 0(e^{-\frac{1}{w}})\right)^2}$$

and since αa_o is $\cong 10$ in the present example, we find indeed that the non-analytic effects can be neglected altogether. Thus, Eq. (6-41) possesses a stable solution as long as T is smaller than

$$\bar{T}\,(P=0) = 2\,\frac{\epsilon}{K}\,e^{-1}$$

A similar analysis carried out in three dimensions results in

$$K\bar{T}(P=0) = \frac{z}{3}\,\epsilon\,e^{-1}\,(1 + 0(\frac{1}{\alpha a}))$$

where z is the number of nearest neighbors. We note that this temperature is not excessively large. Indeed, for f. c. c. lattices, $K\bar{T}(P=0)/\epsilon = 1.48$, that is about twice the value of KT(triple point)/ϵ for the crystals of the rare gas atoms, which are 0. 70, 0. 68 and 0. 72 for Ar, Kr and Xe respectively. For pressures different from zero, we obtain an implicit relation for the lattice expansion which reads

$$\alpha a = \alpha a_o + \frac{3}{4}\,\lambda\alpha^2 + 2\,\ell n\left(1 - e^{-\alpha(a_o - a) - \frac{1}{2}\lambda\alpha^2}\,\frac{P}{\epsilon\alpha}\right)$$

Retaining the linear term in $P/\epsilon\alpha$ and $\lambda\alpha^2$ yields then

$$\alpha a = \alpha a_o + \frac{3}{4}\,\lambda\alpha^2 - \frac{2P}{\epsilon\alpha} \tag{6-42}$$

Inserting this relation into Eq. (6-40) yields to first order in $P/\epsilon\alpha$

$$KT(\lambda, P) = \frac{1}{2}\,\epsilon\lambda e^{-\frac{1}{4}\lambda\alpha^2}\,(1 + \frac{3P}{\epsilon\alpha}) \tag{6-43}$$

and thus

$$K\bar{T}(P) = 2\,e^{-1}\,\epsilon\,(1 + \frac{3P}{\alpha\epsilon}) \tag{6-44}$$

As expected, the limit of stability increases with increasing pressures. Incidentally, if we write Eq. (6-43) in terms of the renormalized Einstein frequency $\omega(T, P)$, via $\lambda = 2KT/M\omega^2$, we find for $P = 0$

$$\omega^2 = \omega_o^2 \, e^{-\frac{1}{4}\frac{4.3}{z}\frac{KT}{\epsilon}\frac{\omega_o^2}{\omega^2}} \tag{6-43b}$$

whereby

$$\omega_o^2 = 2 \cdot \frac{z}{4.3} \epsilon \frac{\alpha^2}{M}$$

and thus, ω^2 at the instability amounts to $\omega_o^2 e^{-1}$ for $P = 0$. If we return, for comparison, to the instability at fixed density for the potential (6-39) we find by numerical analysis that, at the density of static equilibrium $1/a_o$ and as αa_o varies from 1 to 15, $\bar{\lambda}/a_o^2$ varies slowly from 0.19 to 0.27. For $\alpha a_o = 10$, $\bar{\lambda}/a_o^2 = 0.25$, a value which ought to be compared with the zero pressure instability of 0.04. Finally, similar calculations performed in the three dimensional case indicate that $\bar{\lambda}/a_o^2$ varies from 0.09 to 0.14 as αa_o varies from 1 to 15. Remembering that $\lambda = 2\langle u^2\rangle$, we obtain as a rule that the first order s. c. equation (6-34) becomes unstable, in the three dimensional case at

$$\frac{\langle u^2\rangle}{a_o^2} \cong 5 - 7\ \% \tag{6-44}$$

in a way practically independent of the range of the forces and, we repeat, owing essentially to non-analytic effects. Changing the conditions from constant density to constant pressure, or considering second and higher order effects, may change the situation rather radically in producing instabilities at lower w values (20 % or even less) in such a way that the non-analytic effects become comparatively negligible.

The two simple cases selected for the above discussion have served to illustrate how stability analysis of the s. c. Eq. (6-34) can be performed. They have also indicated which parameters are relevant to the problem. We shall now comment on this point, since the same parameters often come into play. Inspection of other situations, dealing also with higher order s. c. equations, shows this indeed. Together with KT/ϵ , $\frac{\beta P}{\rho}$, z , these parameters are

$$\alpha a , \quad \alpha' a \;; \; \lambda / a^2 , \; \lambda \alpha^2 \tag{6-45}$$

and also $\lambda\alpha / a$, which is the geometric mean of the former two. We have, first, useful parameters in the rate of change of the repulsive and attractive parts, respectively, of the interatomic potential functions, that is

$$\alpha a = - \frac{d \ln \varphi_{rep}(a)}{d \ln a} \quad , \quad \alpha' a = - \frac{d \ln \varphi_{att}(a)}{d \ln a} \tag{6-45a}$$

In what follows, the factors αa , $\alpha' a$ will be designated by p and p' . Considering, typically, a Lennard-Jones potential

$$\varphi (R) = 4 \epsilon \left(\left(\frac{\sigma}{R}\right)^{12} - \left(\frac{\sigma}{R}\right)^{6} \right)$$

one obtains $p = 12$, $p' = 6$. In the case of a Coulomb potential, $p = 1$. We see, therefore, that these parameters vary over one order of magnitude, at least. There is next our familiar fluctuation parameter $\lambda / a^2 = w$. To specify the order of magnitude within which w can actually vary, we proceed as follows. At $T = 0$, we have

$$w_o = \frac{\hbar}{M\omega a^2}$$

Introducing a characteristic temperature Θ through $\hbar\omega = K\Theta$ and expressing M, Θ, a^2 in the suitable units

$$M = \hat{M} \; . \; 50 \quad \text{proton mass}$$

$$\Theta = \hat{\Theta} \; . \; 100 \; {}^{o}K$$

$$a^2 = \hat{a}^2 \; . \; 10 \; \text{Å}^2 \tag{6-46}$$

results in

$$w_o = \frac{\hbar^2}{MK\Theta a^2} = \frac{1}{957} \frac{1}{\hat{M}\hat{\Theta}\hat{a}^2} \tag{6-47}$$

We then see that, from the heavy to the very light solids, w_o can vary from, roughly speaking, 10^{-4} to 10^{-1} ; that is to say, over three orders of magnitude. In the classical limit, we have correspondingly, ignoring the fact that $\Theta(a, T)$ for order of magnitude estimate

$$w_T = \frac{2KT}{M\omega^2} = 2 \frac{\hbar^2 KT}{M(K\Theta)^2} = 2 \, w_o \frac{T}{\Theta}$$

which means that, for a given crystal, w usually varies by no more than half an order of magnitude from $T = 0$ up to the triple point. It follows that, with this parameter alone, the theory is not sensitive enough. The next parameter, encountered in the examples treated in this section, is $\lambda\alpha^2$, which we shall designate by y . It corresponds to the most significant eigenvalue of the fluctuation operator $\underline{w} = \lambda \underline{p}^2$ which permitted us to express in closed form the irreducible cumulants $\varkappa_k$ of $\mathcal{K}$. But clearly

$$y \equiv \lambda\alpha^2 = \frac{\lambda}{a^2}(\alpha a)^2 = w\,p^2$$

and here we see that the factor p can amplify by two orders of magnitude the effect of the fluctuation parameter w , most frequently very small. This means that, for $p > 1$, y , rather than w , is the relevant parameter of the theory. Numerical analysis indicates more accurately and in particular that, for

$$p \geqslant 3 \tag{6-48}$$

and

$$w < \frac{1}{p^2} \tag{6-48a}$$

the non-analytic effects mentioned at the beginning of this section can be neglected and that the usual lowest order polynomial expansion of $\varkappa_1$, and $\varkappa_2$ in powers of w is valid†. Inspection of the stability of s. c. equations based on truncated polynomial expansion is, however, subject to some caution. For example, if it is readily found that inclusion of the usual cubic terms of $-\frac{1}{2}\beta\varkappa_2$ in a s. c. equation always yields an instability; it is also found that the result can be rather grossly misleading. The point is that the negative contribution from this term is, in part, offset by positive contributions from $\frac{1}{3!}\beta^2\varkappa_3$. Since $\bar{y}$ and $\bar{\beta}\epsilon$ are found to be of order one, we may have 1° to use unabridged expression for the $\varkappa_k$‡ (still evaluated disregarding non-analytic effects) and 2° to sum up partial series of the irreducible cumulant expansion $\mathcal{K}$. Model analysis of this kind is, in particular, feasible in the wave vector independent limit discussed in the preceding section. Since it is hardly possible to report

† See [3], [4], [7], also J. J. J. Kokkedee' "Many-Particle theory of Interacting Phonons in Crystals" A. N. L. Report 6744, (1963) and K. N. Pathak Phys. Rev. article 139, A 1569, (1965).

‡ e. g. L. J. Sham, Phys. Rev. 139, A 1189, (1965)

more about this subject without entering into lengthy technicalities, we leave it aside and proceed with the study of another aspect of the problem. Up to now we have indeed examined the dependence of the effective potential per atom as a function of λ for fixed interatomic spacing and for fixed pressure. We wish now to inspect the dependence of $\Phi(R,\lambda)$ as a function of R for fixed λ and, in so doing, to point out a few applications of the theory.

As a first example, we consider, in three dimensions, the Morse-type potential function

$$\varphi(R) = \epsilon\left(e^{\alpha(R_o-R)} - 2\,e^{\frac{1}{2}\alpha(R_o-R)}\right) \tag{6-49}$$

and determine its parameters in a way which, in fact, suggested Eqs (6-45a). We start from the well-known Lennard-Jones potential

$$\varphi_{L-J}(R) = 4\epsilon\left(\left(\frac{\sigma}{R}\right)^{12} - \left(\frac{\sigma}{R}\right)^{6}\right) \tag{6-50}$$

and express it in terms of R_o, its minimum position given by

$$\frac{R_o}{\sigma} = 2^{1/6} = 1.115$$

i.e.

$$\varphi_{L-J} = 4\,\epsilon\left(\left(\frac{\sigma}{R_o}\right)^{12}\left(\frac{R_o}{R}\right)^{12} - \left(\frac{\sigma}{R_o}\right)^{6}\left(\frac{R_o}{R}\right)^{6}\right)$$

$$= \epsilon\left(\left(\frac{R_o}{R}\right)^{12} - 2\left(\frac{R_o}{R}\right)^{6}\right) \tag{6-50a}$$

then we exponentiate

$$\left(\frac{R_o}{R}\right)^n \equiv e^{-n\, \ell n \frac{R}{R_o}} \equiv e^{-n\, \ell n\left(1+\frac{R-R_o}{R_o}\right)}$$

and retain the term linear in $\frac{R-R_o}{R_o}$ in the exponent. This yields

$$\varphi = \epsilon\left(e^{12\left(1-\frac{R}{R_o}\right)} - 2\, e^{6\left(1-\frac{R}{R_o}\right)}\right) \tag{6-49a}$$

with, evidently, the values of p and p' given under Eq. (6-45a). We shall accept this determination of αR_o for numerical applications. The depths of the two potentials are, obviously, identical. To figure out quantitatively how these potentials compare, we have plotted below φ/ϵ of Eq. (6-49a) and φ_{L-J}/ϵ

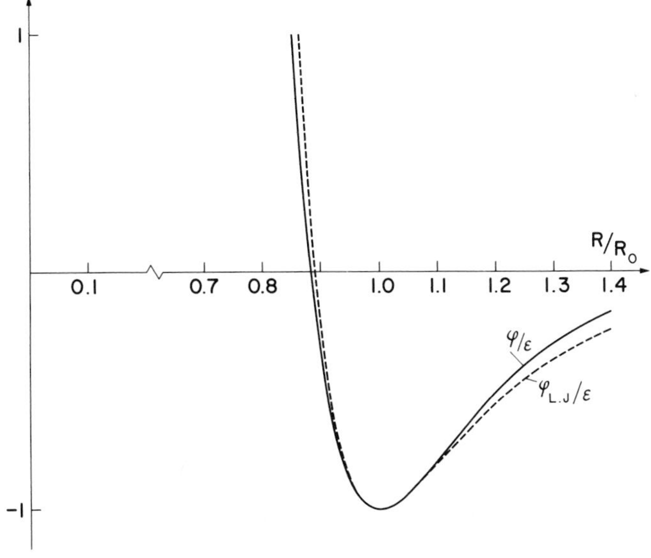

It is seen how φ deviates from φ_{L-J} at large R/R_o owing to its shorter range, and at small R/R_o since it is softer than its partner.

Within 8 % of $\frac{|\delta R|}{R_o}$, however, the differences are barely noticeable. This is what we need, since this range covers the domain of thermal expansions and, in energy, the KT/ε values interesting in practice. For a number of applications, the model potential (6-49a) can therefore be employed. Calculation of the effective potential Φ proceeds as usual. For the repulsive part, we have

$$\Phi_{rep} = \frac{\varepsilon e^{\alpha R_o}}{(2\pi\lambda)^{3/2}} 2\pi \int_0^\infty R'^2 \, dR' \int_0^\pi \sin\vartheta \, d\vartheta$$

$$\times \exp\left[-\frac{1}{2\lambda} (R'^2 + R^2 - 2 R R' \cos\vartheta) - \alpha R' \right]$$

$$= \frac{\varepsilon e^{\alpha R_o}}{\sqrt{2\pi\lambda}} \frac{1}{R} \int_0^\infty dR' \, R' \sum_{\eta=\pm 1} \eta \exp\left[-\frac{(R'-\eta R)^2}{2\lambda} - \alpha R' \right]$$

This yields

$$\Phi_{rep} = \varepsilon \left(1-\frac{\alpha\lambda}{R}\right) \exp\left(\alpha R_o - \alpha R + \frac{1}{2}\alpha^2\lambda\right)$$

$$- \varepsilon \left(1-\frac{\alpha\lambda}{R}\right) \exp\left(\alpha R_o - \alpha R + \frac{1}{2}\alpha^2\lambda\right) . \operatorname{erfc}\left(\frac{R-\alpha\lambda}{\sqrt{2\lambda}}\right)$$

$$+ \varepsilon \left(1+\frac{\alpha\lambda}{R}\right) \exp\left(\alpha R_o + \alpha R + \frac{1}{2}\alpha^2\lambda\right) . \operatorname{erfc}\left(\frac{R+\alpha\lambda}{\sqrt{2\lambda}}\right) \qquad (6\text{-}51)$$

and similarly for the attractive part obtained in replacing α by $\alpha/2$ which need not be written down. In the following figure are plotted the resulting effective potentials as a function of R/R_o, for $\alpha R_o = 12$ and for six values of $\frac{\lambda}{R_o^2} = w = \frac{1}{3}\frac{\langle \delta R^2 \rangle}{R_o^2}$.

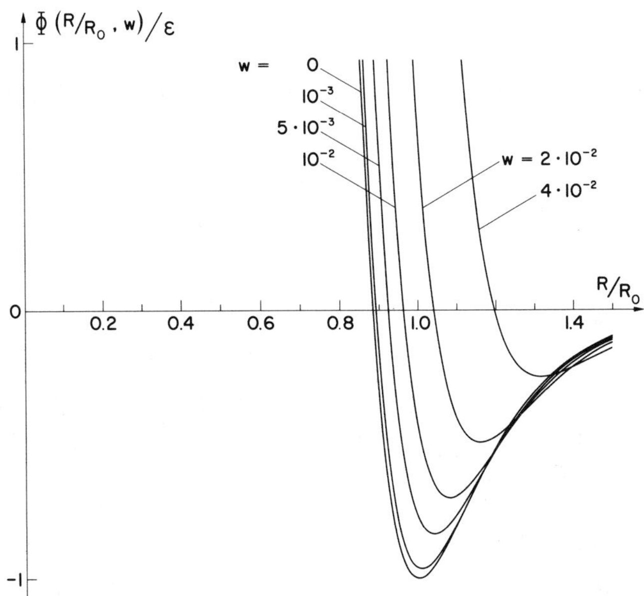

The shift of the minimum of $\Phi(R/R_o, w)$, as w increases, is particularly suggestive of the lattice expansion due to motional fluctuations, of the accompanying rise in mean potential energy, and of the stabilization induced by the renormalization. We observe indeed that for distances $R/R_o \gg 1.11$ the trace of the static force constants, $\Delta\varphi$, is negative. This means that, there, the harmonic frequencies are imaginary. On the contrary, the frequencies in the R. H. A. are neatly stabilized by the motional fluctuations which induce positive force constants. This is a situation characteristic of the quantum solids where the above theory applies. There, for $R/R_o = 1.3$ and considering third nearest neighbours for suitable accuracy, one finds that $\frac{\partial\psi}{\partial w}$ is > 0 from $w = 0.02$, that $\frac{\partial\psi}{\partial w}$ and $w\,\frac{\partial\psi}{\partial w}$ have their maximum at $w = 0.20$ and $w = 0.25$ respectively. At this point we wish to refer particularly to the very interesting work on this subject, conducted and published by L. H. Nosanow et al.[†]. Here we proceed in mentioning a few other applications.

† See Phys. Rev. 146, 120, (1966) and 154, 175, (1967)

See also H. Horner's "Lattice Dynamics of Quantum Crystals", the most recent and elegant article on the subject in Zeits. f. Phys. 205, 72-89, (1967).

As a second example, let us consider the screened Coulomb potential

$$\varphi = \frac{1}{R} e^{-\mu R} \tag{6-52}$$

In this case, we have

$$\Phi = \frac{1}{\sqrt{2\pi\lambda}} \frac{1}{R} \int_0^\infty dR' \, e^{-\mu R'} \left(e^{-\frac{(R'-R)^2}{2\lambda}} - e^{-\frac{(R'+R)^2}{2\lambda}} \right)$$

$$= \frac{1}{R} e^{-\mu R + \frac{1}{2}\mu^2 \lambda}$$

$$- \frac{1}{2R} \left\{ e^{-\mu R + \frac{1}{2}\mu^2\lambda} \operatorname{erfc}\left(\frac{R-\mu\lambda}{\sqrt{2\lambda}}\right) + e^{\mu R + \frac{1}{2}\mu^2\lambda} \operatorname{erfc}\left(\frac{R+\mu\lambda}{\sqrt{2\lambda}}\right) \right\} \tag{6-53}$$

This model can be used as an alternative to the simple exponentials treated above, in approximating $\epsilon(R_o/R)^n$ by

$$\epsilon \frac{R_o}{R} e^{(n-1)(1-R/R_o)}$$

This is the three dimensional analog of the potential (6-35), and we see that $R\Phi$ of Eq. (6-53) differs from Eq. (6-36b) by the sign of the last term but, otherwise, contains the same functions. For numerical applications, these are interesting properties. If, in particular, $\mu = 0$, then

$$\Phi = \frac{1}{R} - \frac{1}{R} \operatorname{erfc}\left(\frac{R}{\sqrt{2\lambda}}\right) \tag{6-54}$$

$$= \frac{1}{R} \operatorname{erf}\left(\frac{R}{\sqrt{2\lambda'}}\right) \tag{6-54a}$$

We note from Eq. (6-54) that the homogeneous solution $\chi = \frac{1}{R} = \varphi$ is independent of λ and thus that the anharmonic effects contained in Φ are due entirely to the non-analytic part of the problem. Let us mention here a few cases where the effective Coulomb potential (6-54a) occurs. In the electronic theory of metals, there is a low density model due to Wigner which pictures the electrons as forming a lattice and vibrating around their mean positions with the plasma frequency. For the theory of the electronic cohesive energy as a function of density, it would then be highly desirable to know more about the stability of Wigner' electron lattice model. Present day understanding on this subject, currently investigated by A. F. Kugler, is summarized in D. Pines "Elementary Excitations in Solids" ([11], p. 91-95) to which we would like to refer†. Another application worth further investigation concerns the theory of the absolute stability of molecular and ionic crystals as put forward by Jansen and Lombardi. Thus far, theirs is a static theory whereby with Jansen's model of one effective electron per atom with gaussian charge distribution

$$\rho(r) = (\beta/\sqrt{\pi})^3 \, e^{-\beta^2 r^2}$$

interatomic potentials of the type

$$\varphi = \frac{1}{R} \operatorname{erf}(\beta R)$$

repeatedly occur in a variety of expressions. Now inclusion of dynamical and thermal effects due to the lattice ions can be, in part, achieved owing to a well-known property of gaussian distributions and results in renormalizing Jansen's βR parameter, so that φ

---

† For the most recent advances in the field, see W. Kohn "Mott and Wigner Transitions" to appear in P. R. L., Vol. 19

becomes

$$\Phi = \frac{1}{R} \operatorname{erf}(\beta^* R)$$

with

$$\frac{1}{\beta^{*2}} = \frac{1}{\beta^2} + 2\lambda \tag{6-55}$$

If interatomic correlations are taken into account, then β^{*-2} becomes a tensor as examplified through Eq. (6-33) p. 294.

A variety of other examples and problems concerning both equilibrium and transport properties of crystals come into mind. Rather than quoting a necessarily fragmentary list†, we return instead to dealing with the hard core problem left behind while approximating φ_{L-J} by an integrable potential and this, in quantitative terms. What we did above is a resolution of the supposedly exact potential φ_{L-J} into a normal part, φ, and a remainder containing in particular the hard core part of the interaction. In section (4-4) it has been said that this resolution was not unique and, in fact, it is largely a matter of convenience.

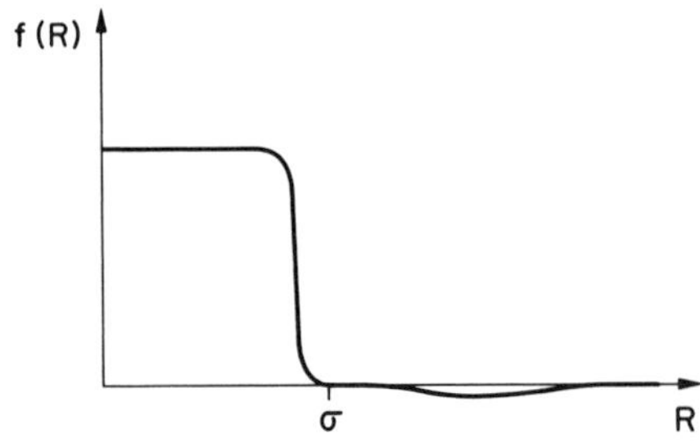

Inserting $\varphi_{L-J} - \varphi$ into f of Eq. (4-76a) one obtains the radial dependence drawn in the facing figure. Following the treatment given in section (4-5), we have the bare pseudo potential

$$\varphi^*(R) = \varphi(R) + KT\ f(\beta\epsilon, R)$$

† Worthy of particular mention here, however, is J.R. Ranninger's work on the lattice thermal conductivity of insulators, in Phys. Rev. 140, A 2031 (1965)

and the effective pseudo potential

$$\Phi^*(R, \lambda) = \Phi(R, \lambda) + KT\ F(\beta\epsilon, R, \lambda)$$

Considering the nearest neighbors interactions as the relevant ones for the problem, we obtain the effective pseudo potential per atom as

$$\psi^*(R, \lambda, \beta\epsilon) = z\ \Phi(R, \lambda) + z\ KT\ F((R, \lambda, \beta\epsilon)$$

If, for simplicity, we treat now the problem in the λ isotropic limit, then, according to the kinetic energy equation obtained here in applying the operation $KT\ Tr \frac{1}{N} \sum_{\tilde{q}} D_{\tilde{q}}^{-1}$ to Eq. (4-89), we find

$$3\ KT = 2 \sum_{\rho} Tr\ \lambda_{\rho} A_{\rho}^{*} = 2\lambda A^{*}$$

$$= \lambda\left(\frac{\partial\psi^*}{\partial\lambda}\right)_{a,T} = z\ \lambda\left(\frac{\partial\Phi}{\partial\lambda}\right)_{a} + KT\ z\ \lambda\left(\frac{\partial F}{\partial\lambda}\right)_{a,T}$$

or, in gathering the factors of KT together

$$3\ KT = \frac{1}{1 - \frac{z}{3}\lambda\left(\frac{\partial F}{\partial\lambda}\right)_{a,T}}\ z\ \lambda\left(\frac{\partial\Phi}{\partial\lambda}\right)_{a} \qquad (6\text{-}56)$$

In its simplest version, we see that the treatment of the hard core effects amounts to producing an enhancement factor multiplying the normal r. h. s. of the s. c. equation. How large is this factor ? We shall answer this question in making the customary approximation of replacing $f(R, \beta\epsilon)$ by a step function as in section 4-4 (p. 163). This amounts to neglecting an extremely weak temperature dependence $(\sim(\frac{KT}{\epsilon})^{\frac{1}{n}}$ for $\varphi \sim R^{-n})$ of the actual position, $\sigma(T) \cong \sigma(KT/\epsilon)^{1/n}$, at which Δf is zero. We can thus borrow Eq. (4-85) for $F(R, \lambda)$.

We have two parameters, σ/R, designated by q in what follows, and $\lambda/R^2 = w$. The latter will be varied from 0.001 to 0.01. The selection of relevant q values can be made with the help of Hirschfelder, Curtis and Bird's data†. With $R = d_o$, the calculated nearest neighbors distance at absolute zero († p. 1043) and σ the core radius determined from second virial coefficients († p. 1110), we obtain q values of 0.87, 0.89, 0.91, and 0.93 for Ne, Ar, Kr and Xe, respectively. For this range of q values, it is interesting to know the analytical expressions for the particular points where $F(w,q)$, $\left(\frac{\partial F}{\partial w}\right)_q$, and $w\left(\frac{\partial F}{\partial w}\right)_q$ have their respective maximum‡ From Eq. (4-85) written in terms of w and q, we find

$$w\,(q,\ F\max) \equiv \hat{w} = q\,(1-q) + 0\,(e^{-2q/\hat{w}}) \tag{6-57}$$

$$w\,(q,\ \frac{\partial F}{\partial w}\max) \equiv \tilde{w} = q^2\,(1-q)^2\,\frac{3+q^2}{(1+q)(1+5q^2)} + 0\,(\tilde{w}^2) \tag{6-57a}$$

$$w\,(q,\ w\frac{\partial F}{\partial w}\max) \equiv \overline{w} = q\,\frac{(1-q)^2}{1+2q} + 0\,(\overline{w}^2) \tag{6-57b}$$

In the following figure, the quantity $wF' = w\,\frac{\partial F}{\partial w}$ is plotted as a function of w for $q = 0.87$ up to $q = 0.93$.

---

† Molecular theory of Gases and Liquids. J. Wiley , New York 1959

‡ One reason is that in supposing the core repulsion simulated by a spherically symmetric potential barrier of range σ and of finite height, Eqs (6-57a, b) would tell us that the inflexion point $\tilde{w} \simeq \frac{1}{3}q^2(1-q)^2$ that is $\langle\tilde{u}^2\rangle \simeq \frac{1}{6}(R-\sigma)^2$ (!), and that $\overline{w} \simeq \frac{1}{q}\tilde{w}$ (!).

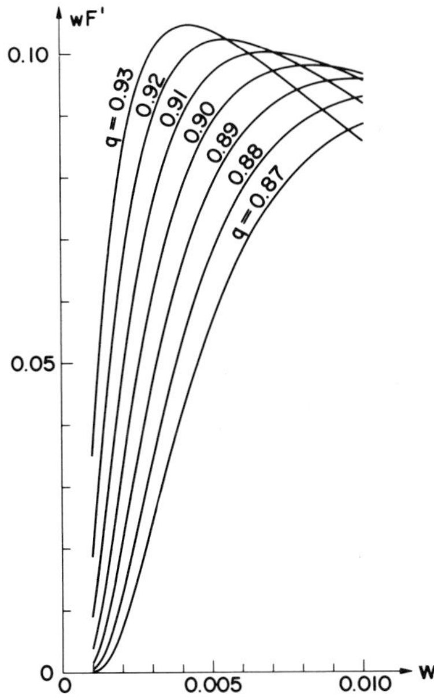

The maximum of wF' is seen to be slightly larger than 0.1 for $q = 0.93$, and to gradually decrease as q decreases. In multiplying wF' by $\frac{z}{n}$, the number of nearest neighbors per unit dimension, we obtain the denominator of the amplification factor. In choosing Eq. (6-49) for the normal part of the bare molecular potential, we calculate finally the r.h.s. of Eq. (6-56). For clarity of the figure, the resulting curves have been plotted below for the three values of $q = 0.87$, 0.90, and 0.93. The lower curve represents $w\psi'$ alone, that is Eq. (6-56) without amplification factor or, in other words, the case where $q = 0$. That the curve with $q = 0.93$ crosses the other two means that, here, the maximum amplification is obtained within the range of w values chosen for the graphical representation. From this analysis, we learn that, for the realistic σ/R ratios considered, no catastrophy occurs since the amplification does not exceed 40 % but, nevertheless, that this factor cannot simply be disregarded without knowing the relevant q and w values of the problem. Knowing this, we could now refine the evaluation of the r.h.s. of Eq. (6-56) in taking φ_{L-J} as of $R \gg \sigma$ for the normal part of the

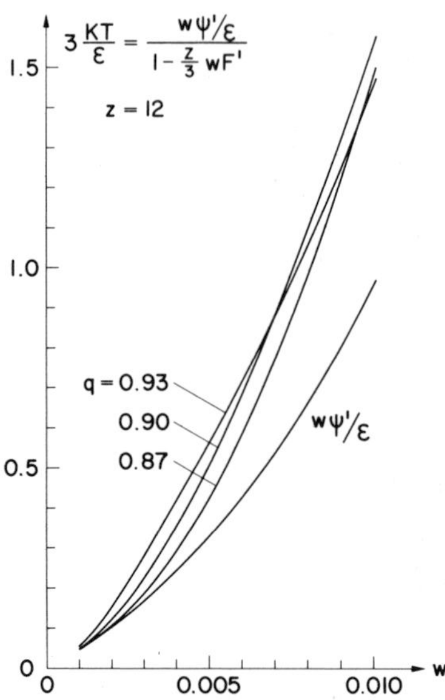

interatomic potential as discussed under Eq. (4-73). This need not be reported here. Anyhow, the "hard core" question raised under Eqs (2-20) and (4-2a), tackled in section (4-4) and further commented under Eq. (6-78, p. 331), receives here a preliminary quantitative answer. Most suitably parallelling and supplementing the approach from the classical theory reported here is the zero temperature, quantum theoretical approach taken up by L. H. Nosanow (see refs p. 313†) and developed for the helium solids in particular. There emerges now the picture that, on the basis of the unifying features brought about by the molecular field theory of lattice dynamics, the differences between the two, apparently extreme, situations are of a quantitative, rather than qualitative, nature.

At this point, a formal conclusion regarding the subject treated in this monograph would be fitting. We propose, instead, to close this text with an outline of investigations concerned with some of the preoccupations referred to in the preface.

† Publication of this work enables us to omit a section that we had originally outlined in this context.

6-3 OUTLINE OF SOME INVESTIGATIONS REGARDING CRYSTALLIZATION

It is convenient to introduce the discussion presented below by the following remarks. Consider the free energy expression for a two-dimensional Einstein-Weiss model, in the classical limit, that is

$$\frac{1}{N} F = -KT \ell n \left(\frac{MKT}{2\hbar^2} \lambda \right) -KT + \frac{1}{2} \psi(a, \lambda) \tag{6-58}$$

where it is recalled that ψ is the mean potential energy per atom

$$\psi = \sum_\rho \Phi(R_\rho, \lambda) = \sum_\rho \int d^2 r \frac{e^{-r^2/2\lambda}}{2\pi\lambda} \varphi(|\underset{\sim}{R}_\rho + r|)$$

$$= \frac{N}{\zeta} \sum_{\underset{\sim}{K}} e^{-\frac{1}{2}\lambda \underset{\sim}{K}^2} \int d^2 r \; e^{-i\underset{=}{K}\underset{=}{r}} \varphi(r) - \Phi(0, \lambda) \tag{6-59}$$

ζ, replacing υ, now being the area of the sample, that $\omega^2 = 2\,KT/M\lambda$, and that the internal state variable

$$\lambda = 2 \frac{1}{2} (\langle u_1^2 \rangle + \langle u_2^2 \rangle)$$

is the stable solution of the implicit equation

$$\lambda = 2\,KT \left(\frac{\partial \psi}{\partial \lambda} \right)_a^{-1} \tag{6-58a}$$

which minimizes the free energy (6-58). The above condition applies to the crystalline state of the system. In the text, however, we have also been repeatedly interested in the imperfect gas limit of the equations of state obtained for the solid state. In this respect, suppose now that we abandon Eq. (6-58a) and impose instead

$$\lambda = \sigma/\pi \tag{6-60a}$$

where $\sigma = \zeta/N$ now is the specific area. Then Eq. (6-58) becomes

$$\frac{1}{N} F = -KT \ln\left(\frac{2\pi M KT}{h^2}\sigma\right) - KT + \frac{1}{2}\psi(a, \sigma/\pi) \tag{6-60}$$

and we observe that, up to small differences in the potential energy (6-59) which arise in particular from the terms with reciprocal lattice vectors $\underset{\sim}{K} \neq 0$, Eq. (6-60) yields, in first order of perturbation theory, the free energy of the 2-dimensional imperfect gas with the correct entropy contribution. On the contrary, in the limit considered in the text, namely $\lambda \sim N\sigma$, it has been shown that the internal energy and thermal equation of state of the imperfect gas were systematically reproduced to all orders of perturbation calculus but, clearly, not the entropy, which differed from the correct one by a factor of $\ln N$ per atom†. It seems, therefore, that in letting $\lambda \to \sigma/\pi$ we obtain an essentially better free energy expression for the fluid. This observation suggests the working hypothesis that a continuous variation of the motional fluctuations, which would go over from the determination (6-58a) to (6-60a), is involved in the dynamics of the transition. Alternatively, a discontinuous variation might be considered as occurring, for example, through the onset of a third root, stable again, of the s. c. equations. Thus far, no reliable evidence for this alternative has been found. The conjecture is accordingly that Eqs (6-60, 60a) and (6-58, 58a) should derive from a unifying scheme.

Setting up this scheme involves quite a few steps. The first one concerns a tailor-made calculus of configuration integrals. What is meant thereby will be illustrated in treating the following key model. For this, we start from the Einstein model of a 2-dimensional lattice of lattice constant a. Omitting for a moment the static part, V_{st}, of the potential energy, we have simply

---

† except, of course, in the "collapsed" case where all $\underset{\sim}{R}_\rho = 0$ since, then, Z is divided again by the usual $N!$.

$$V_E = \frac{1}{2} \sum_j A r_j^2 \qquad (6\text{-}61)$$

whereby A is the force constant $= M \omega_E^2(a)$, $r_j = |\underline{r}_j|$, and j runs from 1 to N. Now, rather than following the conventional but, for our purposes, unsuitable treatment of the Einstein model based on the independent oscillators picture, it is suggested instead to consider the collective coordinate

$$X = \sum_j \pi r_j^2 \equiv \sum_j x_j \qquad (6\text{-}62)$$

where the x_j's represent the areas covered by the isotropically oscillating atoms. Individually these areas vary from 0 to ζ but collectively they are subject to the restriction (6-62) which is the equation of an hyperplane, perpendicular to the (1. 1... 1) direction of an N dimensional vector space, distant by

$$\frac{1}{\sqrt{N}} X \leqslant \frac{1}{\sqrt{N}} \zeta = \sqrt{N}\, \sigma \qquad (6\text{-}62a)$$

from its origin. Clearly, V_E depends on X only, and so does the Boltzmann factor which, in setting $\bar{A} = \frac{1}{2\pi} A$, becomes

$$\exp - \beta \bar{A} X \qquad (6\text{-}63)$$

The volume element

$$d\Omega = \prod_j d^2 r_j$$

is consequently transformed. With

$$d^2 r_j = d\varphi_j \, r_j \, dr_j$$

$$d x_j = 2\pi \; r_j \, dr_j = d\,(\pi r_j^{\,2})$$

$$d\Omega = \frac{d}{dX}\left(\int_{\sum_j x_j \leqslant X} \prod_j d x_j \right) dX$$

$$= \frac{1}{(N-1)!} \; X^{N-1} \, dX \tag{6-64}$$

The configuration integral becomes

$$Q = \frac{1}{(N-1)!} \int_0^{\zeta} dX \, X^{N-1} \, e^{-\beta A X} \tag{6-65}$$

Two interesting limits of this integral are readily obtained, namely if $\beta A = 0$, ζ finite

$$Q_o = \frac{1}{N!} \; \zeta^N$$

whereas, if βA is positive finite but $\zeta = \infty$

$$Q_E = \left(\frac{1}{\beta A} \right)^N$$

Adjoining $Z_{KE} = (2\pi \; M \, KT/h^2)^N$ then yields, in the above limits

$$Z = \begin{cases} \left(\dfrac{2\pi \; M \, KT}{h^2} \right)^N \dfrac{\zeta^N}{N!} = \left(\dfrac{2\pi \; M \, KT \sigma}{h^2} \right)^N e^N & (6\text{-}66) \\[2ex] \left(\dfrac{KT}{\hbar\omega} \right)^{2N} = \left(\dfrac{M \, KT}{2 \hbar^2} \, \lambda_E \right)^N & (6\text{-}66a) \end{cases}$$

which are the most familiar partition functions of the 2-dimensional gas and Einstein crystal, respectively. A closer inspection of Eq. (6-65) is obviously needed. That its integrand possesses a sharp peak at $X/(N-1) = 1/\beta\bar{A}$, which may or may not be reached depending on the magnitude of ζ/N , indicates that the value one of the parameter $\beta\bar{A}\sigma$ will play a particular rôle in this problem. Eq.(6-65) affords indeed an exact solution in the thermodynamic limit. The result appeals to physical **intuition**. Its derivation, however, is not so trivial and will be reported separately. One finds

$$\lim_{N\to\infty} Q^{1/N} = \begin{cases} \sigma e^{1-\beta\bar{A}\sigma} & \text{for } \beta\bar{A}\sigma < 1 \qquad (6\text{-}67) \\ \dfrac{1}{\beta\bar{A}} & \phantom{\text{for }} \beta\bar{A}\sigma \geqslant 1 \qquad (6\text{-}67a) \end{cases}$$

The meaning of this result is clear : as long as $KT > \bar{A}\sigma$, the gas-like character persists, whereas the crystal-like character takes over as soon as $KT = \bar{A}\sigma$. Here, it is convenient to write down a joint expression for the above relations by introducing an internal state variable Δ such that

$$\frac{1}{N}\,\ell n\, Q = \ell n\,\Delta + 1 - \beta\bar{A}\Delta \qquad (6\text{-}68)$$

with

$$\Delta(\sigma, T) = \min\left(\sigma, \frac{KT}{\bar{A}(\sigma)}\right) \qquad (6\text{-}68a)$$

Reintroducing at this stage $V_{st} = N\frac{1}{2}\psi(\sigma, o)$ and noticing that $KT/\bar{A}(\sigma) \equiv \pi\lambda$, we obtain for the free energy of the model

$$\frac{1}{N}\,F = -KT\,\ell n\left(\frac{2\pi M KT}{h^2}\Delta\right) - KT + \frac{1}{2}\psi(\sigma, o) + \bar{A}(\sigma)\Delta \qquad (6\text{-}69)$$

with the subsidiary condition

$$\Delta = \min(\sigma, \pi\lambda) \tag{6-69a}$$

that is, a couple of relations strongly supporting the working hypothesis and conjecture put forward earlier in this section. Interesting consequences can already be drawn from the above model. Let it just be pointed out that the thermal equation of state reads

$$P = P_{st} + \left(\frac{KT}{\Delta} - \mathcal{A}\right)\frac{d\Delta}{d\sigma} - \Delta\frac{d\mathcal{A}}{d\sigma} \tag{6-70}$$

$$= \begin{cases} \dfrac{KT}{\sigma} - \dfrac{d}{d\sigma}\left(\frac{1}{2}\psi(\sigma, o) + \mathcal{A}\sigma\right) & \sigma\mathcal{A} < KT \quad (6\text{-}70a) \\ & \text{for} \\ P_{st} - \dfrac{KT}{A}\dfrac{dA}{d\sigma} & \sigma\mathcal{A} \geqslant KT \quad (6\text{-}70b) \end{cases}$$

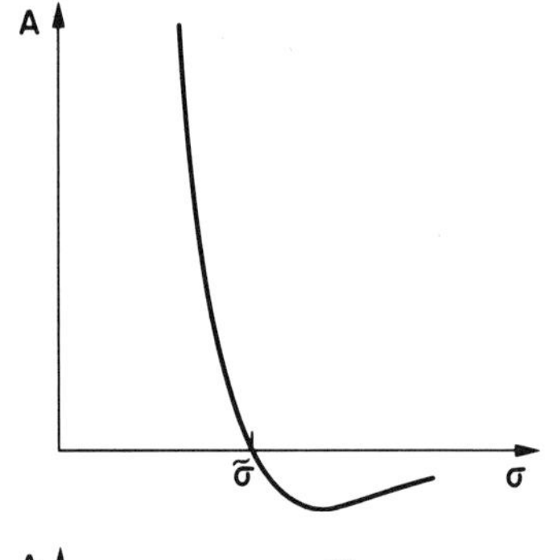

For the illustrative dependence of $A(\sigma)$ schematically drawn in the facing figure, we find the following determination of Δ for a given temperature and the ensuing, self-explanatory, pressure isotherm.†

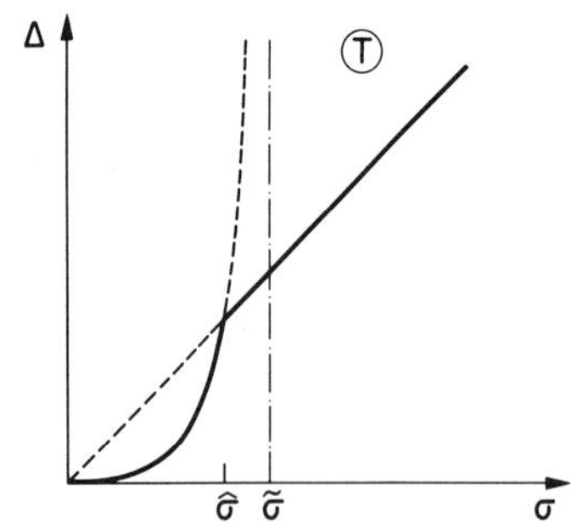

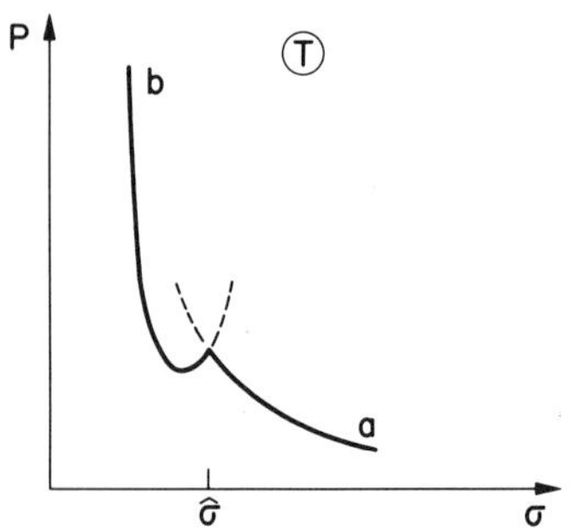

† Note that if $\mathcal{A}$ = const = $\mathcal{A}_o$, then $P - P_{st} = \frac{KT}{\sigma} - \mathcal{A}_o$ for $\sigma < KT/\mathcal{A}_o$ and is zero otherwise.

We note in particular that at $T = 0$, (a) takes over from (b) at the density of static instability, whereas, at $T > 0$, the take-over always occurs before $\sigma = \tilde{\sigma}$. In the other direction we note also that as (b) takes over from (a), the determination $\Delta = KT/A(\sigma)$ reduces the area covered by the fluctuating atoms rather efficiently since, in general, $1/A(\sigma)$ decreases with σ more rapidly than linearly. This latter property helps one to understand why solid-fluid transitions possess no critical point. Cases where this property does not hold will be considered separately. Let us also point out that, at the change-over points, the specific heat C_v experiences a jump of 1/2 K per degree of freedom. A variety of other features displayed by the above model could of course be further discussed. At this stage, however, the main point seems to be that the idea of collective constraint in phase space, as formulated through Eqs (6-62, 62a, 65), may prove a useful one to express the cooperative aspect inherent in crystallization, but more work is undoubtedly needed to support and strengthen this view.

The next step needed to link Eq. (6-60) with Eq. (6-58) concerns the calculus of the mean potential energy appearing in Eq. (6-60). For integrable interatomic potentials the problem reduces to calculating $\langle \exp i\underset{\sim}{k}(\underset{\sim}{r}-\underset{\sim}{r}') \rangle_0$ over the unperturbed fluid state in conforming to the constraint (6-62a). For this, we start from

$$Q_0 = \frac{1}{N!}\zeta^N = \int_{\sum\limits_{j\geqslant 1} \pi r_j^2 \leqslant \zeta} d^2 r_1 \ldots d^2 r_N$$

and we evaluate the one particle mean value

$$\langle e^{i\underset{\sim}{k}\underset{\sim}{r}_1}\rangle_o \equiv \frac{1}{Q_o}\int_o^{\zeta} d^2r_1\, e^{i\underset{\sim}{k}\underset{\sim}{r}_1} \int\limits_{\sum_{j\geqslant 2}\pi r_j^2 \leqslant \zeta - \pi r_1^2} d^2r_2 \ldots d^2r_N$$

$$= \frac{1}{Q_o}\int_o^{\sqrt{\zeta/\pi}} r\,dr \int_o^{2\pi} d\varphi\; e^{ikr\cos\varphi}\,\frac{1}{(N-1)!}\,(\zeta - \pi r^2)^{N-1}$$

$$= \frac{N}{\zeta}\int_o^{\sqrt{\zeta/\pi}} r\,dr \int_o^{2\pi} d\varphi\; e^{ikr\cos\varphi}\,\left(1 - \frac{\pi r^2}{\zeta}\right)^{N-1} \qquad (6\text{-}71)$$

in the limit $N \to \infty$, $\zeta \to \infty$, $\zeta/N = \sigma < \pi\lambda$. We find the remarkable expression

$$\langle e^{i\underset{\sim}{k}\underset{\sim}{r}}\rangle_o = \frac{1}{\sigma}\int_o^{\infty} dr \int_o^{2\pi} d\varphi\; e^{ikr\cos\varphi}\; e^{-\frac{\pi r^2}{\sigma}} \qquad (6\text{-}72)$$

which becomes (see p. 28)

$$\langle e^{i\underset{\sim}{k}\underset{\sim}{r}}\rangle_o = e^{-\frac{\sigma k^2}{4\pi}} \qquad (6\text{-}72a)$$

Thus

$$\overline{\Phi}(k, \sigma/\pi) = \langle e^{i\underset{\sim}{k}(\underset{\sim}{r} - \underset{\sim}{r}')}\rangle_o\, \overline{\varphi}(k) = e^{-\frac{\sigma k^2}{2\pi}}\, \overline{\varphi}(k)$$

that is

$$\Phi(R, \sigma/\pi) = \frac{1}{2\sigma} \int d^2 r\, e^{-\frac{\pi r^2}{2\sigma}} \varphi(|\underset{\sim}{R} + \underset{\sim}{r}|) \tag{6-73}$$

which is exactly our familiar effective potential function (see Eq. 6-59) with, however, σ/π taking the place of λ . From this equation there follows the conjectured continuity, for fixed R_ρ's , of the potential energy (6-59) as a function of the internal state variable Δ .

Continuing, step-wise, the development of the scheme results in the following picture of the system's free energy, now described in qualitative terms only. Let us draw on the figure of p. 302 for instance a vertical line at the cut-off fluctuation $\lambda = \sigma/\pi$ (typically at the mark indicated). Now consider the strip $0 \leqslant \lambda \leqslant \sigma/\pi$. Then, as long as the free energy, plotted there as a function of λ for fixed a and T , has its lowest value where it crosses the border line of this strip, we have the fluid determination. At the temperature $KT = \sigma A(a, \sigma/\pi)$, the minimum of F lies on the border line and below this temperature it moves toward smaller values of λ until, ultimately, the static potential energy is reached at $T = 0$, $\lambda = 0$, provided that the density is larger than that corresponding to the static instability. If not, the lowest value of the free energy remains on the border line of the strip from high to low temperatures. In other words, and more generally, the resulting free energy per atom reads, in a molecular field type of approximation† ($\langle x_j \rangle = \Delta$ for all j)

---

† It is worth comparing here the constraint (6-62a) written as

$$\sum_j \frac{\pi r_j^2}{\sigma} \leqslant N$$

with that of the spherical model in the theory of phase transitions ([12], p. 28).

$$\sum_j \mu_j^2 = N$$

$$\frac{1}{N} F(\sigma, T, \Delta) = -KT\, \ell n \left(\frac{2\pi MKT}{h^2} \Delta\right) - KT + \frac{1}{2} \psi(\sigma, \Delta/\pi) \quad (6\text{-}74)$$

with the subsidiary condition

$$\Delta(\sigma, T) = \min\left(\sigma,\ \pi\lambda = \frac{2KT}{\left(\frac{\partial\psi}{\partial\Delta}\right)_\sigma}\right) \quad (6\text{-}74a)$$

The above equations apply to the case of integrable potential functions. However, nothing seems to prevent us, so far, from borrowing the treatment of the hard core problem given in sections (4-4) and (6-2). Thanks to Eqs (6-72) and (6-74a), the latter being written in term of the pseudo-potential ψ^*, we ought to see rather accurately how and where the hard core effects appear and disappear again as the density is increased from nearly perfect gas to crystal values.

The discussion has, up to now, been limited to classical systems. It is again a consequence of the mean value (6-72) that a generalization to quantum systems seems to be feasible without great effort. If the said mean value can be trusted, this means indeed that gaussian distributions persist throughout the change-over of Δ's determination. If so, the position or Bloch representation (5-15) can be employed to treat the problem in an Einstein-Weiss approximation in particular. In the zero temperature limit, we would simply obtain, always for our 2-dimensional case

$$\frac{1}{N} U(\sigma, \Delta) = \frac{\pi\hbar^2}{2M\Delta} + \frac{1}{2} \psi(\sigma, \Delta/\pi) \quad (6\text{-}75)$$

for the ground state energy per atom and

$$\Delta(\sigma) = \min\left(\sigma,\ \frac{\pi\hbar^2}{M\Delta\left(\frac{\partial\psi}{\partial\Delta}\right)_\sigma}\right) \quad (6\text{-}75a)$$

for the subsidiary condition.

Another aspect of the problem thus far untouched concerns the treatment of interatomic correlation effects. Referring, once more, to the gaussian structure of Eq. (6-72) and to the connection established in Section (6-1, Eqs 6-26 - 6-29a) between the R.H.A. and its wave vector independent limit, we can already infer that $\Phi(R_\rho, \sigma/\pi)$ will become $\Phi(R_\rho, \sigma_\rho/\pi)$, i.e. that σ, like λ, will emerge as depending on the index ρ of neighboring shells of atoms. This brings up the point that in going over from displacements to lattice wave coordinates, the amplitudes $|u_{\underset{\sim}{q}}|^2$, like our previous variables x_j, become subject to collective constraints. For example, eliminating the center of mass coordinate in (6-62a) to make the theory translation invariant results in

$$\sum_{\underset{\sim}{q}\alpha} u_{\underset{\sim}{q}\alpha} u^*_{\underset{\sim}{q}\alpha} \leqslant (N-1)\,\sigma/\pi \tag{6-76}$$

Another example, pertinent to the treatment of correlation effects, may be found in expressing the non-integrability assumption (A.1) of the molecular potential (1.19) $\varphi(|\underset{\sim}{R}_\rho + \eta_\rho \underset{\sim}{u}_s|)$. A sufficient condition under which a theory of anharmonicity can be developed is that, considering the smallest, nearest neighbor, distance R_1, and a small residual core diameter δ

$$|\eta_1 \underset{\sim}{u}_s| \leqslant R_1 - \delta \tag{6-77}$$

Treating this condition in a random phase approximation, that is, retaining the homogeneous part of (6-77) squared, yields then

$$\sum_{\underset{\sim}{q}\alpha} (2 - 2\cos \underset{\sim}{q}\underset{\sim}{R}_1)\, u_{\underset{\sim}{q}\alpha} u^*_{\underset{\sim}{q}\alpha} \leqslant N(R_1 - \delta)^2 \tag{6-78}$$

This constraint provides the basis for the alternative treatment of the hard core problem referred to in Section 6-1 (p. 286). For illustration, applying (6-78) to the one-dimensional perfect fluid yields the well-known equation of state $\beta P(a-\delta) = 1$. The advantages brought about by using relative coordinates instead of absolute ones need not be emphasized. There remains, however, that the inequalities (6-62a, 76, 78) convey the same qualitative feature of phase space restriction which, for some time already†, has been suspected to matter in a theory of crystallization.

Returning to the wave vector independent limit, let us finally remark that, in the 3-dimensional case, we seem to be confronted, at first sight, with the formulation of either an effective specific volume or an effective specific cross-section theory. In the first case, the free energy par atom would read, in a molecular field type of approximation, v being the specific volume υ/N

$$\frac{1}{N} F(v, T, \Delta_3) = -KT \ln \left[\left(\frac{2\pi MKT}{h^2} \right)^{3/2} \Delta_3 \right] - KT + \frac{1}{2} \psi \left(v, \left(\frac{3}{4\pi} \Delta_3 \right)^{2/3} \right) \tag{6-79}$$

with

$$\Delta_3 = \min \left(v, \frac{2KT}{\left(\frac{\partial \psi}{\partial \Delta_3} \right)_v} \right) \tag{6-79a}$$

and

$$\langle e^{i\underset{\sim}{k}\underset{\sim}{r}} \rangle = \frac{1}{\Delta_3} \int d^3 r \, e^{i\underset{\sim}{k}\underset{\sim}{r}} e^{-\frac{4\pi}{3} r^3 / \Delta_3} \tag{6-79b}$$

† In a short Note published in Proc. Int. Conf. Semicond. Phys. Prague 1960 (p. 649) it had been pointed out that unrestricted lattice wave amplitudes entail atomic overruns prohibited by the fundamental ordering hypothesis and by steric hindrances.

whereas in the second case, strictly adapted to the Einstein-Weiss limit of the R. H. A., we would find, in the same approximation

$$\frac{1}{N} F(v, T, \Delta_2) = -\frac{3}{2} KT \, \ell n \left(\frac{2\pi MKT}{h^2} \Delta_2 \right) - \frac{3}{2} KT + \frac{1}{2} \psi(v, \Delta_2/\pi) \tag{6-80}$$

with

$$\Delta_2 = \min \left(\sigma, \frac{3KT}{\left(\frac{\partial \psi}{\partial \Delta_2}\right)_v} \right) \tag{6-80a}$$

and

$$\langle e^{i\underset{\sim}{k}\underset{\sim}{r}} \rangle = \frac{1}{\Delta_2^{3/2}} \int d^3 r \, e^{i\underset{\sim}{k}\underset{\sim}{r}} e^{-\pi r^2/\Delta_2}$$

the relation between σ and v being that $(3\sigma/2\pi)^{1/2} = (3v/4\pi)^{1/3}$, $Q(N)$ of (6-65) becoming indeed $Q(\frac{3}{2}N)$.

It is apparent that a more subtle treatment of this case will have to be proposed. It is also clear that, in forthcoming investigations dealing with the problem of crystallization, the handicap afflicting all of the above discussion - namely, that a single lattice structure has been assumed in treating the configurational and dynamical aspects of the problem - will have to be removed. It is hoped, nevertheless, that the few ideas put forward here will contribute to stimulating more research work on this intriguing subject.

REFERENCES

1. M. Born and K. Huang
Dynamical Theory of Crystal Lattices
Clarendon Press, Oxford, 1954

2. A. A. Maradudin, E. W. Montroll and G. H. Weiss
Theory of Lattice Dynamics in the Harmonic Approximation
Solid State Physics, Supplement 3
Academic Press, New York, 1963

3. M. Blackman
The Specific Heat of Solids
Handbuch der Physik VII, part 1, p. 325-382
Springer-Verlag Berlin, 1955

4. G. Leibfried and W. Ludwig
Theory of Anharmonic Effects in Crystals
Solid State Physics 12, p. 276-456
Academic Press, New York, 1961

5. G. Borelius
The Changes in Energy Content, Volume, and Resistivity with Temperature in Simple Solids and Liquids
Solid State Physics 15, p. 1-48
Academic Press, New York, 1963

6. R. Brout and P. Carruthers
Lectures on the Many-Electron Problem
Interscience Publishers, New York, 1963

7. L. Van Hove
Interactions of Elastic Waves in Solids
M. I. T. 1959. Reprinted in "Quantum Theory of Many-Particle Systems"
W. A. Benjamin, Inc., New York, 1961

7a. L. Van Hove
Selected Topics in the Quantum Statistics of Interacting Particles
University of Washington, Seattle, Washington, 1958

8. E. R. Caianello
Lectures on the Many-Body Problem
Academic Press, New York, 1962

9. A. A. Abrikosov, L. P. Gorkov and I. E. Dzyaloshinski
Methods of Quantum Field Theory in Statistical Physics
Prentice-Hall, Inc., Englewood Cliffs, 1963

10. L. P. Kadanoff and G. Baym
Quantum Statistical Mechanics
W. A. Benjamin, Inc., New York, 1962

11. D. Pines
Elementary Excitations in Solids
W. A. Benjamin, Inc., New York, 1963

12. R. H. Brout
Phase Transitions
W. A. Benjamin, Inc., New York, 1965

13. P. Choquard
On a Method of Summation of First Order Phonon-Phonon Interactions
University of Geneva, 1963

13a. P. Choquard
Selected Topics in Lattice Dynamics
University of Illinois, 1964-65

INDEX